D0655936

FRESHWATER FISH OF BRITAIN AND EUROPE

Bent J. Muus

Illustrated by

Preben Dahlstrøm

Edited by

Alwyne Wheeler

Collins

St James's Place, London

ISBN 0 00 219270 5

EUROPAS FERSKVANDSFISK was
first published in Denmark
by G. E. C. Gads Forlag in 1967.

New edition 1978

Text printed in Great Britain by
Collins Clear-Type Press,
London and Glasgow

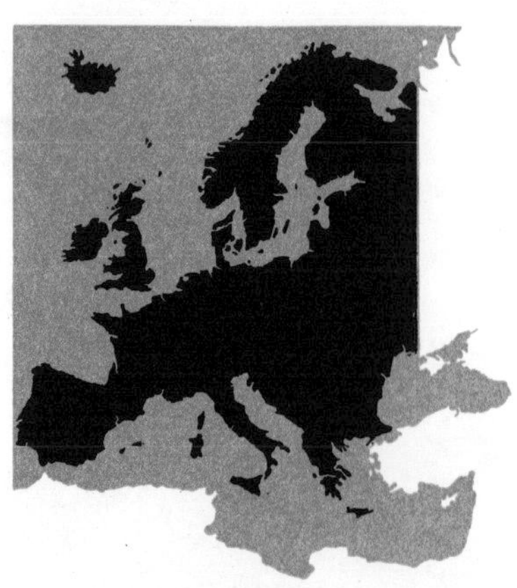

The fish described in this book are found within the area coloured black
Fish marked ◆ are native in Britain
Fish marked (◆) are introduced

Contents

Foreword

Europe has a long tradition for producing fine books about fishes. One of the earliest was Guilliaume Rondelet's *Universiae Aquatilium historiae* . . . published in 1555, which included some twenty-five European freshwater species. Since Rondelet wrote four hundred and more years ago there have been many other books on or including European fishes. Within the last century many of them have been illustrated by beautiful colour plates, some of the most notable having been published in Scandinavia, especially that by B. Fries, C. U. Ekström, and C. Sandevall, best known in its English edition by F. A. Smitt as a *History of Scandinavian Fishes* (1893–95). It is following this great tradition that Bent J. Muus and Preben Dahlstrøm have produced this book on European fresh-water fishes now available in English.

Unlike its forerunners which mostly contained detailed studies of the different kinds of fish found in Europe, this is a book for the twentieth century, with emphasis on the living fish and its environment. Here their natural history is given in broad outline and their life style related to the world around them, their food chains, predators, competitors, and exploiters. Of particular interest is the effect of man on the fish-life of this densely populated continent, the pollution he has produced, and the rape of our rivers by dams, culverts, and water abstraction. Man too has altered the fish fauna in other ways (not always to his own advantage ultimately) by the introduction of exotic forms, and the translocation of stocks of fish, usually in the guise of fishery improvements.

This book deals with the fishes of Europe within the limits shown on the map on page 2, and includes all the species native to the British Isles. For the English edition a few inter-polations have been made to add to its value for the reader in the British Isles, and the scientific names have been revised to accord with the check-list published in my *Fishes of the British Isles and North West Europe* (London, Macmillan; 1969).

To the east in the Caspian and Black Sea basins, many endemic forms live which, although of the greatest interest, are rarely encountered by the western European traveller. They are omitted here for it was felt that the advantage of including them would not compensate for the increase in the size of the book. A note of caution must, however, be sounded. Despite the four centuries of interest in European fishes there are places in which the fish fauna has not been at all well studied. For examples, several of the roach-like fish of the Iberian peninsular, and the forms of dace-like and minnow-like fish in the Balkans have been little studied since they were first described, and more detailed studies may alter their status. The details given here, and particularly the illustrations will help in the recognition of these forms, and point to the areas in which our knowledge is sparse.

The text of the book by Bent J. Muus of Denmark's Fisheries Research Department, gives a reliable but easy to read account of fish-life in our rivers and lakes, It is comp-lemented by, and integrated in a most attractive manner with, the colour illustrations of Preben Dahlstrøm. The result is a book of outstanding appeal, informative, with excellent illustrations presented in an imaginative, often witty, but always decorative manner. It is a pleasure to introduce such a useful and pleasant book to the English reader.

Alwyne Wheeler

THE FISH

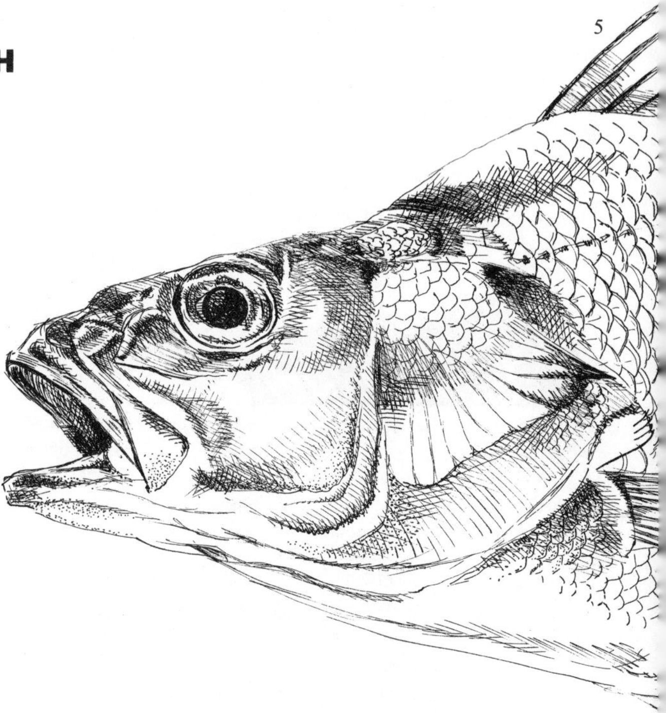

Freshwater fish do not differ essentially from marine fish in biology or appearance; indeed several of them have their closest relatives in the sea. The diversity of freshwater fishes is such that practically the only thing they have in common is that they live in freshwaters of all shapes and sizes, which together account for 1·7% of the land surface, or 2·5 million square kilometres. This is a modest area when compared with the 360 million square kilometres of the oceans. About 5,000 of the 20,000 known species of fish live in freshwater; and new, hitherto overlooked, species are still being described by scientists.

Although most fish are easy to identify, there are groups (e.g. some of the salmonids) which are difficult even for experts, and the beginner needs to know the elementary terms used when describing a fish. The perch makes an excellent example from which to learn:

The *head* is the part from the tip of the snout to the hind edge of the gill-cover; the *trunk* starts here and extends to the anus; the remainder is the *tail*.

The rays of the fins are either rigid, bony spines (spiny rays, spiny fins) as in the first dorsal fin of the perch, or they are

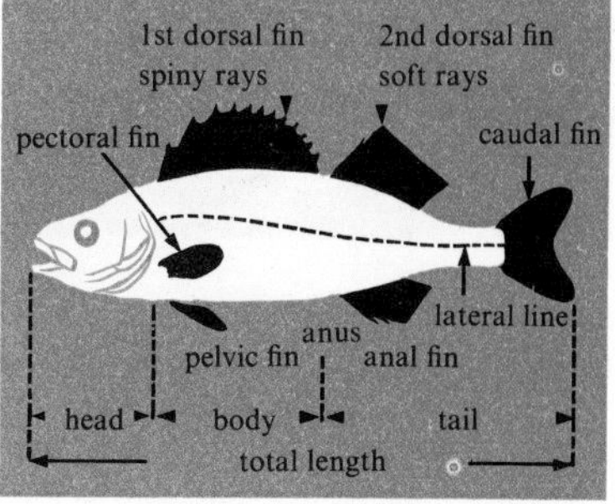

soft, branched and jointed (soft rays, soft-rayed fins) as in the second dorsal fin of the perch. All members of the salmon family have an adipose fin on the tail, a small, fleshy fin without spines or rays.

The fin close behind the anus is the anal fin, and this, the dorsal and the tail fins are known as the unpaired fins. The pectoral

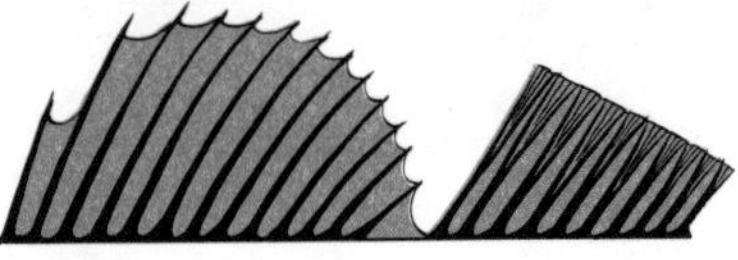

Spiny rays *Soft rays*

and pelvic fins are paired, and placed one on each side of the body (see fig. below). The lateral line is of some importance in the identification of fishes, and consists of a single row of pored scales running along the sides of the fish. (See also p. 12).

Skin and scales

The epidermis is thin, transparent and slimy and covers the scales, which are bony plates lying in pockets in the underlying dermis. In many species with large,

coarse scales the epidermis is often worn away. Several freshwater fishes have either rudimentary scales or lack them altogether on the greater part of the body. Such fishes often secrete large quantities of slime (e.g. eels, loach, wels).

Newly hatched fish have no scales; in the trout, for example, scales begin to form on the anterior part of the trunk when the young are about 3 cm long. In the zander (pike-perch) they begin to form on the tail at a length of 3·5–4 cm.

The scales lie in pockets in the dermis and grow as the fish grows, forming concentric growth rings, like those of trees, which can be used to determine the age of the fish. The free edge of the scale covers the base of the next scale back like tiles and they form regular longitudinal, oblique and transverse rows. Once formed, the number of rows of scales does not change with growth, but lost scales are replaced by regeneration.

Two major types of scale are found in the bony freshwater fishes. Those known as cycloid scales are smooth-edged, while the ctenoid scales have fine comb-like teeth on their free edge. Mirror-scales, as in the carp, are large irregular scales,

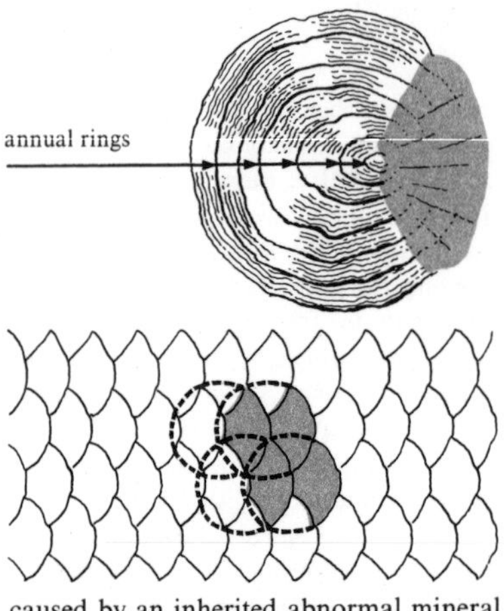

caused by an inherited abnormal mineral metabolism.

Fish which, due to some accident, and often careless handling, have lost some of their scales are often attacked by bacteria and fungal diseases.

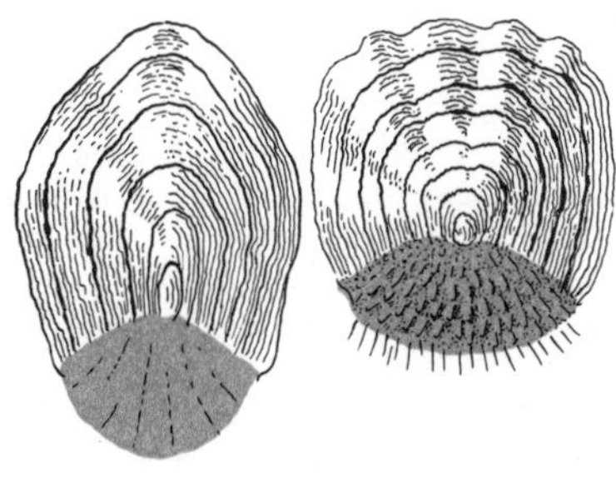

Cycloid scale Ctenoid scale

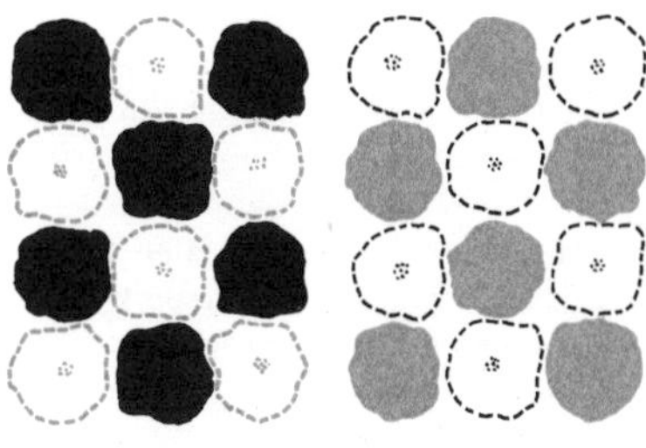

black spread
gold concentrated

black concentrated
gold spread

Chromatophores and colour change

Colour

Fish which usually live in the upper water layers generally have silvery sides and bellies. This colour is due to the reflection of light from microscopic, colourless crystals of guanine, a waste product of metabolism, which forms crystals on the back of the scales or in special colour layers in the skin. Semi-transparent fish, such as the smelt, lack this substance on their scales. Guanine from very silvery fish (e.g. bleak) can be removed from the scales and used as a coating for artificial pearls (*essence d'orient*).

The red, yellow and black pigments in the skin are distributed in thousands of pigment cells known as chromatophores. By contracting or expanding, each pigment granule can be condensed into a spot or can spread to a large and irregular blotch. In this way various colours can predominate, and this is the basis for the ability of fish to change colour. The intensity of the colouration depends on the thickness of the layer of chromatophores and on the concentration of the pigment granules in the individual cells.

Swimming

The most rapid swimmers among fish are those with torpedo-shaped bodies and which swim by flexing the body—particularly the tail. Eel-like fish with long dorsal and anal fins swim with undulating movements of the fin, and can throw this process into reverse in order to move backwards. In general, however, the vertical fins are used as stabilisers and stop the fish rolling while swimming. Pectoral fins may be used as oars for slow swimming or precise orientation, and as volplanes or for sudden braking. The pelvic fins act as stabilisers, although some bottom-living fish use them as supporting limbs.

In the gobies they are modified into a weak sucking disc. The eel has no pelvic fins.

The swimming speed of a fish depends

on its length, the number of swings of its tail and their width. A film of fish swimming in a rotating tank showed that two dace, 9 and 24 cm long, swam 50 and 170 cm in one second, which amounts to 1·12 and 3·8 miles per hour respectively.

A distinction must be made between the normal cruising speed of a fish, and its ability to 'sprint' over a short distance at a much higher speed. Most fish have so-called 'white' muscles which are capable of

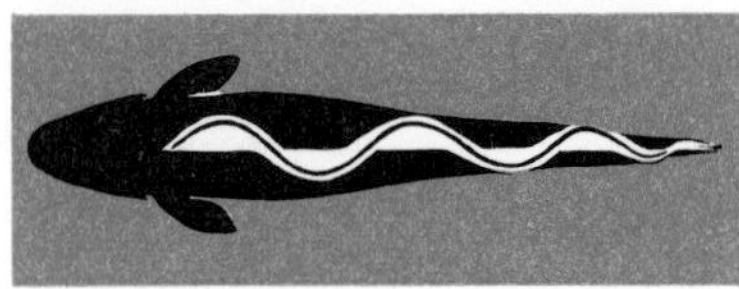

continuous low-energy movements; those in which 'red' muscles (filled with the oxygen-carrying myoglobin) are abundant are notably stronger swimmers with greater staying power. Although all fish are capable of a sprint to escape danger or seize food, few can do so for long. For example, speedy swimmers like salmon and pike can cover a distance ten times their body length in one second, but tire rapidly if forced to swim at this speed for long.

Conservation of energy is the general rule among fish (as in other animal groups); in a strong current fish shelter in the lee of stones or projections and emerge only for short periods. This habit has made available living space for fish that would be otherwise untenanted, and loaches, the miller's thumb and some other fish are found only in such places.

The swim-bladder

The swim-bladder (or air bladder) is a gas-filled buoyancy organ which forms in the embryo as a growth from the intestine. In salmonids and the carp family the swim-bladder is connected with the oesophagus by a narrow air-duct, but in most fish this duct closes shortly after hatching (e.g. in the perch family). At this time the young of those species which have a closed swim bladder must rise to the surface and fill the swim-bladder by gulping air. If young perch, for example are prevented from reaching the surface for 5–8 days, the air-duct closes, the swim-bladder does not fill with air and never functions normally later. The regulation of the amount of gas in those fish with a closed swim-bladder is effected by the blood either supplying gas to, or absorbing it from, the swim-bladder. A special region in the wall of the bladder carries

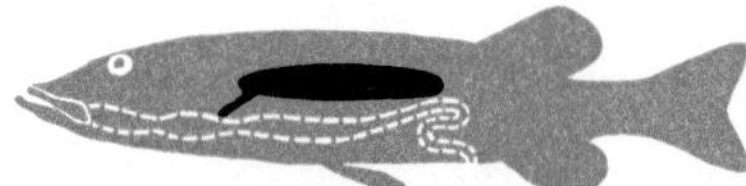

simple swim bladder with air duct: pike and salmonids

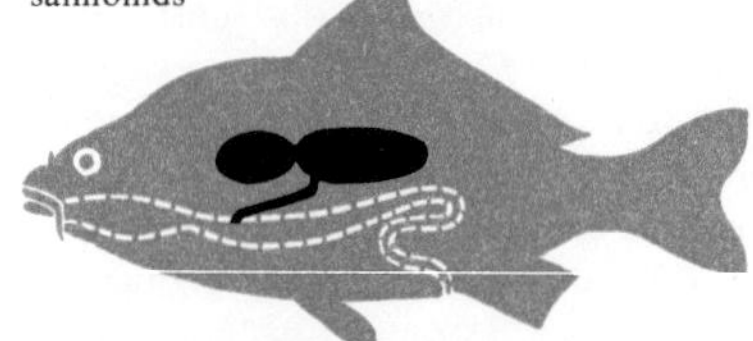

double-chambered bladder with air duct: carps

perch swim bladder with two air ducts and extension to the labynth: herring

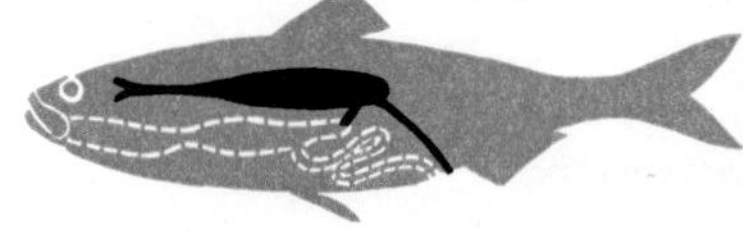

swim bladder without air duct but with gas gland:

out this function (under nervous control) with the result that the specific gravity of the fish is automatically adapted to the water pressure surrounding it. If a fish is hauled up rapidly from a great depth, the air in the swim-bladder expands because of the decrease in pressure and this forces the gut of the fish out of its mouth.

Several bottom-living fish have no swim-bladder, for in their case it is superfluous and degenerates in the larval stage (bull-heads, loaches, freshwater blenny, gobies, and flounder).

Oxygen and respiration

Freshwater always contains some oxygen, obtained partly from the air and partly by the photosynthesis of submerged plants. In running water riffles, weirs and waterfalls provide good aeration, but in stagnant and slow-flowing water the plants are of greater importance as a source of oxygen. As photosynthesis and the resulting production of oxygen stops when it is dark but the consumption of oxygen by animals continues, the oxygen content of such waters decreases during the night and increases in the daytime.

At 15°C freshwater is saturated when it contains 7 millilitres of oxygen per litre; at 5°C saturation is reached with 9 ml/l and at 25°C with 6 ml/l. Below areas of strong water disturbance (e.g. weirs) the water may be supersaturated. The significance of this relationship between saturation and temperature is that at winter temperatures normal rivers are usually saturated, while in summer there may be a deficiency of oxygen. This is unfortunate, for fish usually require more oxygen at higher temperatures.

The gills of fish are thin-skinned, blood-filled filaments placed on rigid gill-arches. Water is taken in through the mouth, which is then closed; the floor of the mouth is raised and the gill-cover is pressed inwards simultaneously, forcing the water past the gills and out under the hindmost fleshy flap of the gill-cover, which functions as a valve. As the water is forced between the gill filaments the blood in them absorbs part of the oxygen dissolved in the water.

On the inner side of the gill-arches are the gill-rakers which form a sieve for retaining food particles. In fish which feed on plankton, e.g. whitefish and shads, the gill-rakers are especially well-developed.

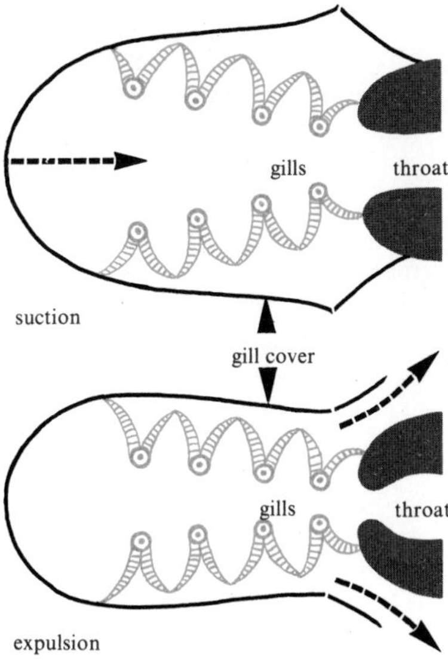

Horizontal section through the head

Many fish obtain some oxygen or lose carbon dioxide by diffusion directly through the skin. Some have refined this process considerably and the pond loach (*Misgurnus*) gets more than half its oxygen through the skin. It also swallows atmospheric air from which oxygen is absorbed in special folds in the wall of the intestine.

In cool, rapid-flowing water the oxygen content is often high, from 7–12 ml/l, and fish accustomed to these regions (typical ones are salmon, trout, loach, grayling and minnow) do not thrive in water of much lower oxygen content.

Deficits of oxygen occur periodically in vegetation-rich, stagnant and shallow lakes, and the fish which thrive in such waters are those which can endure a level of oxygen as low as 0·5 ml/l. Carp, crucian carp, tench and eel are such species. In conditions like this, these fish will be seen to gasp at air-saturated water at the surface.

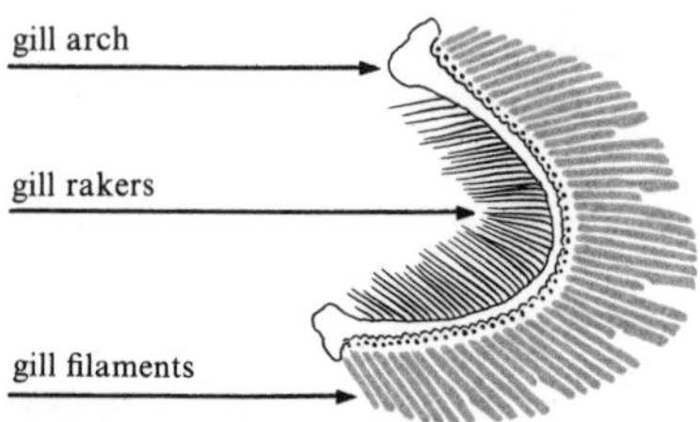

The oxygen demand of the fish is mainly dependent on temperature, but also on condition and on age. At 20°C carp make about 100 breathing movements per minute; during hibernation only 3–4. Well-nourished fish have a larger oxygen demand than lean ones, and the younger the fish the more oxygen is required. Oxygen deficiency occurs when larger amounts are consumed than are produced; the process of bacterial decomposition consumes particularly large amounts of oxygen. Where a heavy crop of plants and much plant debris are present, oxygen becomes deficient during the night. A heavy covering of ice and snow can also cut out light, kill the plants and cause an oxygen deficiency, and organic pollution of any sort also consumes much oxygen.

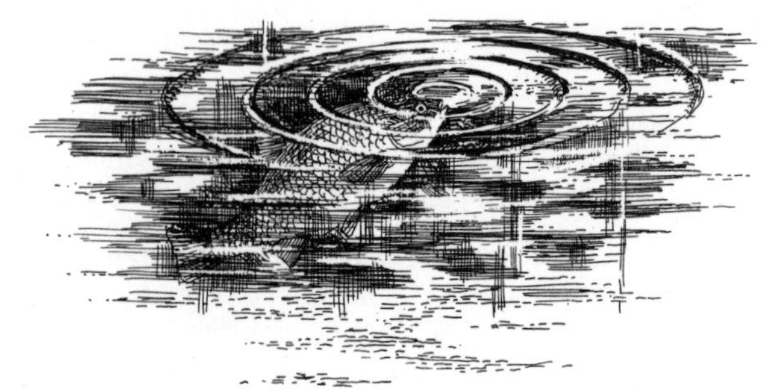

Light and sight

Orientation by sight is of great importance for most fish. The fish eye is large and has a spherical, hard lens. The cornea does not reflect the light as it does in terrestrial vertebrates because it has the same refractive index as water. The lens is placed close to the front of the eye, and bulges through the pupil, so ensuring a wide field of vision. The field of vision for each eye is 160–170° horizontally and about 150° vertically; in front of the fish a field with an angle of 20–30° is covered by both eyes. Because of the particular structure of the retina fish have the sharpest eyesight to the front, while their side vision is well adjusted to detect movement, even if the details are blurred. Special muscles can move the lens closer to the retina if the eye has to accommodate to greater distances.

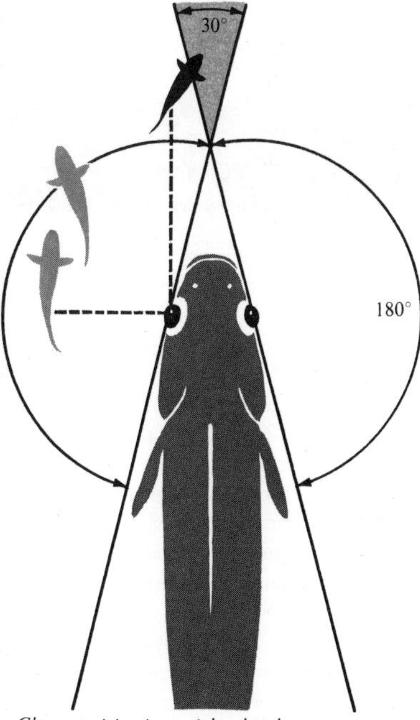

Clearest vision is straight ahead

mammal eye lens alters shape

fish eye lens is moved (as in a telescope)

If a fish looks upwards through the water it can see objects on land or in the air, but only within a total angle of about 98°. Outside this round 'skylight', always just above the fish, the water surface reflects the light and the fish sees a mirror picture of the bottom.

The fish eye is constructed for greatest efficiency at lower light intensities than the human eye—a result of the decrease of light in the water. This is especially the case with nocturnal and crepuscular fishes.

The function of the lateral line

The lateral line is a series of sense organs, small open tubes penetrating the scales and connected by a canal filled with slime. It runs along the sides of the body with ramifications on the head.

Experiments have demonstrated that the lateral line organs form a highly effective sense of distance. While swimming, the fish is surrounded by a 'pattern' of pressure

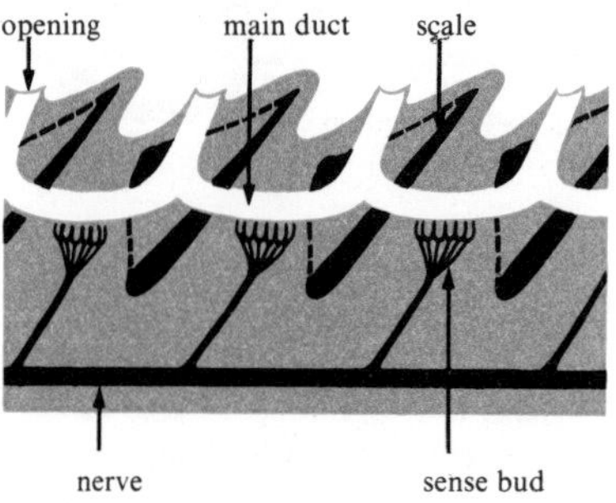

Section through the lateral line

waves; if this pattern is disturbed by other pressure waves from objects in the water (other fish, enemies, stones, etc.) the lateral line sense organs can detect them. The small differences in pressure in the open tubes of the lateral line caused by the disturbances are registered by nerves, and the message is relayed to and decoded by the brain, which automatically estimates the direction and distance of the object. This means that the fish, through its lateral line pores, is constantly receiving a 'picture' of its immediate surroundings. Blind fish, even carnivores like the pike, can survive and thrive simply by the sensitivity of the lateral line.

Hearing

Sound is transmitted more rapidly in water than in air and fish can hear, although to a very variable extent. However, most freshwater fish have excellent hearing. Like other vertebrates, fish have an internal ear, the labyrinth, which is the seat of the sense of hearing, in addition to that of balance and orientation.

The labyrinth has three semicircular canals with three ampullae which house the sense of turning. Below these canals are three bulges each containing an otolith

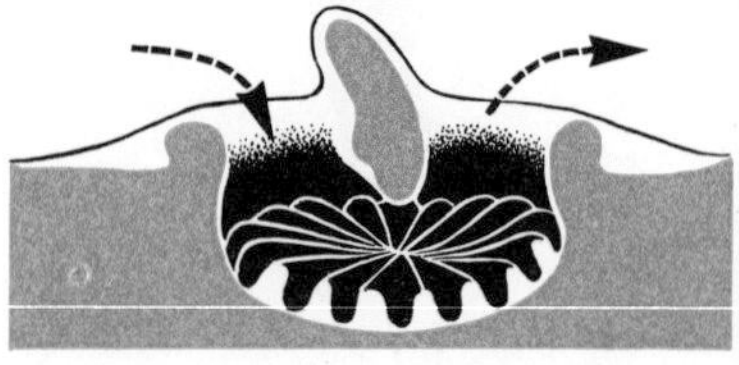

(earstone) resting on a cushion of sensitive hairs. The otoliths are solid, and built of lime. They grow and form year rings which are often useful for age determination. The two lower otoliths (the *sagitta* and the *asteriscus*) react to sound waves, the vibrations being registered by the sense hairs. The upper otolith (the *lapillus*), and the semicircular canals are the sites of the sense of equilibrium.

Herring, the carp family and the wels are fish with a well-developed sense of hearing, because the sound is intensified by the swim-bladder which is connected with the ear either through an extension reaching the labyrinth, or through a system of small movable bones, the Weberian ossicles. In the carp family these transmit the vibrations from the swim-bladder to the ear.

The frequency range at which fish can hear varies from 40–4,700 cycles per second. Von Frisch showed by experiments with minnows that this species was sen-

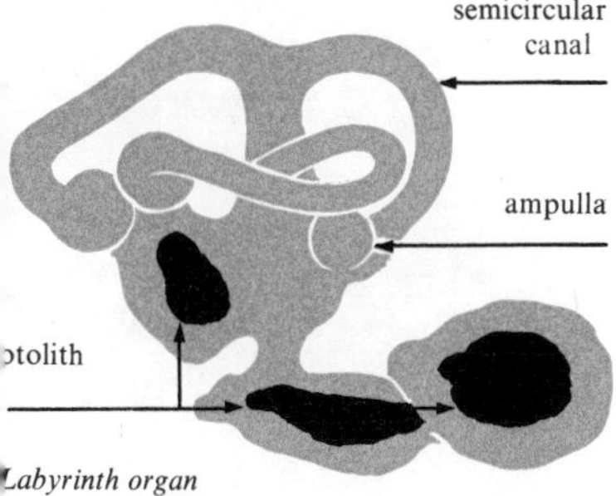

Labyrinth organ

sitive to a range from 16–7,000 c.p.s. Low vibrations (of 5–25 c.p.s.) are perceived by the lateral line. The ability to hear weak sounds (the auditory strength) was as good in the minnow as in man, and the fish could distinguish between tones as close as 3/8 octave (the small third). However, the capacity to hear is less in most carp fishes.

Fish have no vocal cords, but a few can produce rumbling and squeaking sounds by using special muscles to make the wall of the swim-bladder vibrate, or by letting out air from the air-duct. Other sounds made are, however, involuntary and are caused by swimming, eating, burrowing, etc. The underwater world may seem a silent one to us, but there is no doubt that fish communicate and understand a variety of sounds.

The senses of smell and taste

The sense of smell is well-developed and is centred on the nostrils, each of which

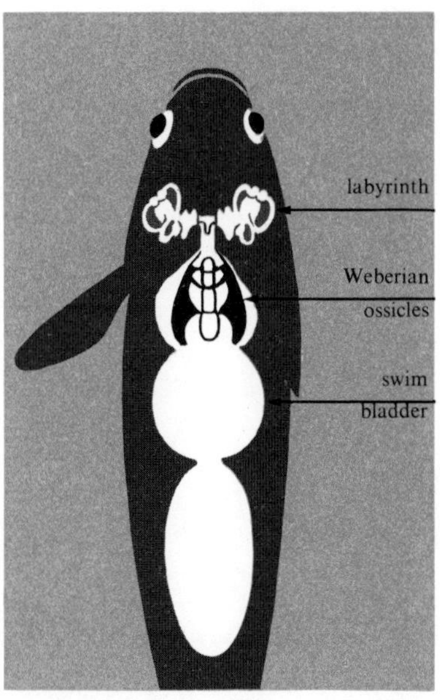

leads to an olfactory pit. In most fish each nostril is divided by a bridge of skin into an entrance or an exit for the water, which passes into the nostrils either during swimming or by active pumping. The eel scents its prey and has particularly well-developed olfactory pits capable of detecting as little as a few molecules of odorous substance. The pike, on the other hand, is dependent more on sight than smell, and its olfactory organs are poorly developed. Fish can recognise other fish by smell and a damaged fish will secrete alarm-substances which frighten others away, although they may attract predators.

The sense of taste is located in the mouth, in sense cells in the barbels, on the underside of the head and spread over a considerable area of the body surface.

BEHAVIOUR AND REPRODUCTION

Shoals

Some species are solitary for preference and, apart from the period of reproduction, live singly. The pike is an example, and the eel, wels and burbot are others; they are all rather large predators.

At the opposite extreme are the social fish species which live in greater or smaller shoals. The young often form dense shoals, but with increasing age the shoaling instinct weakens, and the fish spread or disperse into small groups. Plankton feeders in particular, which live mainly in open water, are apt to form shoals, e.g. whitefish and bleak. Wintering shoals are a special phenomenon of some carp fishes (e.g. bream, young tench, and carp). The fish gather in compact shoals in certain chosen deep places, mostly resting on the bottom. In spring these wintering shoals disperse.

Usually the fish in a shoal are of the same size and age, and as a rule comprise only one species. However, two species will sometimes shoal together and minnows often keep company with young trout, which they somewhat resemble in appearance and movements. Silver bream and bream also shoal together occasionally.

What is the importance of these shoals, outside the breeding period? Statistically a single swimming bleak or a shoal of fifty bleak will have about the same chance of meeting a pike. Fifty bleak swimming alone will, therefore, roughly speaking, be exposed to 50 times as many potentially fatal encounters with pike as they would have when moving in one shoal. In addition there is some mutual protection in a shoal; a predator can approach unobserved only with difficulty, and will often be confused on the dispersal of the shoal.

Migration

Many freshwater fish are rather sedentary in their daily life. The pike remains in a limited area, especially when young, and the same shoal of rudd or the same pair of tench can often be found regularly in some favoured spot over a considerable period. Brown trout and minnows are sedentary and remain within short stretches of their native stream where they know each stone and all the hiding places.

Migratory fish, in contrast, undertake long journeys, particularly before or after the breeding season. According to the direction of their spawning migrations these fish have been termed *catadromous* if they migrate downstream to breed, but *anadromous* if the opposite. The eel is a catadromous fish which spawns in the central north Atlantic Ocean but grows and matures in freshwater; sturgeon, shad, salmon and trout are anadromous species which grow for a few years in the sea before migrating into freshwater to spawn. Several fish of the carp family, e.g. roach and ide, have both a non-migratory and a type of anadromous stock, the latter growing up in brackish waters.

The fish are caused to migrate by hormones formed in connection with the maturation of the gonads; their adjustment to the environment changes physiologically, their senses demand new surroundings and they migrate in order to find them. Salmon have been shown to have an almost incredible capacity for remembering and recognising the smell of the water in which they grew up.

Sex and reproduction

In fish the two sexes generally resemble one another externally, other than in the breeding season, although sometimes there are secondary sexual differences in fin shape or size. The pectoral fin in the gudgeon, the pelvic fin in the tench, and the dorsal in the grayling and four-horned bullhead all show such differences. In the tooth carps of southern Europe differences exist in the colour pattern, or the male is much smaller than the female (e.g. *Gambusia*).

As the gonads reach full maturity the male acquires more vivid colours, and in several species the appearance is so changed that the male can be said to have a special mating dress (salmon, trout and stickleback are examples). In the carp family the males acquire a peculiar rash of white horny pimples, known as the spawning tubercles, especially on the head and the front part of the body. These tubercles disappear after spawning, and their precise function is not known for certain.

Most freshwater fishes spawn in shallow water. The chosen area for spawning varies from a stony bottom in rapid

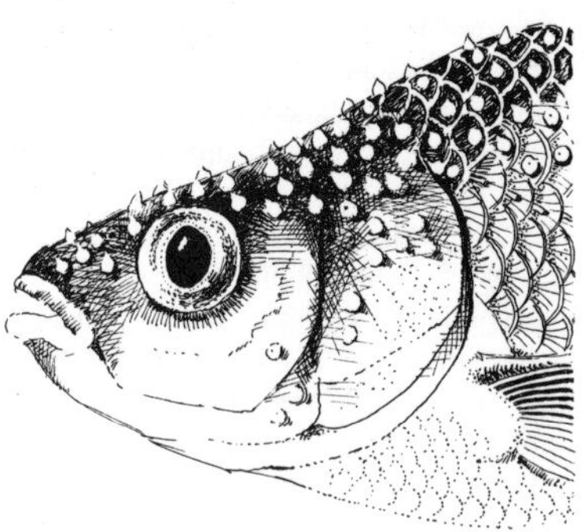

currents (lampreys, salmon, minnow, asp, the nases, barbel, etc.) to vegetation-rich, stagnant water (carp, bream, silver bream, pond loach, perch, etc.).

Outside the spawning season the gonads are quite small, and only with the approach of the breeding season do they swell to form sacs which produce eggs (roe) or sperm (milt) on their inner walls. They open through a short duct just behind the anus.

Maturing of the gonads is of course

regulated by hormones, but before spawning takes place a certain water temperature is often required, and roughly speaking we distinguish between winter, spring and summer spawning fish. Spawning of any species is generally earlier in southern than in northern Europe. Sperm and eggs are shed freely in the water, where fertilisation takes place. A form of copulation with internal fertilisation occurs in some species (some bullheads, gobies), and in *Gambusia*—which is viviparous—the male's anal fin is modified into a copulatory organ. Some species spawn in shoals, others pair off. Among the carp family hybrids are rather common, and the rudd, for example, often joins in the spawning of other species. Most hybrids (e.g. carp × crucian carp) are unable to breed, but some are fertile with the parent species.

In some species all the eggs become mature together and may be spawned at one and the same time (pike, roach, perch). In others the eggs mature more slowly and are shed in two or more portions at intervals of some days (tench, carp, bleak, ide, bream, white bream). Most freshwater fish eggs are transparent or reddish, slightly heavier than water and a little sticky so that they can adhere to stones or plants. Shad and burbot have light eggs which often float in the water until hatching.

The number of eggs depends on their size (constant for each species) and on the age and size of the parent fish. Salmon eggs measure 5–7 mm, 5,000–7,000 eggs making one litre, and 2,000 eggs are spawned for each kg of the weight of the female. Pike eggs are smaller, and a large

development. The egg of the carp needs about 100 day-degrees. Therefore at 20°C the carp egg will develop in 100 divided by 20, or 5 days.

In most cases the parents do not care for their offspring, but some fish do protect their brood to some extent. The eggs are deposited in more or less elaborate nests which are guarded, often by the male (sticklebacks, wels, gobies). The bitterling deposits its eggs inside the protecting shell of living freshwater mussels.

Spawning is for many fish a severe physiological strain. They do not feed, or feed very little, during the spawning season, and after it they are lean and exhausted. Many salmon and all lampreys die after spawning.

Egg just before hatching

Larval development

At hatching the young frees itself from the egg membranes and stretches its body. Its length is about three times the diameter of the egg and it has a large yolk-sac; it

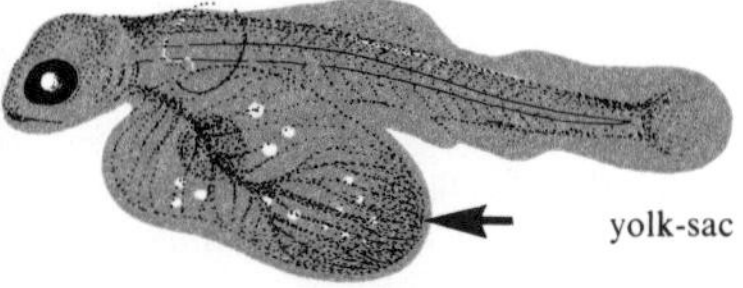

Newly hatched salmon larva

does not resemble the adult and at this stage is called a larva. Most newly hatched larvae remain passive for some days (for several weeks in the salmon) until the yolk-sac is consumed.

During its development the embryo lives off the yolk-mass, which it gradually absorbs so that the last remnants become enclosed in the belly. By this time the mouth is fully formed and open, and the larvae of many species then swim to the surface to fill their swim-bladder with air.

Growth and age

Growth is determined mainly by the amount of food available, but also by many other factors; it is most rapid in the early years. After maturity is reached growth decreases partly because the development of the gonads results in a loss of 10–25% of the body weight at each spawning, and partly because some of the sexual hormones actually restrict growth.

Growth decreases with increasing age, but fish grow during their whole lifespan. This apart, growth during the year is not constant, for in winter fish eat little or nothing but live on the reserves of fat accumulated during summer. The carp, for example, loses 5–15% of its weight during winter. The growth of the fish

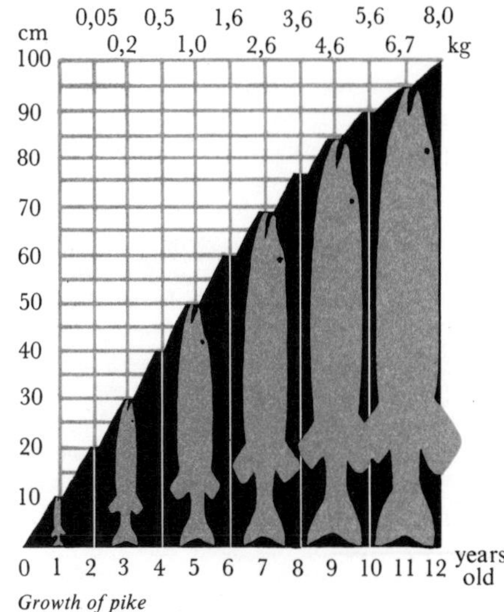

Growth of pike

shown as a graph therefore increases in steps. It is, of course, obvious that different species of fish have different maximum lengths and that their annual growth increments vary also.

Measuring increasing length is obviously only measuring one of the dimensions of growth. Growth in height and width is proportionate to growth in length, and the relation between weight and length can be expressed as follows: weight $= a \times L^n$, where (a) is a constant, (L) is length, and the exponent (n) is, as a rule, about 3. As fish grow throughout their life no absolute figures can be given for the maximum size attained; the maxima mentioned in this book mean that fish exceeding the given length are very rare.

Most fish are eaten or caught before they become senile. Many of the smaller species only reach an age of 1–4 years, but for members of the larger carp family the age-limit is 10–20 years. The carp is known to live for longer than 40 years, and the sturgeon is said to live more than 100 years.

FOOD AND FEEDING

The intense competition between fish species has forced them to exploit every possibility to find living space and food. Fish therefore occur in all kinds of freshwaters, and indeed most other freshwater animals are utilised as food by one fish or another, and sometimes by several.

Fish species can roughly be divided into (1) plant-eaters, (2) animal-eaters, and (3) predators. Most species, however, have a rather mixed diet.

The plant-eaters form the smallest group. They feed on green algae, which they rasp from stones and wood, or they nibble the green shoots of water-plants. Very often, at the same time, they eat small animals hiding in the vegetation (e.g. small crustaceans, worms, the larvae of midges), thus supplementing their diet. The sterlet and nases are mainly plant-feeders.

The animal-eaters form by far the largest group. They feed on worms, bivalves, snails and crustaceans, but especially on the larvae of insects so characteristic of the freshwater fauna (see pp. 32–5).

The predators mainly eat other fish, although they will eat frogs, water-shrews or other small vertebrates if they are available. However, even the food of carnivores may be mixed, and in ponds with relatively few fish even pike may deign to eat such small insignificant animals as water-slaters.

The search for food

When their yolk-sac is absorbed, the young generally shoal in shallow water, and feed near the surface on microscopic planktonic organisms, especially rotifers, the larvae of small crustaceans and diatoms. The eyes of the young are relatively large and well-developed, and they search for food by sight. Indeed, for many surface-living fish sight remains an essential sense in the search for food. The lateral line gradually assumes an increasing importance with growth, particularly for those fish which hunt for actively moving prey.

For fish which after their first growth stages begin to feed on bottom-living animals, the importance of sight decreases and the senses of taste and smell become more developed. These bottom fishes have particularly well-developed sensory cells around the mouth, and many also

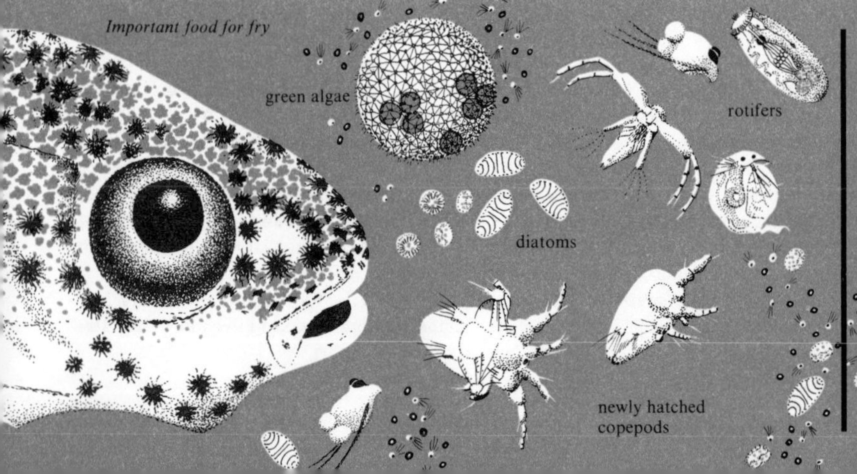

Important food for fry

have barbels well supplied with sensory cells (burbot, wels).

Fish which rely on their sight to find food feed mainly in the daytime and stop feeding at night. The wels, burbot and eels, on the other hand, are nocturnal fish which are guided by well-developed senses of taste and smell.

Feeding

The shape of the mouth, jaws, teeth and throat varies with different feeding habits. Most fish have teeth not only in the jaws, but also on several other bones in the mouth. These palatine and vomerine teeth are often very numerous and can be used to identify some species; for example, in salmon and trout there are differences in the teeth on the vomer in the roof of the mouth. Predatory fish usually have a large mouth with pointed or sharp, often backwardly pointing teeth, suitable for catching and holding large prey. The mouth may also be protractile as in the bream and sturgeon, where it is used to suck in the larvae of midges, or colonies of worms from the bottom. In the lampreys the mouth has the form of a sucking disc with which they fasten themselves to their prey or to stones. The lamprey then uses its toothed tongue to rasp a hole in the skin of its prey.

Vomerine bones

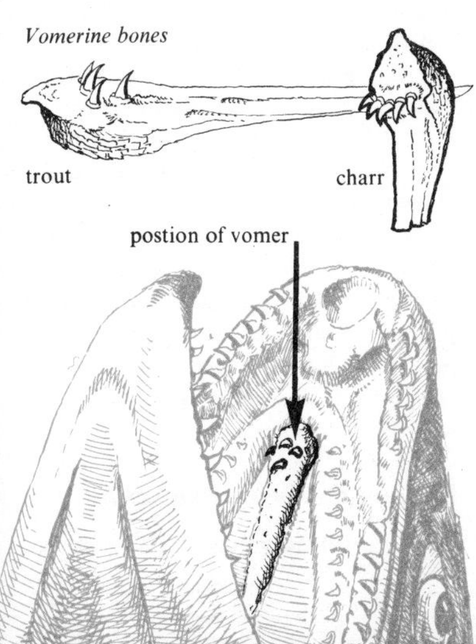

Plant-eaters, such as the nase, may have a sharp, horny lower lip suitable for scraping algae from rocks and submerged wood. Teeth are totally missing or are minimally developed. Plankton-feeders, living on microscopic organisms, have only a moderate-sized mouth without teeth or at most with weak teeth. The gill-rakers form a dense sieve preventing small food items from passing out through the gills when water is expelled during respiration.

The predators swallow their prey whole, and a pike can engulf a fish as large as half its own length. The cyprinid fishes have no teeth in their mouth, but crush their food before it reaches the intestine by means of the pharyngeal teeth. These are placed in from one to three rows on the lowest pair of pharyngeal bones just beyond the last of the gill-arches. These teeth are distinctively shaped and occur in relatively constant numbers and arrangement in different species, but in this book, where only external characters are considered for the identification of species, they will not be fully described.

The pharyngeal teeth are moved by strong muscles and grind against a horny plate in the roof of the pharynx, crushing and tearing the food as it passes. The teeth are either simple and conical (as in in the asp), or they have a serrate face (as in the rudd) or a knife-shaped edge (as in the nases). In the carp they have blunt crushing faces. They are lost in the spawning season, and afterwards replaced by new ones which are formed in the tissue close to the pharynx. They are finally attached firmly to the pharyngeal bones.

The grey mullets have no teeth, or only very small ones on their lips. Their food, which is mostly vegetable, is pressed into a solid mass in a strongly muscular walled part of the foregut which resembles the gizzard of birds.

Examples of pharyngeal bones, from above

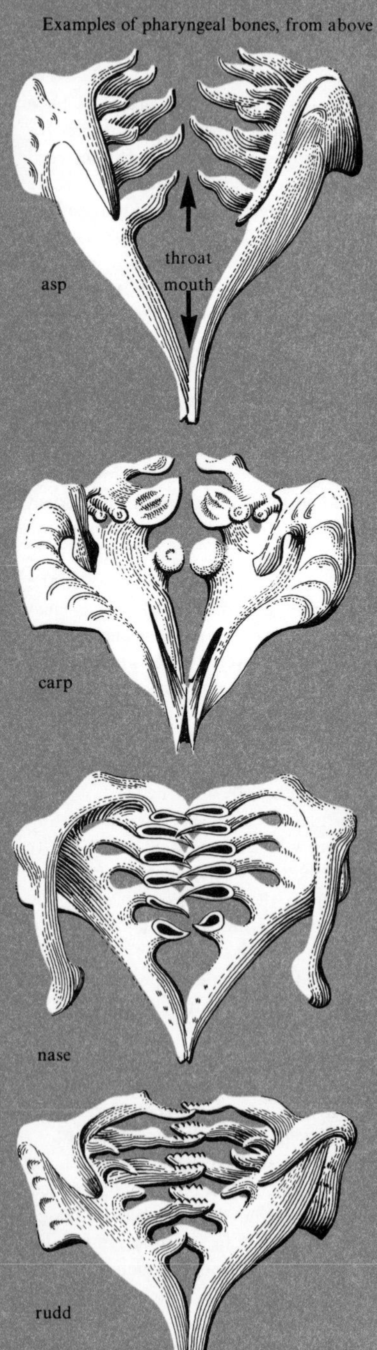

The gut and digestion

The development and appearance of the stomach and the intestines varies with the type of food eaten. In predators the stomach is large, and the intestine is often shorter than the body. Fish with a mixed diet have a small stomach and a longer intestine, which in the purely plant-eaters is often 5–10 times the body length. Food is partly digested in the stomach, and large prey reaches the stomach alive. The cyprinid fishes, however, have no stomach, and in this group the oesophagus is directly connected to the intestine.

At the point where stomach and intestines meet there are often a number of short pyloric appendages, which secrete enzymes and neutralise the strongly acid stomach contents before they reach the intestine. The liver is large and rich in oil with a high vitamin A and D content.

In the lampreys, digestion begins with the pumping of digestive enzymes into the wound, while the lamprey is fixed to its prey by its sucking mouth. The flesh of the prey is broken down into a soup which is then sucked in by the lamprey; these enzymes also prevent the blood of the prey from clotting. Animals as different as squids, spiders, the larvae of dragonflies and water-beetles digest their prey in a similar way.

The time it takes a fish to digest its food depends upon the temperature and the kind of food concerned. A roach may take four hours to digest midge larvae at a temperature of 20°C, but 9 hours to digest mussels or snails. At 10°C these times are doubled or trebled. Worms are digested quickly, but food rich in calories is only slowly digested, and for large prey (e.g. fish) the period of digestion may last as long as several days.

How much does a fish eat?

Food serves two functions: it is con-

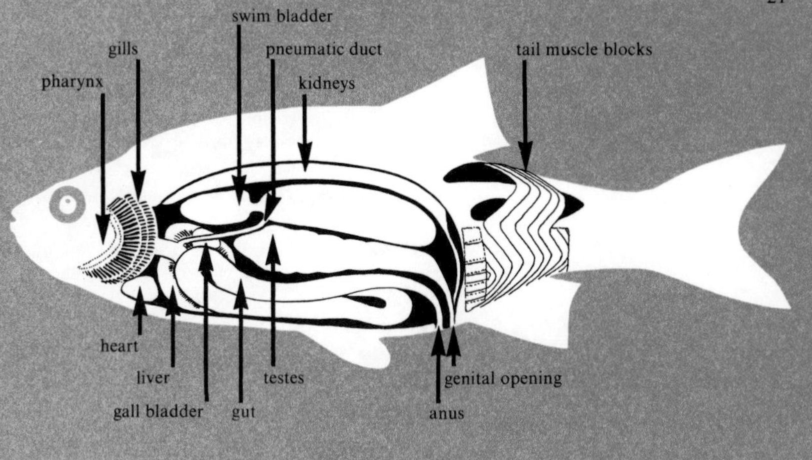

verted into energy and the surplus is used for growth. The rate of growth is thus dependent on the nutritive value of the food (the number of calories) and on the amount eaten.

Freshwater fish commonly eat an amount of food corresponding to half, or even more of their own weight daily while they are growing, and the main bulk of it is used for growth. However, when the food is low in calories and contains much waste matter (e.g. water-fleas) the fish must consume three times as much as when the food consists of solid digestible protein. Young fish eat 2–3 g of mixed food for each gramme of increase in body weight; this may be expressed as the coefficient of nourishment being 2–3. (The coefficient of nourishment (CN) therefore denotes the number of grammes of food necessary to give an increase in body weight of one gramme).

It appears that the CN increases with age, that is a gradually decreasing part of the food is used for growth, while the amount used for the production of energy becomes greater. An old pike needs 10–30 grammes of food, roughly the weight of one bleak, to increase its weight by only one gramme. Generally, the coefficient of nourishment for fish in good health and in their prime is around 4–8.

The coefficient depends not only on the nutritive value of the food and on the age of the fish, but also on the abundance of food. Regular, large meals cause the fish to fail to utilise the calories fully, possibly because the food's passage through the digestive tract becomes quicker than normal. The coefficient of nourishment therefore becomes relatively high. After a period without food, or when it is scarce, the food is utilised very efficiently.

HABITATS

Freshwaters offer fish as many different possibilities of life as does the sea. It is no wonder, then, that the fish living in a cool mountain brook are not also found inhabitating a peat-pit in the lowlands. The types of habitat available are therefore of considerable interest. In rivers, a number of regions are recognised (and named according to the fish species which seem typical of them), although they are less obvious in the British Isles, where the fauna is poor and the rivers relatively short, than in mainland Europe.

Mountain brooks and spring brooks

Brooks are characterised by swiftly running water, with rapids and waterfalls alternating with deep hollows where the water is quieter. The bottom consists of pebbles or coarse gravel. Even in summer the temperature is low and does not exceed 10°C, but the water is clear and well oxygenated. The invertebrate fauna is made up of animals adapted to this running water, the larvae of insects capable of clinging to stones, and often living in shelters (larvae of caddis-flies, mayflies, stoneflies).

Here the brown trout is non-migratory, and this area is called the *trout region*. Right up to an altitude of 2000 m the brown trout and the bullhead are found, and in some places we also have wild stocks of the brook trout introduced from North America.

Brooks rising from springs in the lowlands have a less steep descent than the mountain streams, but they also should be considered to belong to the trout region. The remainder of the fish fauna of this region includes lamperns, spiny loach, common loach and minnow.

Rapidly flowing streams

Where brooks converge to form wider streams with deeper water, but still with a rapid current, we reach the *grayling region*. The bottom is stony where the current is rapid, but there are long stretches of gravel or coarse sand, sometimes with plant cover of water thyme, water starwort and bullrush. The water is still well oxygenated and clear, but somewhat warmer than in the trout region.

Here the grayling is found as a permanent inhabitant. The remaining fauna includes gudgeon, chub, and in south and central Europe, nase. The burbot may also occur here, and salmon and migratory trout spawn in the region. It is also the home of the pike, which may be common in the deeper hollows and among the submergent weeds where there is shelter from the current.

The upper reaches of the rivers are dominated by the salmonid fishes but the grayling region is the last of these. Below it begins that part of the river which is dominated by members of the carp family.

Streams and rivers with a good current

Here the stream is deeper and in places has a soft bottom with vegetation. The water flows rapidly but in summer may reach temperatures of around 20°C. In central Europe the dominant species is the barbel, and this part of the river is therefore known as the *barbel region*.

Here we find dace, asp and ide, but also shoals of roach and rudd. Perch and pike are also common, the latter particularly in sheltered bays. In southern Europe the zingel, streber and the Danube ruffe live in the barbel region.

Rivers and broad, slow-running rivulets

The fish fauna in slow-running water is very rich. The bottom is soft, the water may be deep and it is often turbid, while the vegetation in the bank-zone is rich. This reach of the streams is termed the *bream region,* and here we find the same species of fish as in the lowland lakes of cultivated areas: besides the main species, the bream, we have silver bream and tench, the roach is numerous, and carp and zander (pike-perch) may occur. There is a large stock of eels, and wels (sheat-fish) in central and south Europe. Naturally the pike is present also in this region.

The lower bottom-living fauna is generally rich. Especially numerous are larvae

of midges and may-flies, and also freshwater worms.

The bream region of the rivers is a temporary refuge for many migratory fish such as sea-lamprey, sturgeon, shad, and also sea fishes such as mullets, bass and flounder.

Estuaries and brackish waters

Near river mouths freshwater and sea water become mixed due to the tidal movement of the sea. Many freshwater fish can tolerate low salinities and a number of species are found in what would appear to be salt water. All the migratory species of freshwater fish pass through the estuary with its brackish water. Young salmon, for example, stay there for a short period in order to accustom themselves to the salt water and to the change in diet.

The Black Sea has a relatively low salinity and a number of the members of the carp family have developed migratory forms, which grow up in the Black Sea before ascending the rivers (e.g. the Danube) to spawn. The Baltic too is less salt, and cyprinids and pike occur in it, particularly in the northern part.

Growth in brackish water is generally quicker than in fresh water because food is more abundant and the choice of diet wider.

Lakes

According to their size, depth, mineral content and temperature lakes are as different from one another as are rivers, and the fish fauna is adapted to these differences.

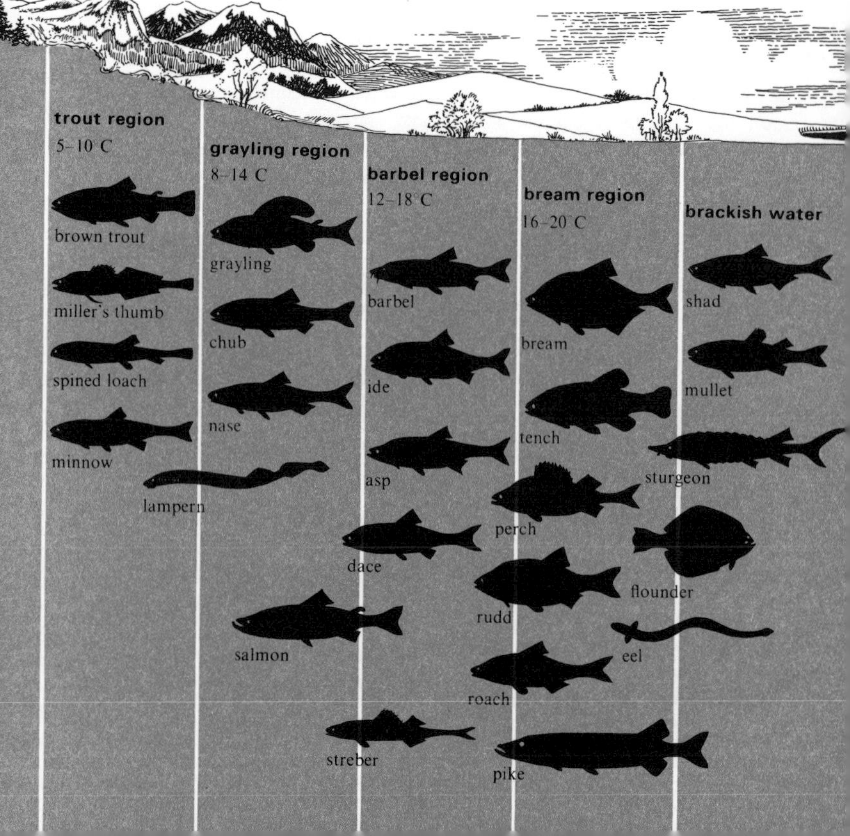

Lowland lakes

In lowland areas, lakes are rather shallow, and in cultivated districts or in built-up areas are often rich in nutrients (eutrophic) with a large production of plankton and rather turbid water during summer. At this time the water close to the surface is heated by the sun, its specific gravity decreases, and consequently it stays near the surface as a warm layer (the *epilimnion*) several metres thick, above the colder, deeper water mass (the *hypolimnion*). Between these two layers is a transitionary layer called the *thermocline*.

The deeper parts of the lake below the thermocline are thus cut off from the better oxygenated, warm surface layers. Only during autumn and winter, when the surface water becomes colder and the difference between the specific gravity of the hypolimnion and the epilimnion is less, does a general mixture of the water-masses take place.

If we imagine cutting a section through a lake we would be able to see the following sequence of habitats:

Along the beaches are stony surf-zones and wide reed-swamps. Beyond the reeds, at depths of 2–5 m, is the erect, submerged vegetation—long plants with submerged leaves, especially pondweed, water-milfoil

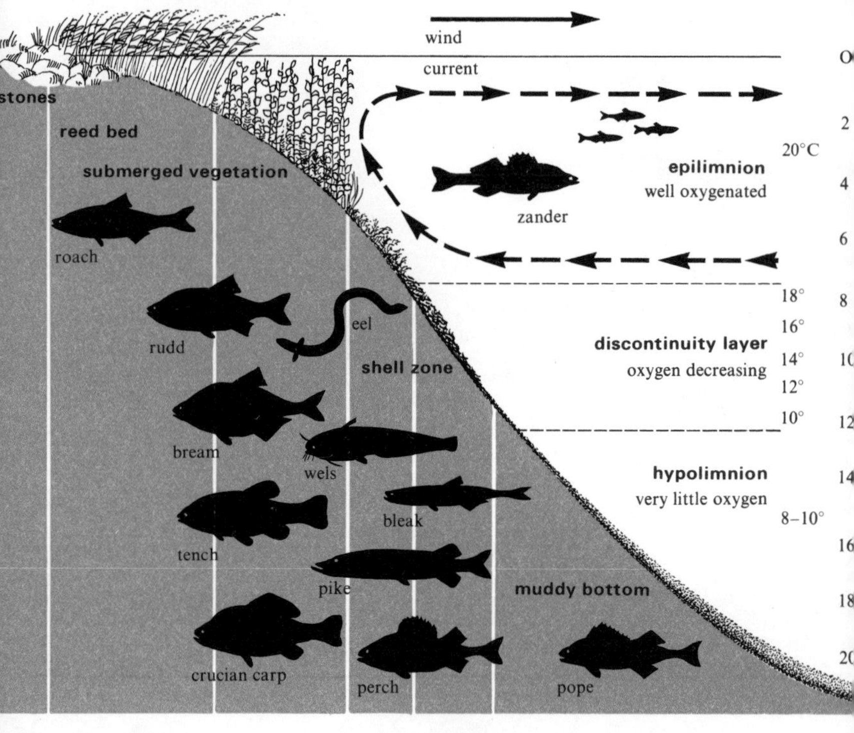

and watercrow-foot. In still deeper water there is often a bottom growth of submerged algae and mosses, mainly stonewort, water-moss and silkweed. At a depth of more than 7 m the bottom is soft and bare, often with a band of empty shells (pond snails and mussel shells) along the lower zone of the bottom vegetation.

The fish fauna in a eutrophic lowland lake resembles that of the bream region of the slow-flowing big rivers. In the zone of erect, submerged plants we find bream, silver bream, rudd, roach, tench, and pike. Fry, too, seek this zone and the outer part of the reed-swamp. Along the surf beaches, which have a strong water movement, live several species also found in running water, e.g. loach, minnow, and bullhead.

In the outer part of the zone of erect, submerged plants are found shoals of bleak and perch. Perch also occur farther out in deeper water over the bare floor and here too the zander lives; it can compete best with pike and perch where the water is coloured. Dense populations of ruffe are also often found in this deeper water.

Ponds and swamps

These waters are usually small and overgrown with weeds, and their fish are hardy species which can tolerate a low level of oxygen. They are very often overcrowded with stunted fish, and food supplies are usually insufficient.

The carp, crucian carp and perch find these conditions tolerable but unless carefully managed will become overcrowded to form what have been called 'thousand-brother communities'. Other species thriving in such ponds are sticklebacks, the European *Leucaspius*; in central Europe pond loach, mud minnow and bitterling, and in southern Europe the cyprinodonts. Ponds can be extremely productive fisheries if suitably managed (see pp. 205–8).

Cold lakes and mountain lakes

Many lakes in northern Europe and in the foothills of the Alps are cool, deep and rather poor in nutrients (*oligotrophic*). The water is well oxygenated. Here the fish fauna is dominated by the whitefish species and lake trout which are found particularly in the open water, while the fish near the shore include some of the common cyprinid fish, besides pike, perch and in Europe, burbot.

Alpine lakes up to a height of 2000 m are poor in nutrients and have only a short summer. Here only trout, charr, minnow and bullheads occur.

A warning about theoretical divisions

One of the attractions of nature is that it is never completely amenable to strict arrangement in categories. The various terms and categories used in this account of rivers and still waters are really only convenient pigeon-holes to contain some general observations. By no means all rivers and lakes will fit into them, some streams will probably be known to the reader where one or more regions are missing, while others will, more than likely, know of atypical lakes. The summary of freshwaters given here is therefore a very simplified account of the situation.

Key

Species or groups marked with an asterisk are native and long established introductions to British waters; an asterisk in brackets indicates that the fish is present due to recent introduction.

Key to main groups

1 Body eel-like but without paired fins; no jaws, mouth a rounded sucking disc .... ***Lampreys,** p. 42
Otherwise **2**

2 Body with 5 rows of bony plates; tail-fin asymmetric upper lobe the largest .... ***Sturgeons,** p. 44
Otherwise .... **Bony fish,** key 1

Key 1. Bony fish.

3 Body a flattened oval, with long fins; skin smooth but with prickles along the lateral line and the bases of dorsal and anal fins .... ***Flounder,** p. 176
Body eel-like; dorsal, tail, and anal fins continuous; pelvic fins absent .... ***Eel,** p. 148
Otherwise **2**

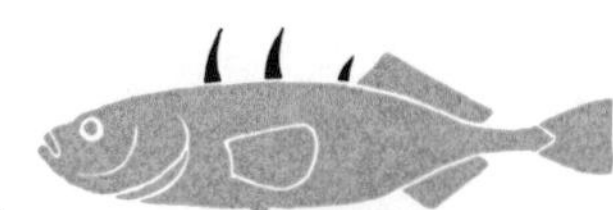

2 Small scaleless fish with 3–10 free spines on back in front of the dorsal fin . . . . ***Sticklebacks,** p. 174

Small scaled fish with pelvic fins fused . . . . ***Gobies,** p. 170

Otherwise **3**

3 Body scaleless (or the scales minute and only just visible to the naked eye) **4**

Body with distinct scales (except the leather carp which is nearly scaleless) **7**

4 With a pair or more of barbels around the mouth **5**

No barbels around the mouth; small fish **6**

5 Small fish, body slender; one short dorsal fin; ventral mouth surrounded by short barbels . . . . ***Loaches,** p. 140

Large fish with broad, flat head and at least two long barbels on upper lip . . . . **(*) Catfishes** p. 144

With broad flat head, and a barbel on the chin; short first dorsal fin; second dorsal and anal fins long . . . . ***Burbot,** p. 154

6 One long dorsal fin; a small fleshy flap over each eye . . . . **Blenny,** p. 170

Two dorsal fins, the first with spiny rays. Broad, flat head, spiny gill-cover, eyes on top of head . . . . ***Miller's Thumb,** p. 172

7

Two dorsal fins, the first with rays, the second a small, rayless, adipose fin . . . . ***Salmon family,** p. 50

Two dorsal fins, or the dorsal fin divided into two parts; a first fin with spines, the second with soft rays **11**

One dorsal fin with soft rays only **8**

8

No lateral line; at least one distinct, black spot behind the head; belly scales form a sharp toothed edge . . . . ***Shads,** p. 48

The dorsal fin placed far back on the body, mouth and teeth large . . . . ***Pike,** p. 78

Otherwise **9**

9

The margin of the tail-fin convex or rounded; small fish less than 12 cm long **10**

The margin of the tail-fin concave or forked . . . . ***Carp family,** p. 82

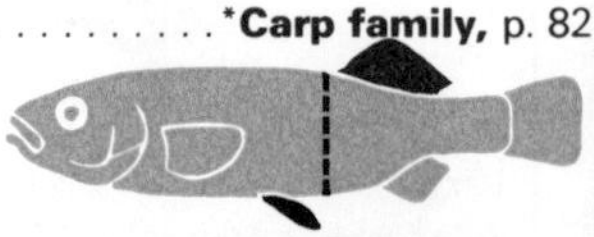

10

Pelvic fins clearly in front of a vertical line from from the dorsal fin origin . . . . **Toothcarps,** p. 152

The base of the pelvic fins just below the dorsal fin origin . . . . **Mud-minnows,** p. 80

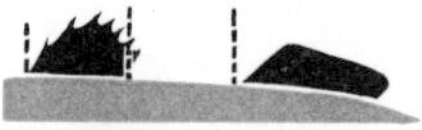

11

Two dorsal fins separated by a space almost as long as the base of the first dorsal fin **12**

Dorsal fins separate, but either joined at the base, or separated by a small space **13**

Dorsal fins not separate **14**

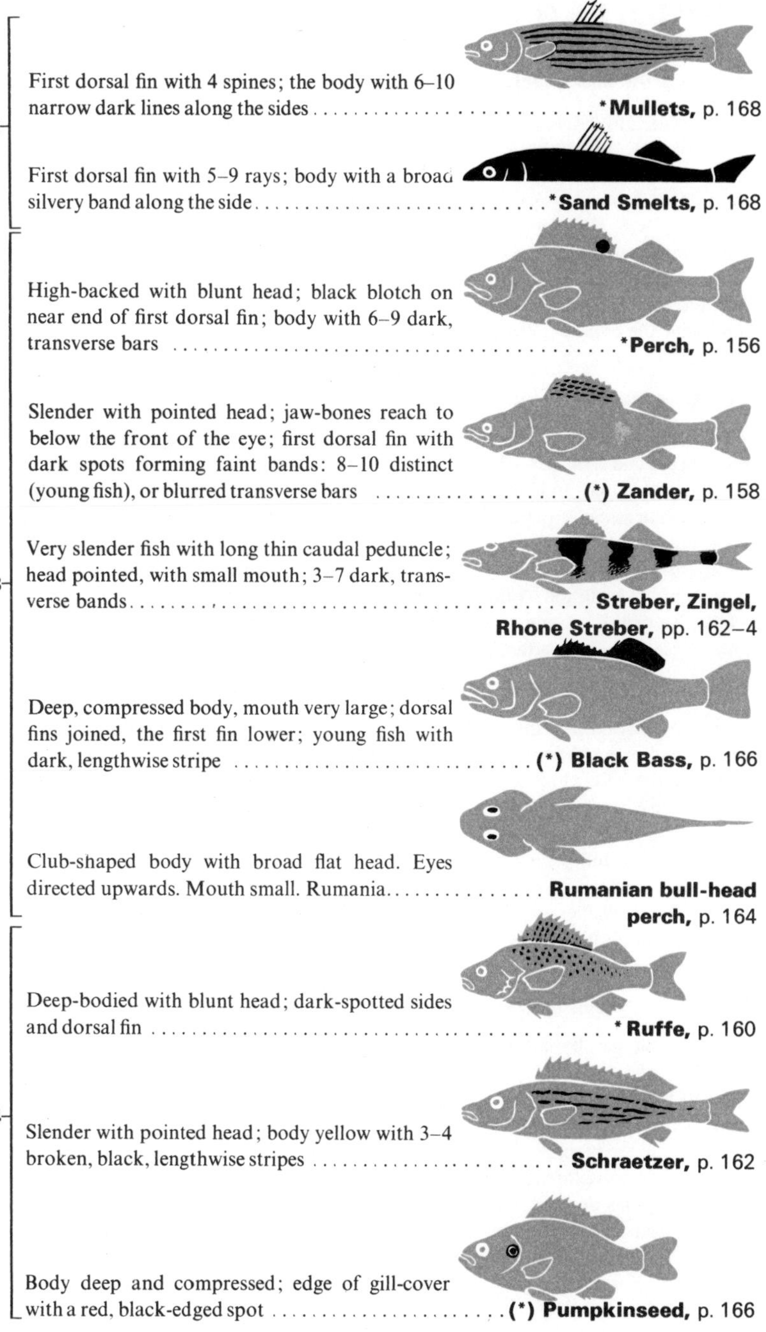

12 First dorsal fin with 4 spines; the body with 6–10 narrow dark lines along the sides . . . . ***Mullets,** p. 168

First dorsal fin with 5–9 rays; body with a broad silvery band along the side . . . . ***Sand Smelts,** p. 168

High-backed with blunt head; black blotch on near end of first dorsal fin; body with 6–9 dark, transverse bars . . . . ***Perch,** p. 156

Slender with pointed head; jaw-bones reach to below the front of the eye; first dorsal fin with dark spots forming faint bands: 8–10 distinct (young fish), or blurred transverse bars . . . . **(*) Zander,** p. 158

13 Very slender fish with long thin caudal peduncle; head pointed, with small mouth; 3–7 dark, transverse bands . . . . **Streber, Zingel, Rhone Streber,** pp. 162–4

Deep, compressed body, mouth very large; dorsal fins joined, the first fin lower; young fish with dark, lengthwise stripe . . . . **(*) Black Bass,** p. 166

Club-shaped body with broad flat head. Eyes directed upwards. Mouth small. Rumania . . . . **Rumanian bull-head perch,** p. 164

Deep-bodied with blunt head; dark-spotted sides and dorsal fin . . . . ***Ruffe,** p. 160

14 Slender with pointed head; body yellow with 3–4 broken, black, lengthwise stripes . . . . **Schraetzer,** p. 162

Body deep and compressed; edge of gill-cover with a red, black-edged spot . . . . **(*) Pumpkinseed,** p. 166

IMPORTANT FOOD ANIMALS

True worms and Leeches *(Oligochaeta and Hirudinea)*

A number of species of true worm live in freshwater. *Stylaria* is very common, particularly in ponds, and is often found among floating water-plants in clear water. They are transparent, 1·5 cm long, have a "tentacle" at the front end, and reproduce by transverse division to form chains of animals. *Tubifex* worms form large colonies, especially in polluted places. They form tubes in the mud from which project their red tails, which act as gills. Leeches are close relations of the true worms, and are mostly blood-suckers, although a few eat whole small animals. The fish-leech (*Piscicola,* p. 188) is a parasite. The gnathobdellids, e.g. the medicinal leech, have three exceedingly sharp jaws. The common horse-leech and the common erpobdellid leeches feed on small worms, larvae of insects and snails.

Crustaceans *(Crustacea)*

The large crustaceans (Decapoda), such as the mitten crab and crayfishes, are eaten by eels, burbot and wels. More important as fish food are the water-slater (Isopoda), particularly in still water, and the freshwater shrimps (Amphipoda) living among stones and vegetation in streams and in still water. The plankton on which almost all young fish and many adult fish rely is composed mainly of entomostraceans, water-fleas (Cladocera) and copepods (Copepoda). Many species within these groups are also found close to the bottom or in vegetation. A third group of entomostraceans are the ostracods (Ostracoda), which live mainly among vegetation. The entomostraceans feed mainly on diatoms and green algae; all are important fish food.

Dragonflies, Alder-flies, Stoneflies *(Odonata, Neuroptera Plecoptera)*

Dragonfly larvae, like the adults, are predators. Those of the true dragonflies have a two-jointed pair of hooks under the chin which can be shot towards the prey. Their gills lie inside the body close to the anus and water can be pumped in and out so that they shoot themselves forward by a strong jet of water. Damselflies are light-weight dragonflies, whose larvae have three flat external gills posteriorly. They crawl among the vegetation or on the muddy bottom. The larvae of alder-flies feed on other animals, especially the larvae of midges.

Larvae of stoneflies are particularly numerous on or below stones in rapid streams (the trout region). Their bodies are flattened and they can be recognised by their two long tail-threads. Most are carnivorous, although some are vegetable-feeders.

Mayflies *(Ephemeroptera)*

As adults mayflies have only a short life (for some of them just a few hours) they do not feed. After their mating flight, which takes place in large swarms near the bank, the female deposits her eggs on the surface of the water either by flying low over it, dipping her abdomen, or (in some genera) by crawling underneath the water to deposit the eggs on stones. These larvae are perhaps the most common animals in freshwater, and can be recognised by their three long thread-like tails and by their rows of external gills on the sides. They feed on diatoms and green algae, which they browse from stones and wood with their brush-shaped jaws. Some species are confined to running water, while others are found only in still water. Mayflies form an important part of fish diet, both as larvae and as adults.

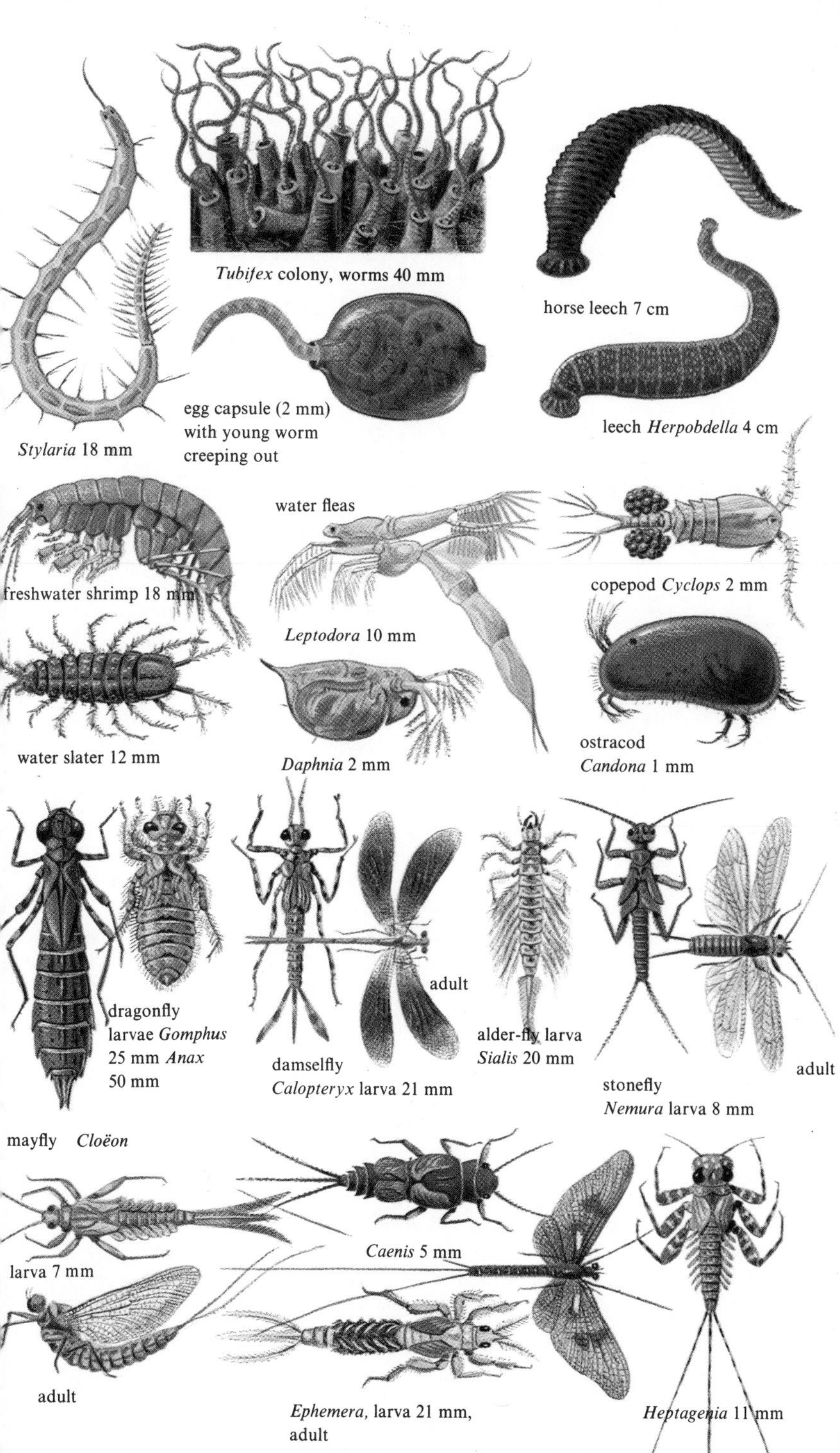

Tubifex colony, worms 40 mm
horse leech 7 cm
egg capsule (2 mm)
with young worm
creeping out
leech *Herpobdella* 4 cm
Stylaria 18 mm
water fleas
copepod *Cyclops* 2 mm
freshwater shrimp 18 mm
Leptodora 10 mm
water slater 12 mm
Daphnia 2 mm
ostracod
Candona 1 mm
adult
dragonfly
larvae *Gomphus*
25 mm *Anax*
50 mm
alder-fly larva
Sialis 20 mm
damselfly
Calopteryx larva 21 mm
adult
stonefly
Nemura larva 8 mm
mayfly *Cloëon*
larva 7 mm
Caenis 5 mm
adult
Ephemera, larva 21 mm,
adult
Heptagenia 11 mm

Caddis-flies (*Trichoptera*)

The larvae of caddis-flies are as common as those of may-flies. Most of them build tubes in which they protect their soft abdomens, and each species constructs a characteristic case using pieces of leaves, sticks, sand-grains, or empty snail shells. Some can swim while carrying this case. In running water the edges and undersides of all large stones are often covered by caddis cases built of small stones woven together and sometimes anchored by means of silk threads. Other species spin silken webs and even funnels in running water which act as fixed nets to capture edible particles carried by the current. Most caddis larvae are carnivorous, though some are entirely vegetarian. The larvae pupate in their cases, and the adults are moth-like insects always found near water, with long antennae, and dull-coloured, rather weak wings.

Beetles (*Coleoptera*)

Many beetles spend part or all their lives in freshwater. Water-beetles live in ponds and the adults are active swimmers and carnivores. They store their air beneath the horny wing-covers and come to the surface frequently to breath. The larvae are voracious, eating fish larvae, tadpoles, etc. The lower jaw is curved and sharply pointed and a digestive fluid is pumped through the hollow points into the prey, breaking up the tissues of the body so that the resulting 'soup' can be sucked up. The hydrophilid beetles are mostly small (although one reaches a length of 4 cm) and live in vegetation, feeding on the plants. The underside is provided with a layer of unwettable hairs in which air is trapped and which the beetles have to renew. Although the adult *Hydrous* is a plant-eater the larvae are carnivorous, and attack principally snails and tadpoles.

Gnats, Midges and Mosquitoes (*Nematocera*)

The larvae of mosquitoes (*Culex, Anopheles*) hang head down from the surface-film with their tail gills in contact with the air. They eat algae and small animals, and their pupae are very active. *Corethra,* the phantom-midge, has two pairs of swim bladders. It is transparent, breathes through its skin, and feeds on entomostraceans.

The larvae of midges live among plants or in the mud. Many make tubes, including the red larvae (blood-worms) of the *Chironomous* midges which live in oxygen-poor mud.

Black-flies (*Simulium*) live attached to stones in rapidly running, preferably slightly polluted, water. The females of many species are blood-sucking, give a painful bite and may occur in very large swarms.

Mussels and Snails (*Lamellibranchia, Gastropoda*)

Among mussels, the pea-mussels (*Sphaerium* and *Pisidium*) provide food for many fish. In turn they feed on small algae and plant debris, and are found even in small pools among water-plants or decaying leaves.

The snails are mainly pulmonates and at intervals have to come to the surface to breathe. They feed on algae and vegetation and are therefore especially common in overgrown lakes and ponds. The spiral-shelled pond snails and the rams-horn, *Planorbis*, are common and well known. In running water the low, cap-shaped river-limpets are found (*Ancylus* and *Acroloxus*), and another form occurs in lakes. Among the operculates which can close their shell with a lid, the freshwater winkle, a large viviparous species (*Viviparus*), is well known.

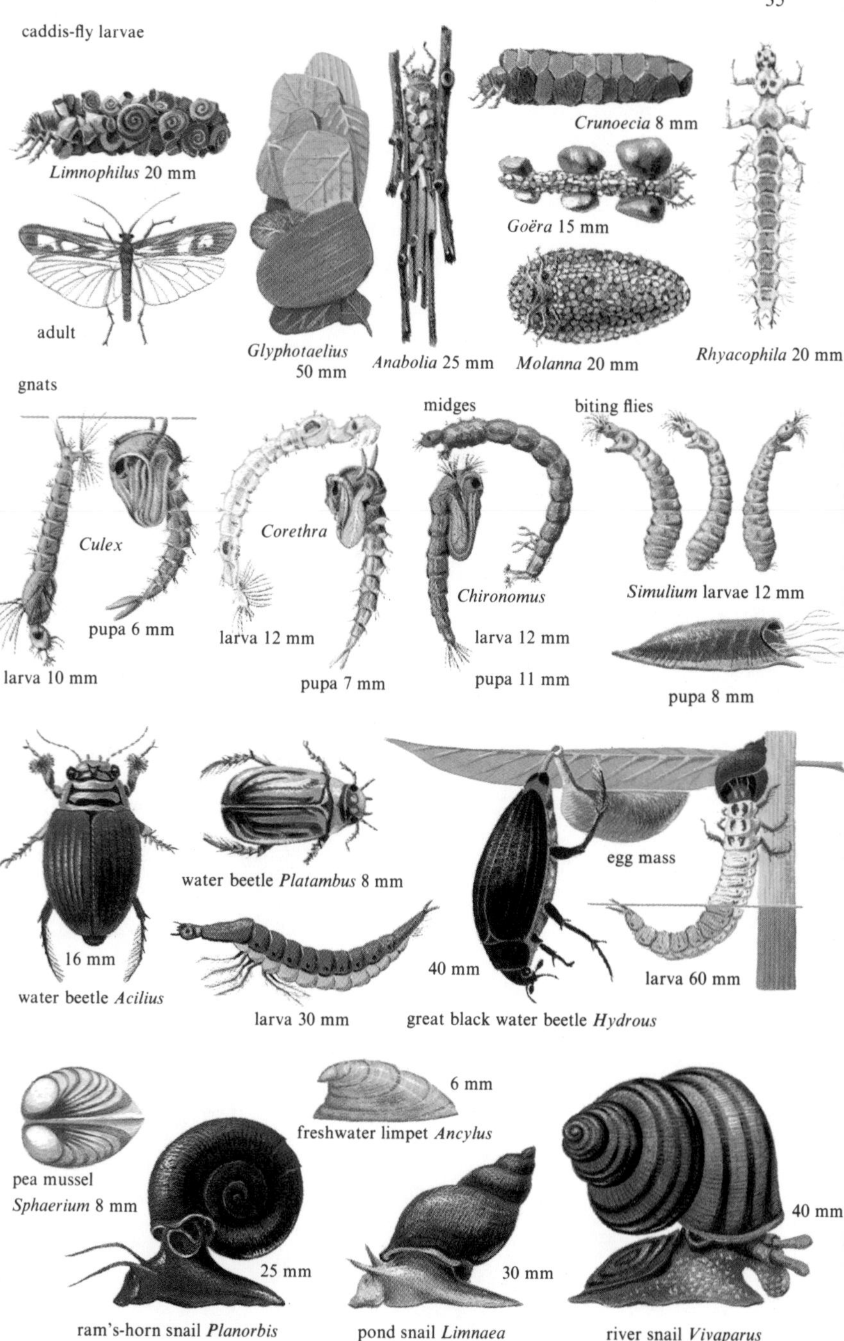
caddis-fly larvae
Limnophilus 20 mm
adult
Glyphotaelius 50 mm
Anabolia 25 mm
Crunoecia 8 mm
Goëra 15 mm
Molanna 20 mm
Rhyacophila 20 mm
gnats
Culex
pupa 6 mm
larva 10 mm
Corethra
larva 12 mm
pupa 7 mm
midges
Chironomus
larva 12 mm
pupa 11 mm
biting flies
Simulium larvae 12 mm
pupa 8 mm
16 mm
water beetle *Acilius*
water beetle *Platambus* 8 mm
larva 30 mm
egg mass
40 mm
larva 60 mm
great black water beetle *Hydrous*
pea mussel
Sphaerium 8 mm
6 mm
freshwater limpet *Ancylus*
25 mm
ram's-horn snail *Planorbis*
30 mm
pond snail *Limnaea*
40 mm
river snail *Vivaparus*

ILLUSTRATIONS AND DESCRIPTIONS OF THE SPECIES

External features of a fish

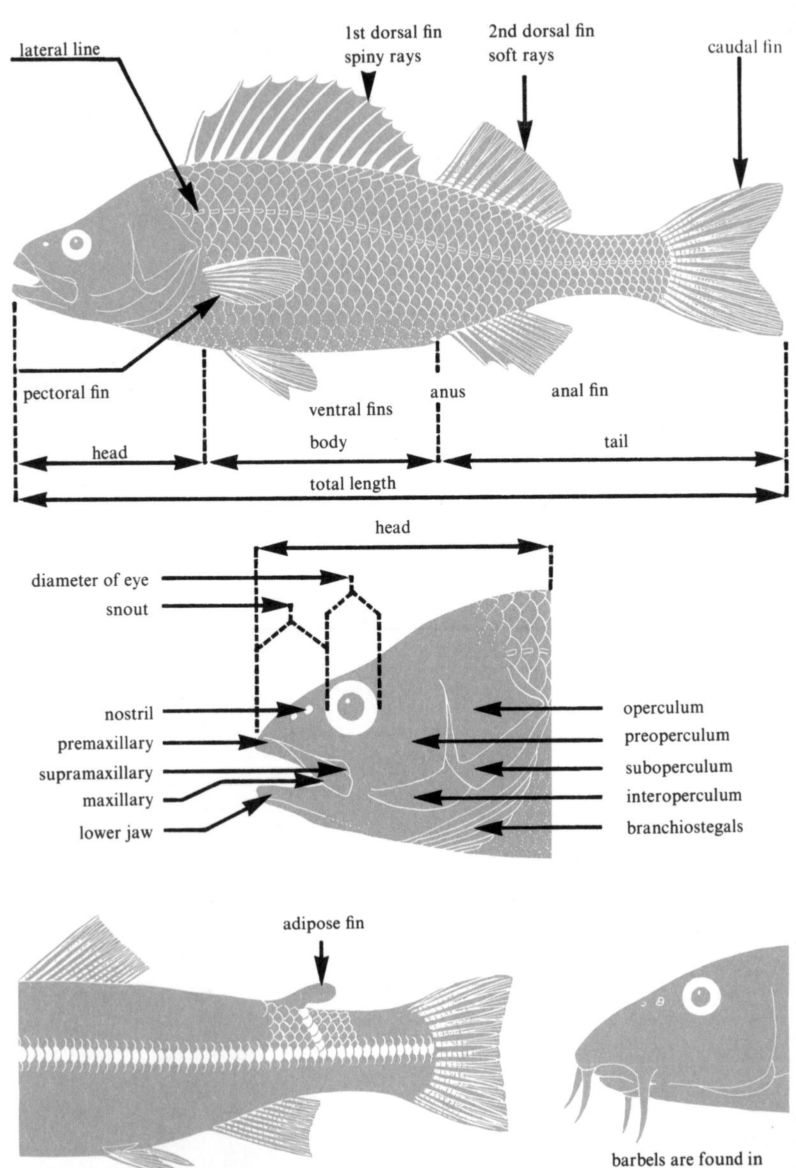

salmonids have an adipose fin. The white scales (much enlarged in this drawing) show how one counts them for identification purposes.

barbels are found in various lengths and numbers in sturgeons, some of the carp family, catfishes, loaches and cod.

CYCLOSTOMES

The cyclostomes (class Cyclostomata), which in freshwater are represented by lampreys, are morphologically so primitive that modern zoologists no longer regard them as fishes. They are only distantly related to the 'true' fishes and have followed their own line of development for 4–500 million years. The class Cyclostomata includes the marine hagfishes as well as the lampreys. The approximately 45 described living species are descended from the armoured cyclostomes (Ostracodermi), which were covered by bony plates, and lived (possibly in freshwater) about 300 million years ago.

The cyclostomes are the most primitive vertebrates known. Unlike all other vertebrates, they have no jaws, and their name derives from the circular sucking mouth which bears horny teeth. There are no paired fins and even the vertical fins are weakly developed. The body is eel-shaped, naked and slimy, while the skeleton is lightly developed and made of cartilage.

The gills and breathing mechanism differ from those of the bony fishes. Near the head, a sac extends backwards from the front of the intestine, and on each of its sides 7 openings lead into 7 gill-chambers, each connecting with the outside by a narrow aperture. In respiration, water enters through the mouth and is expelled through the gills, but it can also be pumped in and out directly through the gill-openings. This is useful when the lamprey is clamped by its sucking mouth to its prey (it is a blood-sucker and carrion-eater). This mouth also allows the lamprey to 'keep station' in a current by clinging to stones.

The larvae (ammocoetes) of lampreys live buried in the mud. They have a horseshoe-shaped lip, no teeth, and the eyes are very small and covered by skin. They are not parasitic, but filter bacteria, diatoms and other microscopic organisms from the water during respiration.

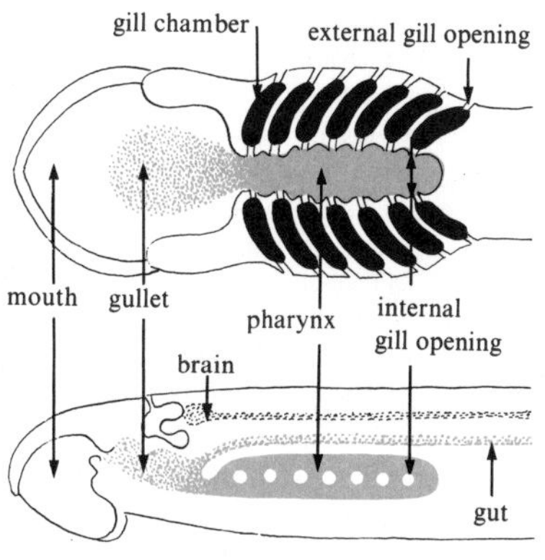

Horizontal and vertical sections through the front end of a lamprey

1. Lampern

Lampetra fluviatilis (L.)

Distinctive features: Both parts of the dorsal fin separated by a space; the mouth-disc with few, strong teeth; the tooth-plate at the upper edge of the disc with two widely separated teeth.

A closely related species the far-eastern lampern (*L. japonica*), is found from the White Sea to Korea.

Size: c. 32 cm, rarely 40 cm. The females are larger than the males.

The lampern migrates from the sea into rivers and brooks in August–November or in early spring. Some over-winter in the rivers without feeding. On reaching maturity the body becomes shorter, the dorsal fin increases in size, an anal fin is developed in the female, and the intestine degenerates.

Spawning takes place on a stony bottom in February–June. The female attaches herself to a stone while shaping a pit by lashing her tail. The male then uses his disc to fasten himself to the female, usually to one side of her head and, twisting his body round hers, fertilises the spawned eggs. The eggs number from 4,000–40,000 and have a diameter of 1 mm. The adults die after spawning. The ammocoete larva is blind and toothless, and lives buried in river mud for 3–5 years. Only after metamorphosis, at 9–15 cm, does it migrate to the sea where it remains 1–2 years.

In the sea the lampern lives by sucking blood from herring, young cod etc., or as a carrion-eater. It rasps a hole in the skin of its prey, and secretes a fluid which dissolves the tissues and keeps the blood from coagulating.

Caught in nets and traps, lampreys are eaten—particularly in the Baltic countries—smoked, fried or cured.

2. Brook lamprey

Lampetra planeri (Bloch)

Distinctive features: Resembles a small lampern. Thin eel-shaped body; the two dorsal fins are more or less contiguous. The teeth are blunt.

Considered by many workers to be a non-migratory form of the lampern. Very closely related species or races in Siberia and North America.

Size: rarely over 12–16 cm long, at 3–5 years.

The brook lamprey spends its entire life in brooks and the upper reaches of the rivers. Spawning takes place in March-June as for the lampern. The eggs are laid in a spawning trough on a bottom of coarse sand or gravel in shallow water. The eggs are a little larger than those of the lampern, but they number only *c.* 1,500. The adults die after spawning. The eggs hatch in from 3–4 days. The blind, toothless larvae live for 3–5 months on all kinds of small bottom organisms, until in the autumn they start to metamorphose in to the adult stage. The sexual organs begin developing towards the end of the larval period, and during metamorphosis eyes and teeth develop, but the intestine degenerates. In spring metamorphosis is completed, and the animal is mature. The adults are not parasitic and do not feed.

Sometimes used for bait, but are otherwise not utilised.

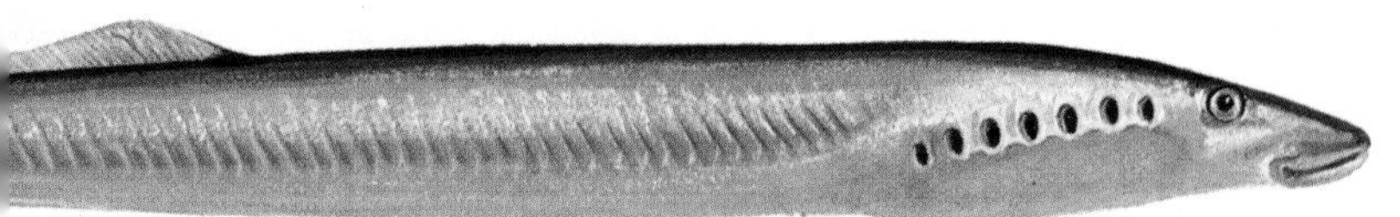

33 cm

♦ 1. LAMPERN
Lampetra fluviatilis

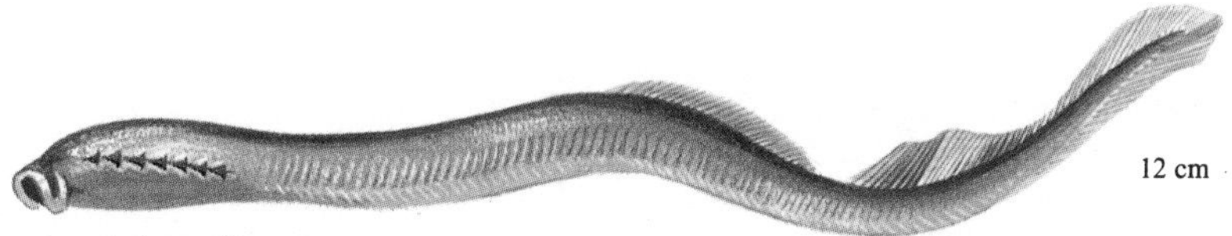

12 cm

ammocoete larva of lampern

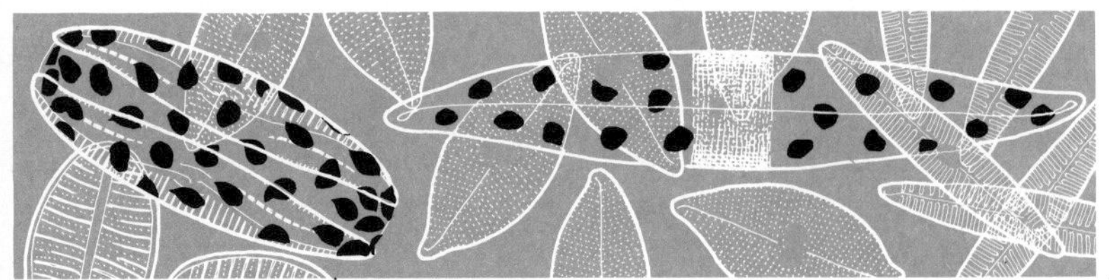

principal food: diatoms, enlarged about 700 times

14 cm

♦ 2. BROOK LAMPREY
Lampetra planeri

DANUBIAN LAMPREYS

In the Danube-system live three closely related freshwater lampreys.

3. Danube lamprey

Eudontomyzon danfordi (Regan)

Distinctive features: The body is thickest at the middle; the tongue-tooth (see opp. page) has 9–13 well-developed points, the central one the longest.
Size: 18–30 cm.
Distribution: Lives in the upper tributaries of the Danube (trout region), but perhaps not in the Danube itself. Due to former confusion with the two following species the exact distribution is not known.

It preys on loaches, bullheads, small barbel, chub and salmonid fishes, often eats waste from slaughter-houses and is numerous in fish-ponds.

Migrates far up into the headwaters to spawn in April-May. The larvae hatch among stones in fast-running water and are carried to still, shadowy places in the stream. Here they live for 3–4 years in the muddy bottom, feeding on diatoms and small animals caught by a slimy band in the pharynx. Metamorphosis occurs in August, and for 5–6 months before maturity the adult feeds parasitically.

4. Vladykov's lamprey

Eudontomyzon vladykovi Zanandrea

Distinctive features: Front of body thickest. The tongue-tooth (see opp. page) has 5–9 points, the central one only conspicuous. The large lateral teeth in the innermost ring of teeth have 2–4 points.
Size: 18–21 cm.
Distribution: Occurs in the Danube and its tributaries, but mainly in more southerly areas than *E. danfordi*.

Metamorphosis begins in the autumn and ends with maturity in spring. The adult does not feed.

5. Ukranian lamprey

Eudontomyzon mariae Berg

Distinctive features: Front of the body is thickest. The tongue-tooth has only 5 points; the central one is the strongest, the others being very small.
Size: 18–21 cm.
Distribution: In the eastern Black Sea rivers. It resembles *E. vladykovi* in biology, and does not feed as an adult.

6. Sea lamprey

Petromyzon marinus L.

Distinctive features: Sucker disc with numerous rings of teeth (see opp. page).
Size: 60–75 cm.

Migratory fish which ascend rivers from the sea to spawn in February-June. 200–240,000 eggs, 1 mm in diameter, are spawned on a stony bottom (see lampern). The parents die after spawning. The eggs hatch in 1–2 weeks; the larva lives in the mud for 2–5 years and metamorphoses at a length of 15–20 cm. It then migrates to the sea, where it feeds parasitically as a blood-sucker on cod, mackerel, herring, etc. for 3–4 years.

In parts of western Europe it is captured when ascending rivers in autumn. Its flesh is rich in fat and tasty.

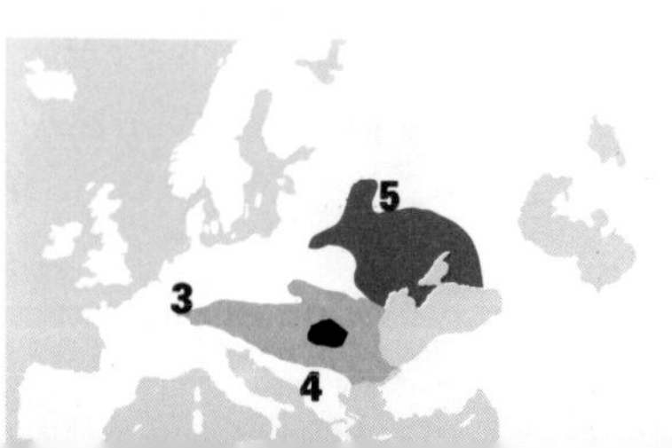

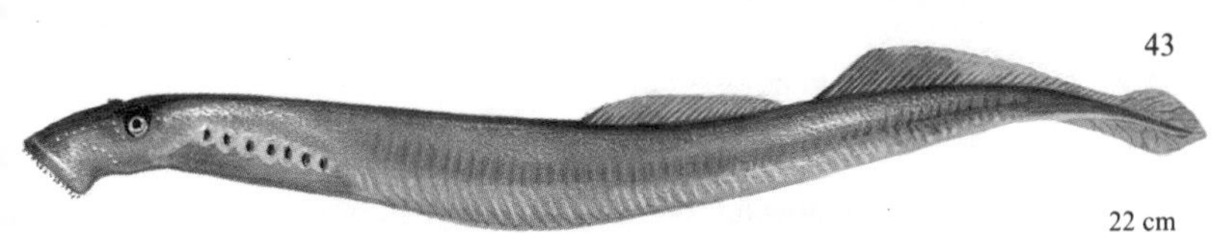

22 cm

3. DANUBE LAMPREY
Eudontomyzon danfordi

76 cm

♦ 6. SEA LAMPREY
Petromyzon marinus

dentition:

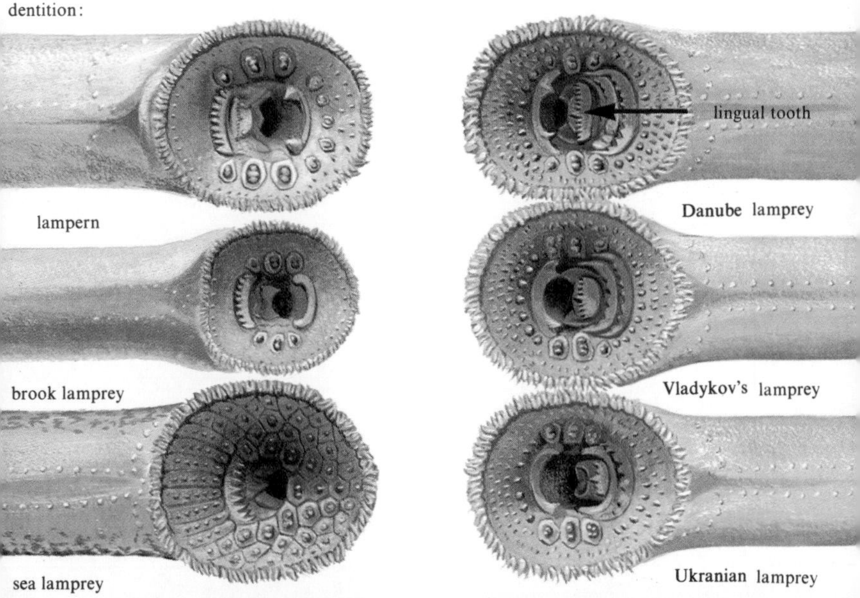

lingual tooth

lampern

Danube lamprey

brook lamprey

Vladykov's lamprey

sea lamprey

Ukranian lamprey

BONY FISHES

The bony fishes (Class Osteichthyes) include the sturgeons (Chondrostei) and the true bony fishes (Teleostei), to which all other European freshwater fishes belong.

The 19,000 or so species known comprise the majority of recent fishes, and they are distinguished from the cartilaginous fish (sharks and rays) by their bony skeleton, gill-covers, and bony fin-rays, as well as by usually having scales or bone-plates on the body.

STURGEONS

The body is elongate and covered by 5 rows of large bony plates. The upper lobe of the tail is the largest. The head is armoured, and the small, protractile, toothless mouth is ventral in position. Below the snout are 4 barbels. Sturgeons feed on small bottom-animals.

Most of the 26 species live in Russian and Asiatic rivers. The annual catch in the U.S.S.R. is from 12–16,000 tons from the Black Sea regions and around the Caspian Sea. The stocks of sturgeons have greatly diminished due to the increasing pollution in large rivers.

As several species occur in the Danube area and in the larger rivers of the Mediterranean, a short key to the species is given below. However, it must be noted that several species hybridise, and that some show great variation in the shape of the snout and number of bony-plates.

KEY TO THE STURGEONS

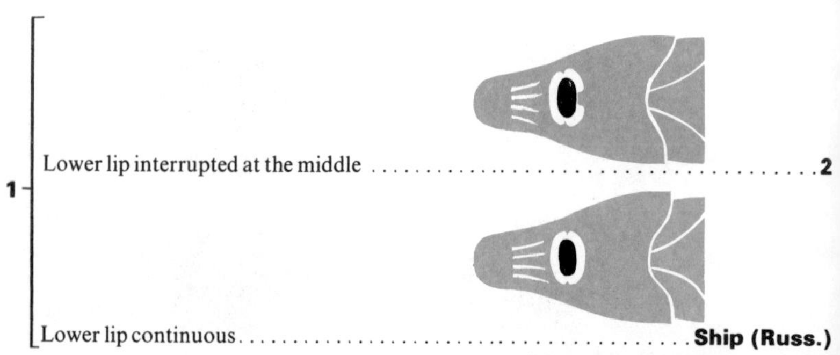

1 — Lower lip interrupted at the middle **2**

— Lower lip continuous . . . . **Ship (Russ.)**

Acipenser nudiventris LOVETZKY

2 The ends of the barbels are distinctly frayed. More than 60 plates along the side .... **Sterlet,** p. 47

Barbels smooth or almost smooth; fewer than 60 plates along the side **3**

3 Snout long, narrow and pointed, and forming up to 60% of the head length .... **Sevnjuga (Russ.)** *A. stellatus* PALLAS

Snout length at most 50% of the head length **4**

4 Barbels flattened; when laid back reach beyond the front of the mouth .... **Beluga (Russ.),** *Huso huso* (L.)

Barbels round in cross-section, placed closer to the snout than to the mouth, not reaching the mouth when laid back **5**

5 Lateral plates well separated, the lateral line visible in the spaces .... **Waxdick (Ge.)** *A. guldenstadti* BRANDT

Lateral plates continuous, each being twice as high as broad; snout broadly rounded from above .... **Adriatic sturgeon,** *A. naccari* BONAPARTE

Lateral plates continuous but not twice as high as broad; snout pointed when seen from above .... ***Sturgeon,** p. 46

7. Sturgeon

Acipenser sturio L.

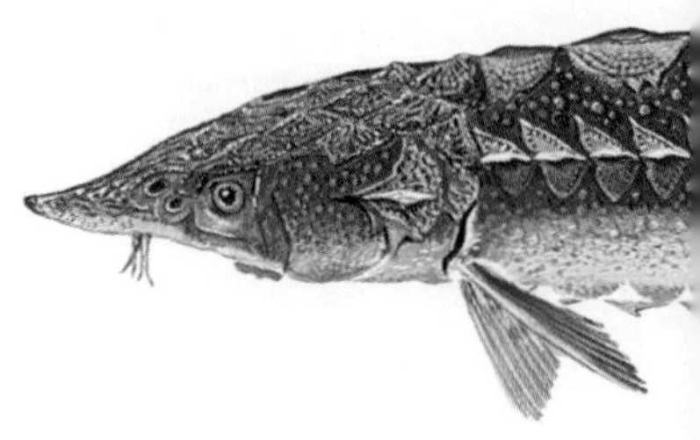

Distinctive features: The four barbels are round in section, and not frayed; 24–40 lateral plates, 11–13 ventral plates.
Size: 1–2 m, maximum 5–6 m, 400 kg in weight, over 100 years old.

Lives as a bottom-fish, migrating into the sea. In Lake Ladoga (U.S.S.R.), however, there is a stationary stock. Migrates in April-June to the rivers, to spawn in water 2–10 m deep and with a strong current. The eggs number 800,000–2,400,000, and measure 3 mm in diameter. They stick to stones, and hatch in 3–6 days. After 1 or 2 years the young migrate to the sea where they spend 7–14 years, the males maturing when 7–9 years old, at 110–150 cm in length, the females when 8–14 years old, at 120–180 cm. Their food consists of bottom-animals, especially the larvae of midges and worms. Caviar is produced from the roe. The only important fishery in recent years has been in the region of the Black Sea.

8. Sterlet

Acipenser ruthenus L.

Distinctive features: The pointed, narrow snout is curved slightly upwards; the 4 barbels in front of the mouth are fringed; 60–70 small plates along each side of the body; 10–18 larger plates on each side of the belly.
Size: 35–40 cm long when 5 years old. Can attain *c.* 80 cm and an age of 20 years.

One Siberian and one European race. It lives in rivers and large lakes, and in the northern part of the Caspian Sea penetrates into brackish water.

The most important food items are the larvae of mayflies, which it 'grazes' from submerged pieces of wood and stakes. It feeds also on larvae of chironomids, small snails and worms. It over-winters in deep places in the rivers, and hardly takes any food; in spring it migrates upstream, further than the sturgeon, to spawn. The males arrive earliest and from May-June spawning takes place in running water over a stony bottom. The adhesive eggs measure 1·5 mm and, according to their size, females spawn 11,000–140,000 eggs, which hatch after 4–5 days. The young remain close to the spawning place, but gradually spread into more shallow water. At an age of 4–5 years at *c.* 35 cm in length, the males become mature, the females not until 5–9 years at 40–45 cm.

Sterlets are fished mainly in the River Volga and the Don with hooks, in seine or in special traps. Following successful Russian experiments with hatching and rearing, the sterlet has also been stocked in many artificial waters and fish-farms. It has no value as a game-fish. Its flesh is considered tasty; the roe produces a fine-grained caviar and the swim-bladder a glue of high quality.

The Russians have succeeded in producing valuable hybrids between the sterlet and the closely related sturgeon species *Acipenser guldenstadti.*

105 cm

♦ 7. STURGEON
Acipenser sturio

principal food in brackish and salt water:

fly larvae 12 mm

crustaceans, worms

molluscs

sand-eels

larva 10 mm

26 cm

8. STERLET
Acipenser ruthenus

principal food:

caddis-fly larvae 12 mm

fly larvae 10 mm

green algae

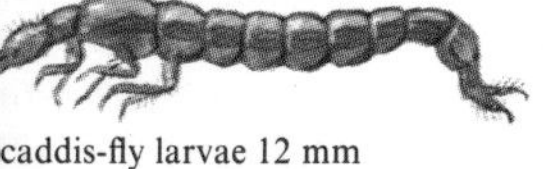

head, from below

THE HERRING FAMILY

Slender, pelagic, shoaling fish with a short dorsal fin and without an adipose fin or a lateral line. Most species live in the sea, and about one-third (or 14 million tons) of the total global catch of fish is made up of the different kinds of herring-like fish. The species are mainly migratory. Several of them ascend rivers, and a few have even formed non-migratory stocks in lakes.

SHADS

Two representatives (both of the genus *Alosa*) of the herring family occur commonly in the mouths of European rivers, namely the twaite and allis shads which resemble one another closely. In Dutch rivers they are reported to form hybrids capable of reproduction. They spawn in freshwater and are closely related to the Black Sea herring, genus *Caspialosa,* which has 7 species in the Black and Caspian Seas. Both European species are migratory, but due to the increasing pollution of the rivers they have become much reduced in numbers.

9. Twaite shad

Alosa fallax (Lacépède)

Distinctive features: One short dorsal fin and no lateral line; the eye has a 'fat cover', i.e. a thick, transparent membrane across the front and rear parts. The gill-cover is furrowed and the gill-arches have only 40–60 gill-rakers. Along the side are 60–65 scales and 6–10 black spots.
Size: 35–40 cm at 6–7 years, maximum *c.* 55 cm; 1½–2 kg in weight (presumably at 20–25 years).

The twaite shad is non-migratory in some lakes: Lugano, Como, Maggiore, Iseo, Garda, Skadarsko and Killarney.

In the sea, it lives in shoals from the surface down to 100 m depth, and feeds on shrimps, mysids and other pelagic or semipelagic crustaceans.

In May-June the mature fish gather in shoals and enter rivers. The eggs number 80,000–200,000 and at first measure 1·6 mm but swell in the water to 4·5 mm. They are shed freely on a bottom of sand or gravel over which they may float slowly with the current. They develop in 2–8 days depending on the temperature, 15–25°C being the most suitable. In the autumn the young migrate to the sea where rapid further growth takes place, reaching 8–14 cm in length after 1 year. Maturity is attained after 3 years, at a length of 30 cm.

Fished for with seine, drift-net, and fixed gear during the adult migrations into freshwater, when they are at their best. The catch is nowadays rather unimportant, but is often sold smoked.

10. Allis shad

Alosa alosa (L.)

Distinctive features: One short dorsal fin and no lateral line; the eye has a 'fat cover' as in the twaite shad; the gill-cover is furrowed, and there are 90–120 gill rakers. 70–80 scales along the side and usually 1 dark spot (occasionally up to 5) on each side.
Size: 35–40 cm at 6 years, maximum *c.* 70 cm. In its mode of life it resembles the twaite shad (see above), but its range extends less far to the east.

It is mainly an estuarine form although during the spring migration to the rivers it can be found up to 800 km upstream. It has suffered from pollution even more than the twaite shad, and is now a relatively rare fish in Europe.

41 cm

♦ 9. TWAITE SHAD
Alosa fallax

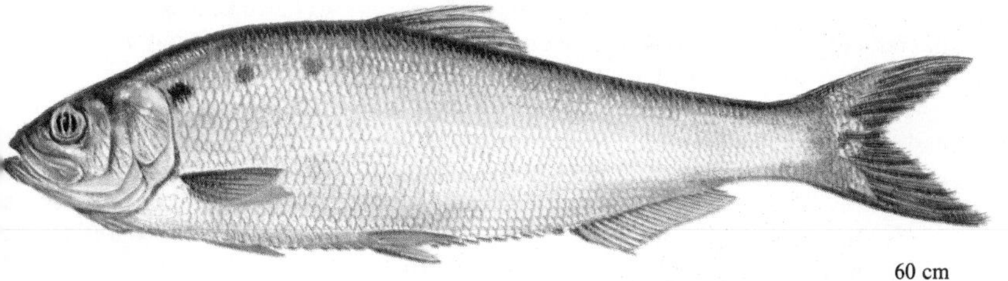

60 cm

♦ 10. ALLIS SHAD
Alosa alosa

principal food for young in fresh water:

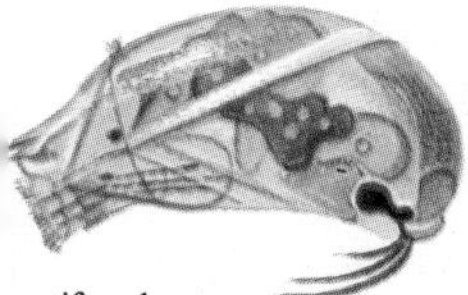

rotifers 1 mm

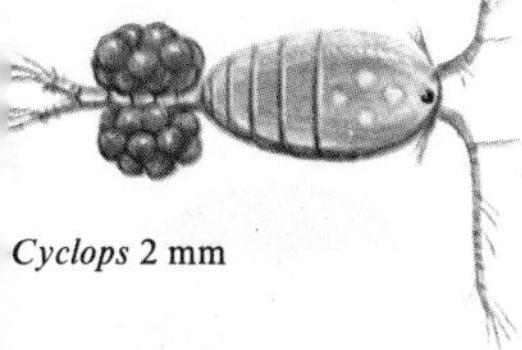

Cyclops 2 mm

Daphnia 1 mm

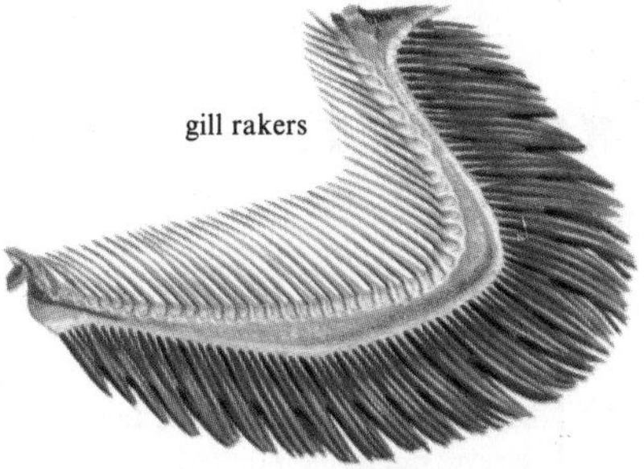

gill rakers

gill arch of twaite shad

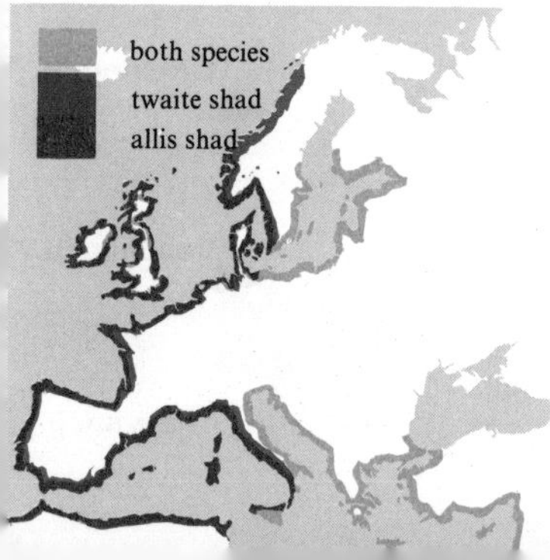

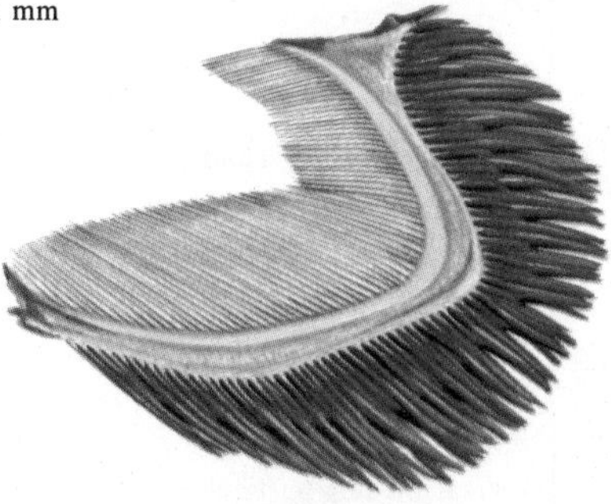

gill arch of allis shad

both species
twaite shad
allis shad

THE SALMON FAMILY

The salmonid fishes are slender, and can be distinguished by the small, rayless adipose fin situated between the rayed dorsal fin and the tail-fin. The gill-slits are large, and the gill-arches have well-developed rakers on their inner edges. There are no barbels and the scales are rather small.

The ovaries are large, and the mature eggs lie free in the abdominal cavity. They are shed through an opening behind the vent, but some usually remain in the abdominal cavity after spawning and slowly degenerate (residual eggs).

The salmonid fishes are naturally distributed over the northern hemisphere but have been widely introduced in the southern hemisphere. They include both migratory forms which spawn in freshwater but spend a longer time in the sea (anadromous fish), and non-migratory forms which spend their entire life in lakes and rivers. The family as a whole is associated with oxygen-rich, cool water, and the fish spawn in the cooler months.

A number of the species tend to form local races or forms which vary greatly in biology and appearance.

In addition, many of them—especially the migratory forms—become greatly changed in appearance in the spawning season. On account of these seasonal and sexual changes in appearance, and the great variability within the species, considerable confusion has existed in the precise recognition of some salmonid fish species.

Some of the salmonids occurring in European waters were originally introduced from America. They are stocked in fish-farms and are often used as sport-fish.

The salmon fishes have great commercial value, and the annual world yield can be estimated at *c.* 600,000 tons.

KEY TO THE SALMON FAMILY

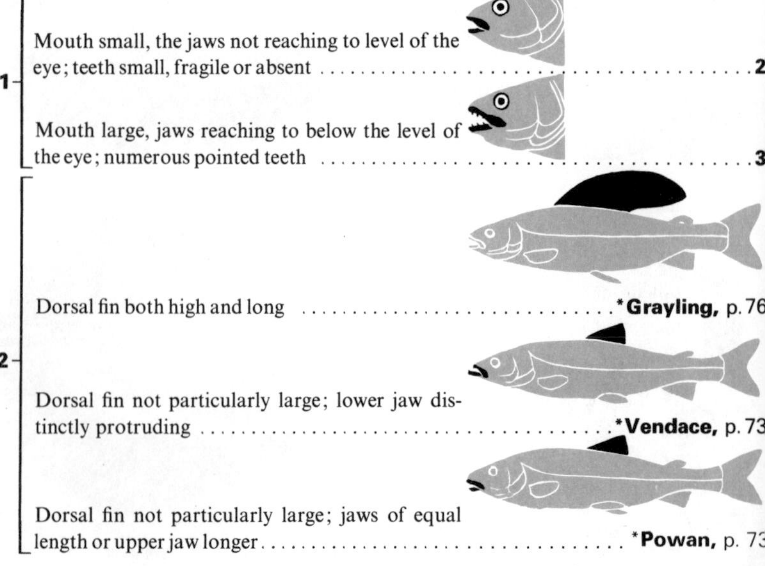

1
- Mouth small, the jaws not reaching to level of the eye; teeth small, fragile or absent 2
- Mouth large, jaws reaching to below the level of the eye; numerous pointed teeth 3

2
- Dorsal fin both high and long .... ***Grayling,** p. 76
- Dorsal fin not particularly large; lower jaw distinctly protruding .... ***Vendace,** p. 73
- Dorsal fin not particularly large; jaws of equal length or upper jaw longer .... ***Powan,** p. 73

3 No spots or pattern on the body; lateral line short (ends over pectoral fin) .... ***Smelt,** p. 74

With spots or pattern on body **4**

4 With a more or less distinct purple band along the sides; tail-fin with numerous dark spots .... **(*) Rainbow trout,** p. 60

Throat with a red, crosswise bar .... **Cut-throat trout,** p. 60

Otherwise **5**

5 Fore-edges of pectoral, pelvic and anal fins white; mouth very large; scales small, 160–240 along the lateral line **6**

Fore-edges of pectoral, pelvic and anal fins not white; scales may be small **7**

6 Pectoral, pelvic and anal fins red with white fore-edges; dorsal fin not spotted .... ***Arctic charr,** p. 67

Pectoral, pelvic and anal fins orange with a white and black double stripe on their fore-edges; dorsal fin darkly spotted .... **(*) Brook trout,** p. 68

Pectoral, pelvic and anal fins rose coloured with a white band on the fore-edge; back and dorsal fin with grey "hieroglyphs" .... **American lake trout,** p. 69

7 Scales moderately large (120–130 in the lateral line, 11–19 rows between the adipose fin and the lateral line); body flattened .... ***Salmon and trout,** pp. 52, 58

Scales very small (180–220 in the lateral line). Body rounded. (Only in the Danube system.) .... **Huchen (Ge.),** p. 62

Scales very small (150–240 in the lateral line) 14–15 rays in the anal fin. (Strays from introductions into the White Sea.) .... **(*) Pacific salmon,** p. 64

♦ 11. SALMON

Salmo salar

11. Salmon

Salmo salar L.

Distinctive features: Difficulties are occasionally encountered in distinguishing salmon from trout. The salmon is more slender, the head more pointed and the caudal peduncle thinner (the rule of thumb holds, 'you can hold the salmon around the tail, the trout slips from your hands'). The tail-fin generally has a deeper fork than in the trout. Between the adipose fin and the lateral line there are 11 to 15 (generally 12–14) scales, counting obliquely backwards and including the lateral line scale. The gill-rakers on the first arch are all slender (see p. 53), and the gill-cover has few or no black spots while that of the trout usually has many.

Size: The maximum length of the male is *c.* 1·5 m (36 kg in weight), the females are rarely more than 120 cm (20 kg). The usual life-span is 4–6 years, on rare occasions up to 10.

The larger salmon come from the sea to the mouth of the rivers on their spawning migration late in winter (winter salmon), the smaller ones later in the year (summer salmon), but this varies from river to river. They are fat and in good condition. From entering the river until after spawning they do not feed, but for some weeks retain the reflex to bite at apparently edible items, to the delight of the game anglers. The ability, persistence and strength of the salmon in surmounting waterfalls and other obstacles during their ascent is well known. Big salmon can jump about three metres in the air provided they can start from deep water. They can leap higher, continuing the jump by vigorous swimming in the water-jet.

During the journey up river considerable reserves of fat are transformed into energy, and the ripening of the sexual organs in autumn makes a further demand on the reserves. At this time the transition from clean to coloured salmon takes place, the skin turns tough and thick and the males develop a hook on the lower jaw (the kype).

The redd (spawning place) chosen must satisfy a number of conditions: the bottom must be of gravel, the current moderate

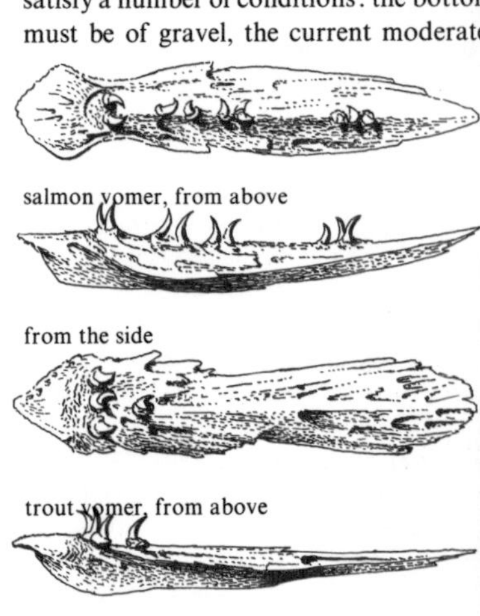

salmon vomer, from above

from the side

trout vomer, from above

from the side

see also page

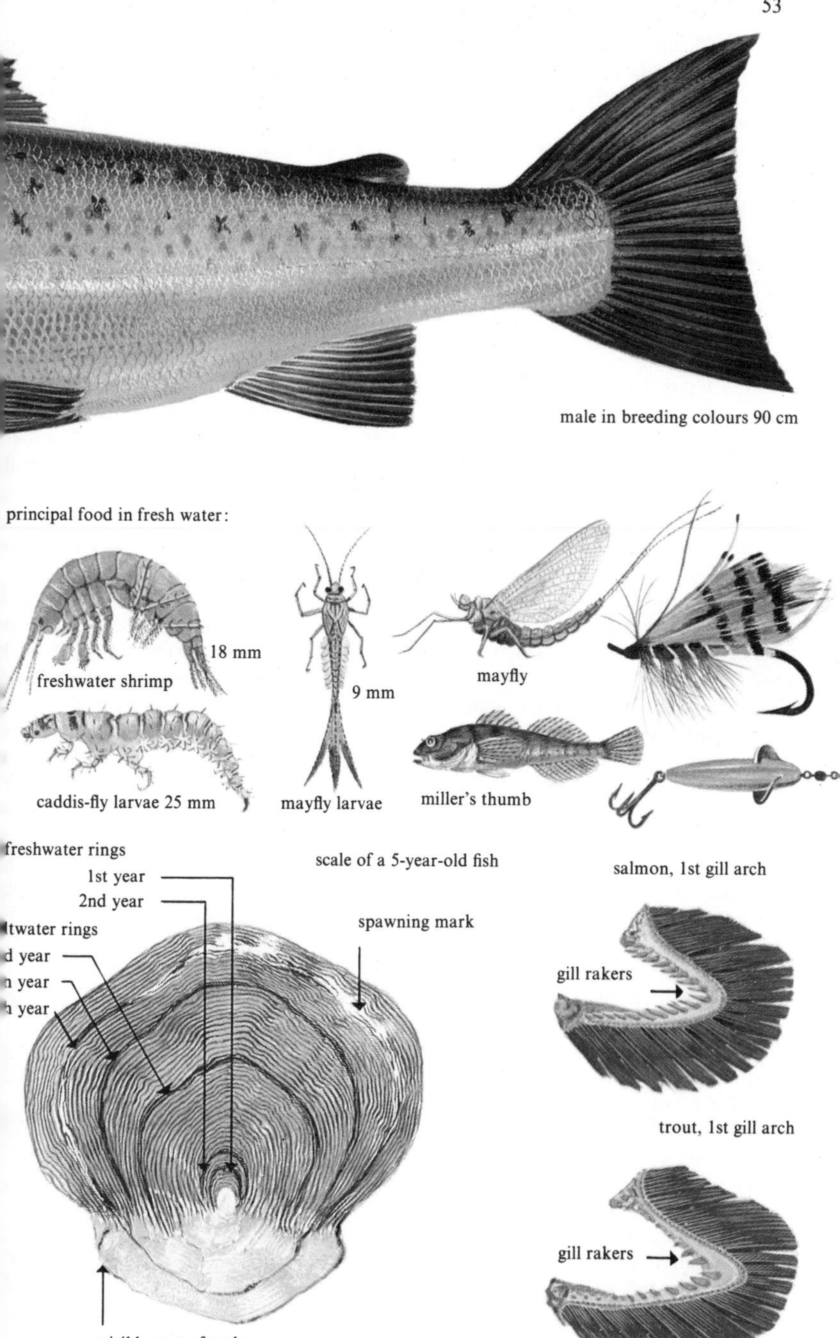

male in breeding colours 90 cm

and the depth from 0·5–3 m. The redd is selected in late autumn by the female, who excavates the gravel by vigorous movements of the tail, thus making a hollow which can be 10–30 cm deep and up to 3 m long.

During spawning the male lies alongside the female, and roe and milt are shed into the redd. The act of spawning is accompanied by considerable involuntary movement including violent trembling and gaping of the jaws. The eggs are deposited in several spawnings at 5–10 minute intervals. They become covered with stones and gravel when the female excavates another redd upstream of the first. Spawning lasts for 3–14 days, interrupted by resting pauses in which the salmon remain in deep holes. The male keeps other males away but it is not unusual for large salmon parr to join the adults on the redds, and even to participate in spawning.

The eggs measure 5–7 mm. There are 5–7,000 to one litre or *c.* 2,000 per kg. of body weight. They often amount to 25% of the body weight. They are heavier than water, slightly sticky and remain buried between the stones throughout the winter.

After spawning, the spent salmon, which are known as kelts, are very exhausted—they may have lost up to 40% of their body weight since they left the sea. Many, especially the males, die after spawning, or are infested with fungus (*Saprolegnia*), or in their feeble state become stranded. Others winter in deep holes or drift downstream towards the sea. The spawning coloration is gradually replaced by silvery colours, and the kype disappears. Few spawn a second time—in some rivers only 4–6% of the spawning fish are mended kelts. The number spawning a third, or rarely a fourth, time are very few, though the proportion varies from river to river.

Those kelts that survive recover quickly in the sea. With the rich feeding at sea they can increase their weight by 1 kg per week, and 1–2 years later they spawn again. Mended salmon which have spawned previously have more black spots than the virgin clean salmon, and their earlier life-history can also be 'read' on their scales.

The eggs hatch in April-May after 70–200 days, depending on the temperature; on average it is *c.* 440 day-degrees (that is the number of days multiplied by the temperature of the water in degrees centigrade). The newly hatched young measures 20 mm and has a large yolk-sac, from which it draws nourishment for 1½ months. During this period it lies quiescent, and then begins to eat small animals, and later the larvae of insects and worms.

The young salmon are distinguished by their 8–10 distinct blue-grey 'finger-marks', (with a single red spot in between each), known as the parr marks, and the young are termed salmon parr. Young trout have less distinct blue-grey marks and many red spots on the sides surrounded by light rings. The adipose fin is grey-green in salmon parr, orange in trout parr.

The young salmon stay from 1–5 years in freshwater; longest in northern Norway, from 2 to 5 years in British rivers and only 1 year in the Rhine. Curiously enough some males become mature while in freshwater, when they are only 1½ years old and 10–15 cm long.

Most of the parr gradually become

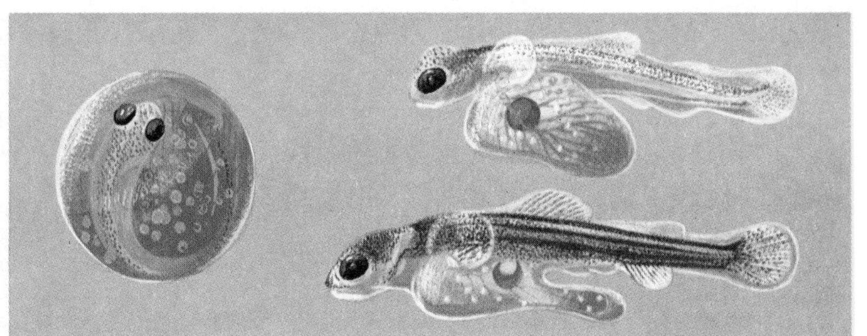

egg near hatching 5.8 mm

larvae with yolk-sacs, 16 and 23 mm

11. Salmon

development:

3 cm

11 cm

at 2 years, 18 cm

principal food:

mayfly larvae 12 mm

freshwater shrimp 15 mm

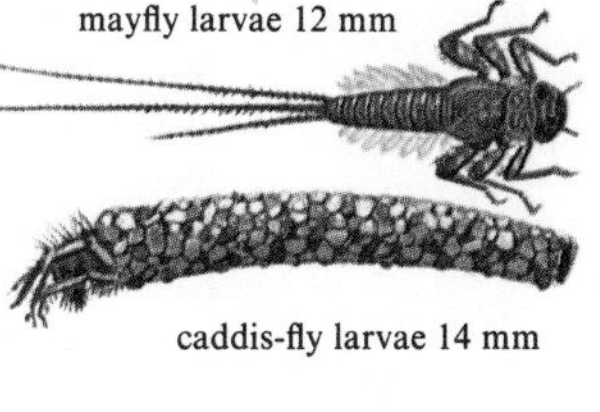

caddis-fly larvae 14 mm

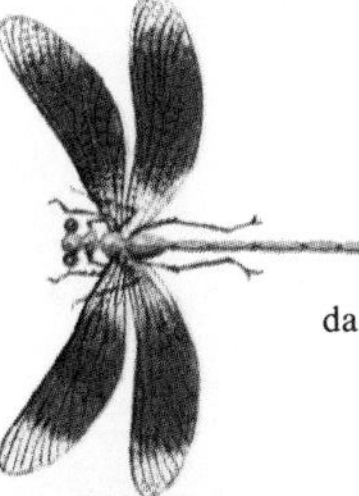

damselfly

silver at about 10–19 cm long, and around that time move towards the sea. This migration takes place in spring and is stimulated by the increasing temperatures. The smolts stay in the river mouth for some time, acclimatising to the salt water and the new diet. Their food now consists of gammarids and other crustacea, as well as sticklebacks and other estuarine fish.

Growth in freshwater is slow, but in the sea very rapid. After 1 year in the sea the salmon measure 50–65 cm ($1\frac{1}{2}$–$3\frac{1}{2}$ kg in weight); after 2 years 70–90 cm (4–8 kg), and after 3 years 90–105 cm (8–13 kg). In the sea the salmon migrate far and wide as active, predatory fishes in the upper water-masses. Their food consists mainly of sand-eels, small herring, sprat, sticklebacks and crustaceans.

After 1–4 years in the sea the salmon returns to freshwater to spawn. It finds its way in the open ocean by an innate biological compass and near the coast by an incredibly acute sense of smell which enables it to recognise the scent of the river in which it grew up. Tagging experiments have shown migrations of up to several thousand kilometres with an average speed of 50–100 km per 24 hours.

In some lakes, which no longer have a passage to the sea, non-migratory, landlocked stocks of salmon occur. They are often dwarf forms, and some of them have received the recognition of vernacular names. In many cold north-eastern American lakes lives the 'Sebago salmon', a

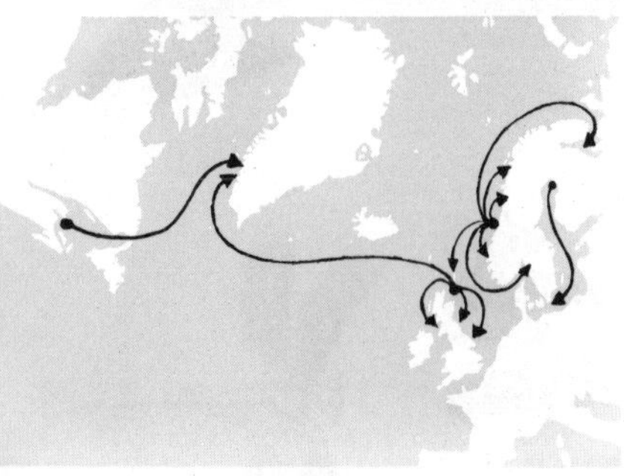

non-migratory form. In Lake St. John and the Saguenay River occurs the so-called 'Ouananiche', an important game-fish, while in Norway the dwarf form 'Blegen' is found in several lakes in the River Otra system. It never grows longer than 30 cm. In Lake Vanern (Sweden) and Lake Ladoga (U.S.S.R.) there are non-migratory stocks of salmon reaching lengths of up to one metre (12 kg). Finally, a completely isolated race of salmon lives in Dalmatia in Lake Ohrid, a relict form from the last glacial period. Some ichthyologists consider it to be a separate species, *Salmothymus obtusirostris* (Heckel). These non-migratory groups of salmon as a rule spawn in the tributaries to the lakes.

In the sea salmon are caught during their migrations along the shores. The immensely valuable fishing off Greenland is conducted relatively close inshore. They are generally caught with fine-meshed drift nets, though some are taken in set nets and trawls, and a few on floating long-lines.

In freshwater as well as in the sea the yield of the fisheries fluctuates from year to year, and the reasons for this are numerous and complicated. The salmon are caught commercially during their ascent to the spawning places in seines, nets, on lines and fixed gear of many different kinds, often in places where the water is dammed up, e.g. at water-mills. The fishing rights on good salmon rivers command such high prices that the rent paid by game-fish anglers often gives as good a return as any other means of exploiting the fish stocks. The annual European yield averages about 6,000 tons.

The increasing pollution of the rivers, particularly in their lower reaches, and dams without adequate salmon ladders have greatly damaged the European stock. As a migratory species the salmon has been particularly severely affected. All countries have introduced conservation measures but in many areas too late. Restocking rivers with young salmon from hatcheries, the provision of fish-ladders round obstructions in rivers, and control of pollution are necessary, and have to some extent remedied the damage.

on leaving the sea, 92 cm

11. Salmon

principal food in salt water:

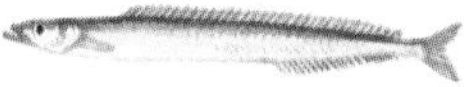

sand-eel

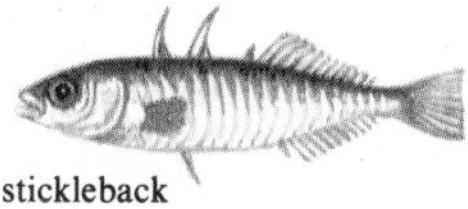

stickleback

herring

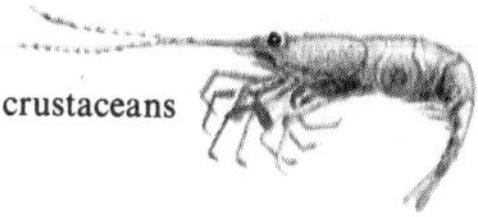

crustaceans

salmon tag

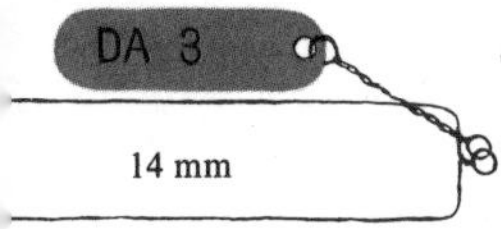

14 mm

position of tag

principal methods of capture:

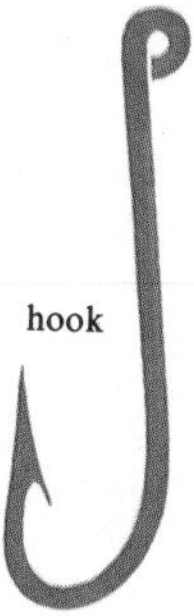

hook

floating lines

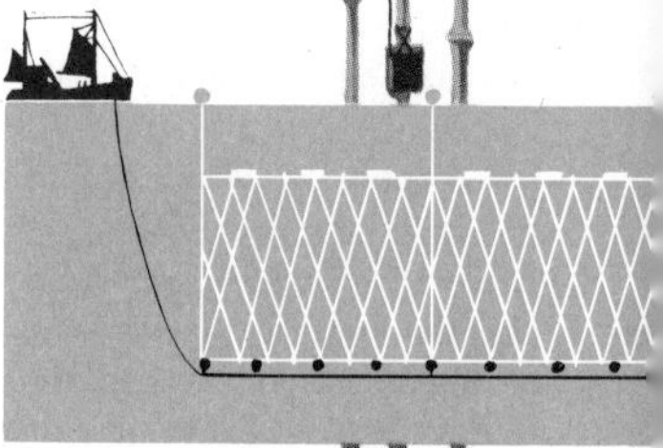

drift net

utilization:

canned

frozen

seine net

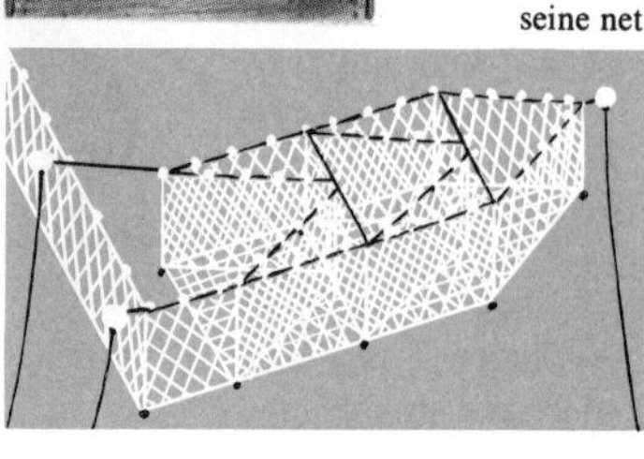

smoked

12. Trout

Salmo trutta L.

Distinctive features: It can be difficult to distinguish trout from salmon. The trout is stouter than the salmon in the body, the head is more blunt and the caudal peduncle broader. The hind margin of the tail-fin is less concave, and is often almost square cut. Between the adipose fin and the lateral line there are 14–19 scales, usually 16, counted obliquely backwards and including the lateral line. The gill-rakers on the upper limb of the first gill-arch are blunt and thicker than those on the lower limb which are slender (see page 53).

Size: Normally rarely over 80–100 cm, (10–15 kg in weight), maximum 140 cm and *c.* 50 kg—Caspian trout. The average life-span is 4–6 years.

The biology of the trout resembles that of its near relative the salmon. However, it is less migratory and tends to form populations in freshwater which never migrate to the sea.

The trout family has been divided into a complexity of forms and subspecies. The differences between these subspecies are basically environmental and behavioural, and are not morphological or genetic. The sea trout is a migratory form distributed from the White Sea to the north of Spain. It lives from 1–5 years in freshwater (longest in the northern region), and descends to the sea at a length of 15–25 cm. It stays in the sea for 6 months to 5 years, growing rapidly. During its spawning migration the trout—like the salmon—develops a mating coloration and body shape. It spawns in winter, later than the salmon, and often upstream in the rivers. Most individuals spawn several times, and the post-spawning mortality is not high. It produces 10,000 eggs (*c.* 1,500 kg of body weight), and the eggs hatch in spring (*c.* 410 day-degrees centigrade are needed).

Young trout (parr) can be distinguished from salmon parr by the large blue-grey spots being less distinct and by the large

number of white-ringed red spots on the sides. The adipose fin is orange.

The lake trout (*S. t. lacustris*) is a migratory form living in large, cool Alpine or boreal lakes but spawning (from September-October) in the rivers feeding these lakes. The young live in these rivers until at 1–3 years of age they migrate into the lake, generally in early summer. They mature at 4–7 years. Lake trout can be quite as big as sea trout.

The brown trout (*S. t. fario*) is a non-migratory form spending its whole life in rivers. It does not pass through a silvery, smolt stage as do sea trout and lake trout, but progresses directly from the transverse barring of the trout parr to the mature colouring. In small streams it reaches a maximum length of *c.* 15–20 cm and matures at an age of 2–3 years. The number of eggs in these fish is low (100–300). In larger rivers they may grow to 50 cm (1–1·5 kg in weight), becoming mature at 4–5 years. The brown trout is rather sedentary and the individual fish often has a preferred station, sheltered from the current behind stones and roots.

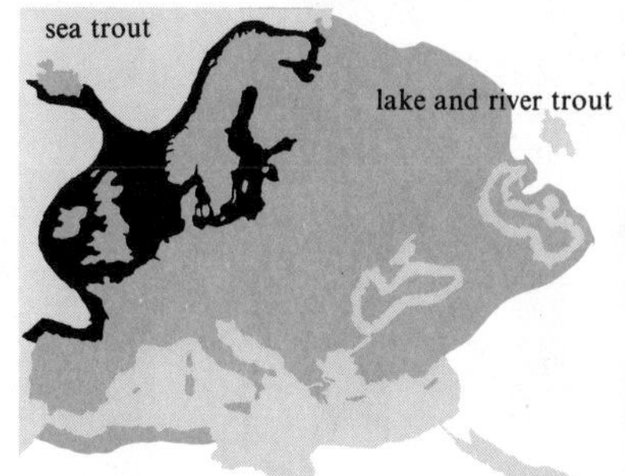

52 cm

♦ 12. TROUT
Salmo trutta

male in spawning colours 47 cm

principal food in salt water:

herring

crustaceans

stickleback

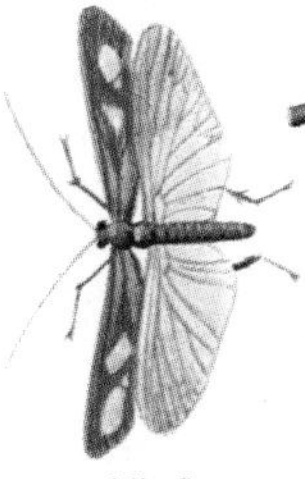

caddis-fly

principal food in fresh water:

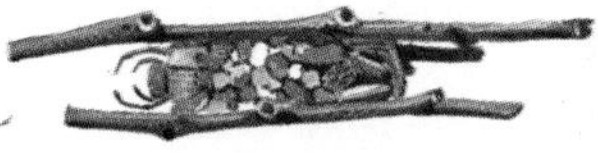

caddis-fly larvae 40 mm

minnow

24 cm

♦ BROWN TROUT
Salmo trutta fario

13. Rainbow trout

Salmo gairdneri Richardson

Distinctive features: Resembles the brown trout in body form, but has a broad purple band along the sides, and the tail-fin is spotted with black.

Size: maximum 70 cm, *c.* 7 kg in weight.

In the 1880's different forms of this species were introduced to European fish-farms where they became mixed by interbreeding. The American steelhead (*S. gairdneri irideus*), is a coastal and migratory fish from the west coast of North America, and its biology in America corresponds roughly to that of the sea trout. The American rainbow trout (*S. g. shasta*), however, is like the brown trout, a less migratory subspecies living in mountain rivers of the Sierra Nevada.

The rainbow trout is above all a fish for the ponds of the fish-farm (see section on pond-farming, p. 202). Near fish farms it is sometimes found living in the wild, and in certain places in central and south-eastern Europe, i.e. in Austria and Yugoslavia, local breeding populations are found which have established themselves after stocking. Most attempts to establish free-living populations through stocking have failed. Rainbow trout are, however, widely and frequently introduced to angling waters. Presumably, fish whose ancestry contains strong elements of steelhead stock will be inclined to migrate to the sea after 1 or 2 years in freshwater, while trout with many of the hereditary characters of the *shasta* form will produce non-migratory, wild-living stocks also in Europe.

The rainbow trout spawns from November-April, the *shasta* type earliest, the steelhead later. Egg number: 1,000–5,000. The young trout (up to 15 cm) have 11–13 large, dark spots on the sides of the body. The *shasta* type resembles the brown trout in biology, but generally grows better and in the Austrian mountain rivers reaches 20–26 cm (120–250 g) in two summers. In 2–3 years it becomes mature. Preliminary studies indicate that locally it may replace the river trout, but that the two species usually utilise different sections of the streams.

The rainbow trout is more tolerant of higher temperatures and poor-quality water, and appears to make use of a wider range of food than the brown trout.

14. Cut-throat trout

Salmo clarki Richardson

Another western American trout, characterised by the red colour of the throat. In biology it resembles the lake trout. This species has occasionally been introduced in Europe, mainly in fish-farms, for food and for game-fisheries, and has hybridised with the rainbow trout in places.

26 cm

(♦) 13. RAINBOW TROUT
Salmo gairdneri

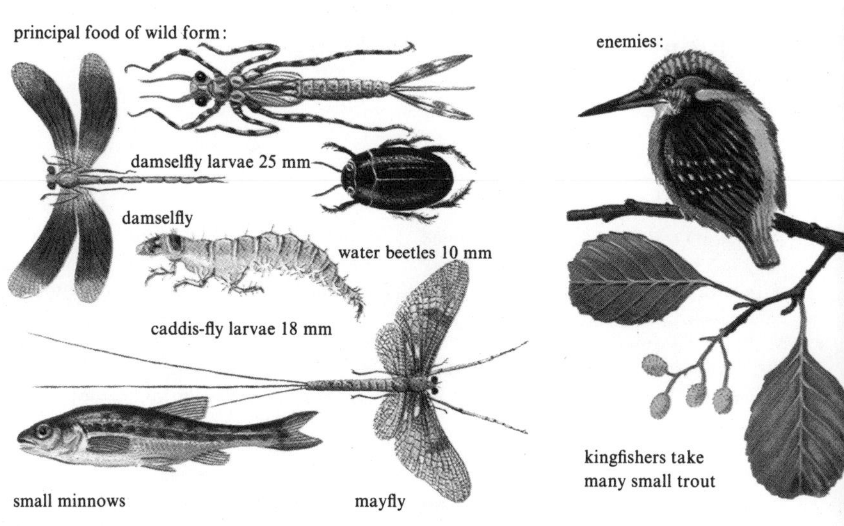

14. CUT-THROAT TROUT
Salmo clarki

15. HUCHEN
Hucho hucho

15. Huchen
Hucho hucho (L.)

Distinctive features: Elongate rounded body with greenish back and silvery sides with coppery lustre. The vomerine bone is short and thick, with teeth only on the front portion.
Size: About 70 cm (2–3 kg) at 5 years, maximum *c.* 150 cm (over 50 kg) at *c.* 15 years.

The huchen is found in the Danube and parts of its tributaries, and only exceptionally in lakes. It is a noticeably non-migratory fish, making only short migrations during spawning time and not descending to the Black Sea. It usually stays in the main stream, living in deep hollows, undercut riverbanks or below bridges, and requiring unpolluted water rich in oxygen. The food mainly consists of the nase (*Chondrostoma*), but also minnows, grayling, barbel, gudgeon, frogs, etc.

Spawning coincides with the melting of ice in March-April, when the fish moves into the lower reaches of the Danube or its tributaries. Spawning takes place over a bottom of gravel or stones, where the female digs a shallow pit. The eggs measure 5 mm and the number is relatively low, as a rule 1,000 per 1 kg of body weight. They are covered loosely with gravel. At a temperature of 8–10°C eyed eggs develop in 19 days, and hatch after 30 days. When the yolk is used up the fry remain near the spawning redd, feeding on small bottom-animals. Growth is rapid and after one year the young measure 15 cm. Young huchen feed on the fry of carp, minnow, nase, and gudgeon, and attain maturity at 5 years of age.

The huchen is unfortunately becoming rare. This has been said to be due to the reduction of the stock of its food-fishes, intense hook-fishing, etc. However, the main reasons appear to be those that have affected other salmonid fishes: pointless industrial pollution, the reckless abstraction of river water, inadequate, or lack of, fish-passes to dammed-up waters. Restocking depleted populations is difficult, for artificial hatching and rearing meet many practical difficulties, and experimental transplantations from other rivers have been unsuccessful. The species is highly esteemed as a game-fish, and is caught by spinning, but the legal minimum size that can be taken in many European countries should be increased to *c.* 70 cm (from the present 50–55 cm).

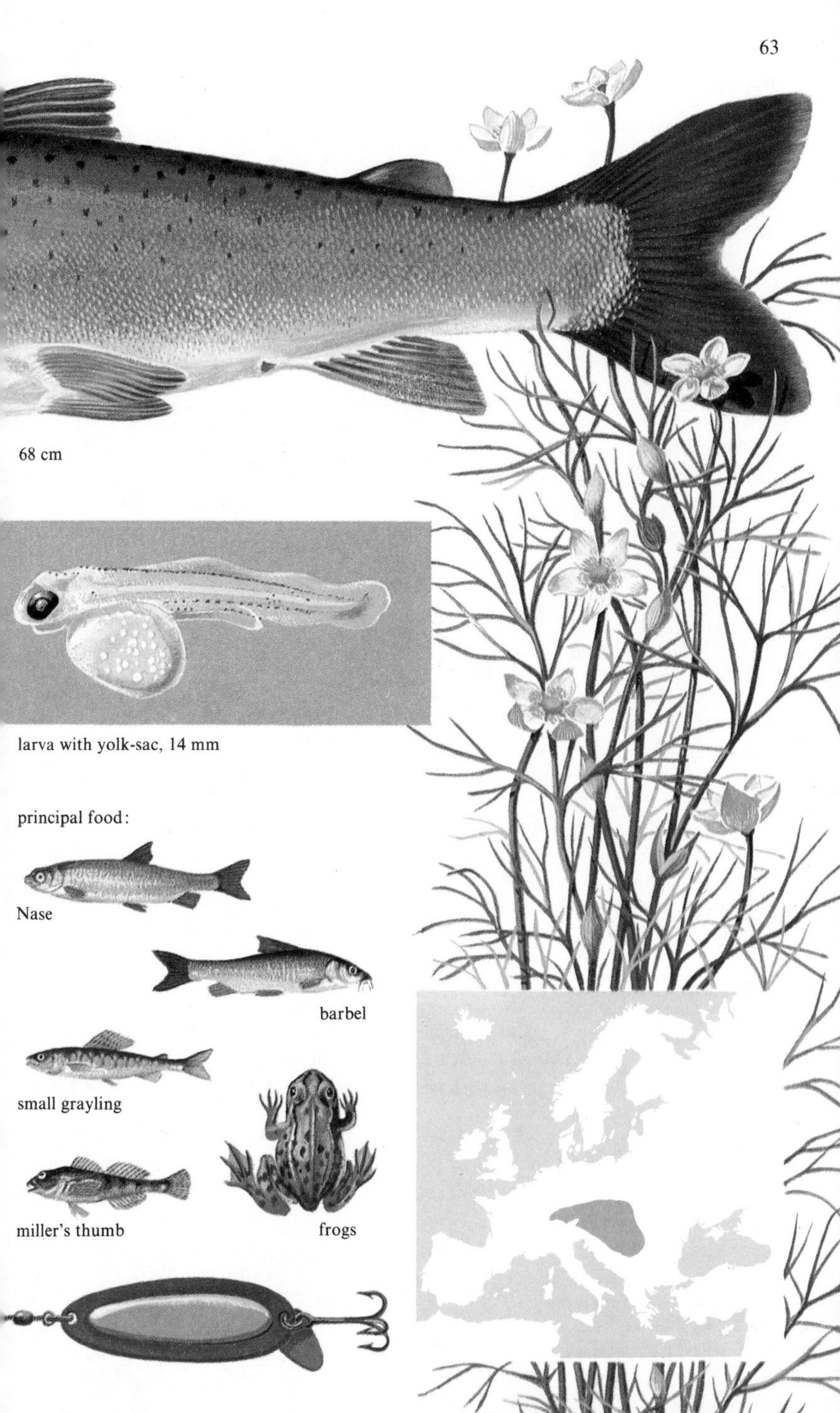
68 cm
larva with yolk-sac, 14 mm
principal food:
Nase
barbel
small grayling
miller's thumb
frogs

PACIFIC SALMON

This group includes migratory fish spawning in rivers running into the northern Pacific, and also distributed in the Arctic U.S.S.R. Two species may be found in northern European seas and even rivers as a result of successful transplantations of young fish in the region of the White Sea. The Pacific salmon belong to the genus *Oncorhynchus,* distinguished from other salmonid fishes by the long anal fin with 12–20 rays.

16. Humpback salmon

Oncorhynchus gorbuscha (Walbaum)

Distinctive features: First gill-arch with 28 gill-rakers; scales very small, 180–240 in the lateral line; dorsal and tail-fins black-spotted.

Size: Usually not longer than 40–50 cm (2–3 kg), or over 2 years in age. It spends almost its entire life in the sea, feeding on sand-eels, other fishes and crustaceans, ascending the rivers in July. The male has a special spawning coloration and develops a hump on the front of its back. Spawning is from August-September in places with a strong current over a bottom of stones or gravel. The eggs (only *c.* 1,500) are shed in a hollow dug by the female, and hatch after 4 months. The parents die after spawning. The newly hatched larvae each have a large yolk-sac and lie passively between the stones until spring. They then migrate directly into the sea where during the first months they remain in dense shoals along the shore. During their early stages and while migrating, they are preyed on extensively by other fish.

The young then migrate far out to sea, but little is known about their life in the ocean. Growth is very rapid and maturity is reached in 2 years. The humpback salmon is distinguished from other Pacific salmon by its short, 2-year life-cycle, and like many other salmon it can be divided into local forms. In these forms rich and poor year-classes may alternate regularly for long periods. The poor year-classes generally have the fastest growth.

In the Pacific there are several important fisheries, notably at Kamtchatka and Alaska. The species has been introduced into the White Sea, and some individuals have migrated westwards and been caught off Iceland, southern Norway, Scotland and northern England.

17. Chum salmon

Oncorhynchus keta (Walbaum)

Distinctive features: First gill-arch with *c.* 24 short gill-rakers; at the most 160 scales along the lateral line. The fins are dark and there are faint, dark cross-bands on the sides.

Size: 50–70 cm (2–5 kg) at 3 years, maximum *c.* 1 m (*c.* 6 kg) at 6 years.

Spends 3–4 years in the sea feeding on sandeels, herring and codling. On entering the rivers to spawn the coloration is a dull red. Two types are distinguished: the smaller summer salmon which ascend rivers in July-August, and the autumn salmon which ascend in August-September. The speed of migration is 40–50 km a day.

Mating takes place in a moderate current in a place selected by the female. Spawning takes 3–5 days and the eggs are shed in an elongated hollow. The eggs are large (7 mm) and number 2,000–5,000. After spawning the male leaves the nest,

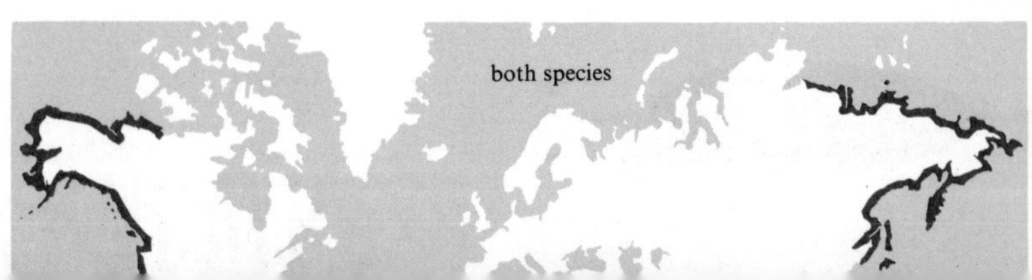

silvered male 28 cm

(◆) 16. HUMPBACK SALMON

Oncorhynchus gorbuscha

principal food in salt water:

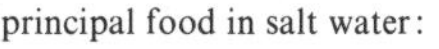

sand-eel

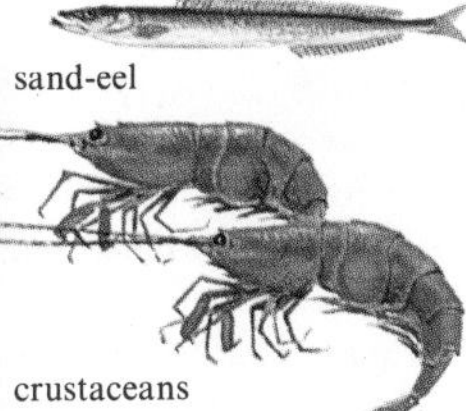

crustaceans

male in spawning colours

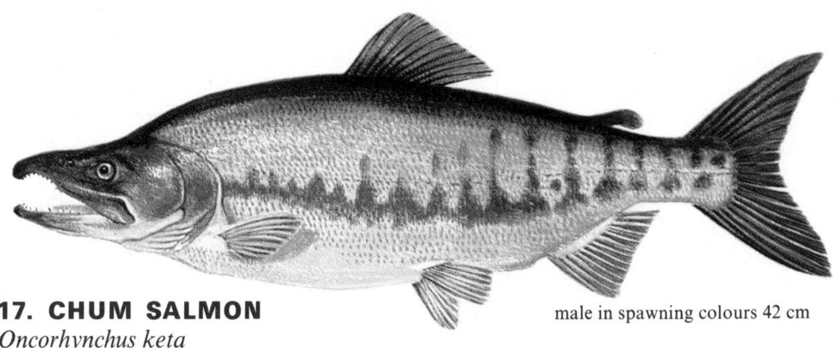

17. CHUM SALMON

Oncorhynchus keta

male in spawning colours 42 cm

principal food in salt water:

herring

small cod

silvered male

which is guarded by the female for about 10 days against other spawning salmon. All the spawning fish die shortly afterwards.

Hatching occurs in from 100–120 days. The newly hatched, 23 mm-long larvae react negatively to light and remain hidden between stones. Only when the yolk has been consumed after 2–3 months do they come out and feed on small animals, until in summer or autumn they migrate to the sea.

The chum has been introduced into the White Sea by the Russians. It may spread westwards into the Atlantic ocean, but has not so far been reported. In the North Pacific it is of considerable importance to the fishing industry but does not fetch the same high prices as other salmon.

18. Arctic charr

Salvelinus alpinus (L.)

Distinctive features: Front edges of pectoral, pelvic and anal fins as a rule bright white; in the spawning season these fins and the belly are blood-red, especially in the male. The scales are very small and inconspicuous: 190–240 in the lateral line, 36–37 rows across the body.

The species is very variable, and a large number of subspecies have been described, some of which are dwarf forms.

Size: Growth and size attained varies from stock to stock, but the size of the migratory forms is often 50–60 cm, 1·5–3·0 kg after 5–8 years, and rarely 80 cm, 8–10 kg at 10–12 years. Many lakes contain populations of stunted dwarf forms of 10–15 cm maximum length.

Distribution: Occurs in all coastal areas of the northern Arctic seas and in rivers leading to them. Also found in cold, clear lakes in the British Isles—Ireland, Lake District, Wales, Scotland; in the Alps, in Sweden, Norway, Finland, northern Russia, Siberia, North America, Greenland and Iceland.

The species is a decided cold water form with non-migratory races in many lakes, and in the northern part of its range has migratory populations which spend the summer in the sea.

The life-cycle of the migratory populations is as follows. From September-October migration from the sea to freshwater takes place; and during this the silvery appearance is lost and replaced by an intense breeding coloration. Spawning takes place on stony ground late in autumn or in winter. The number of eggs for a female of 1 kg is 3–4,000. They measure 3–4 mm in diameter and lodge between the stones until hatching in spring. The spent charr return to the sea in June.

The newly hatched young measures 15 mm and has a large yolk-sac, which it absorbs within a month; after this it starts feeding, particularly on water-fleas and the larvae of midges (chironomids). The young spend the summer in the lower reaches of the rivers and in brackish waters. Maturity is reached after 3–6 years. The adults feed during summer, mainly on small cod in the coastal areas of the Polar Sea.

Non-migratory forms in the large lakes include both autumn and spring spawners, and are often divided into smaller stocks each with its own biological characters. In the Alpine lakes the following types

female 30 cm

♦ 18. ARCTIC CHARR

Salvelinus alpinus

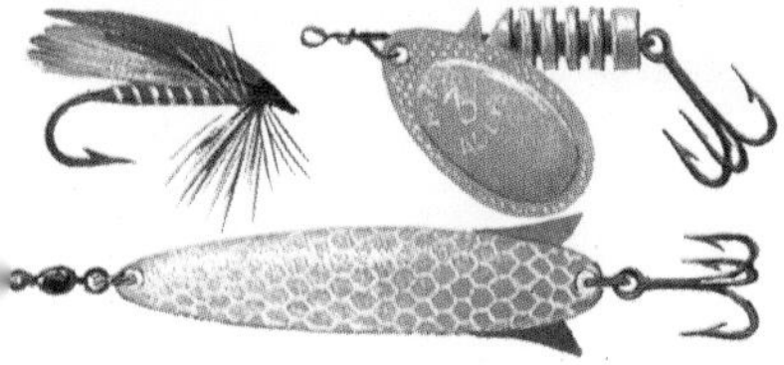

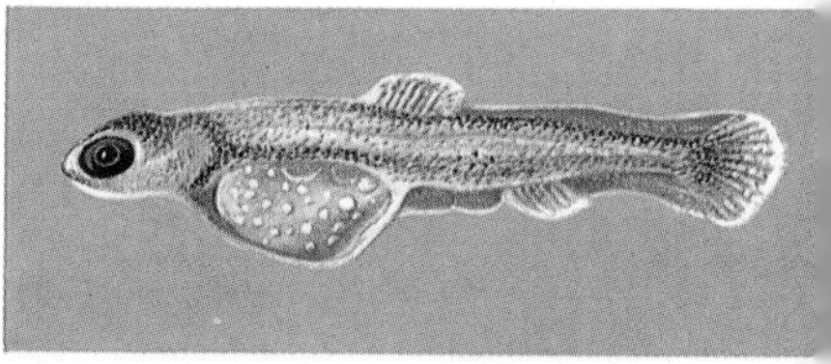

larva 19 mm

16 cm

dwarf form of charr

may be found: (1) the typical lake form feeding on planktonic crustaceans and bottom-animals; (2) a rapid-growing deep-lake form preying on other fish; (3) a dwarf form growing to 10–15 cm (German: *Schwarzreuter*), eating pelagic water-fleas inshore; and (4) a dwarf form in deep water (German: *Hungersaibling*), feeding on bottom-animals. These forms have different spawning places and seasons.

The charr is an excellent game-fish with spinner and fly. It is of great importance to fisheries in the Arctic regions, where it is caught during its ascent from the sea.

(♦) 19. AMERICAN BROOK TROUT

Salvelinus fontinalis

19. American brook trout

Salvelinus fontinalis (Mitchill)

Distinctive features: Resembles the brown trout and the charr but is most closely related to the latter. It is recognised by its large jaws, the light, mottled back and by the front edges of the pectoral, pelvic and anal fins being white bounded by a black margin.

Size: 30–40 cm, (0·5–1 kg) at 3–5 years. Rarely over 45 cm. In many places often rather small.

Distribution: It was introduced from North America with the rainbow trout at the end of the nineteenth century. It is now established in several European countries, living especially in cool, spring-fed brooks and mountain streams with rapid currents (the charr region). Although introduced into the British Isles it is not widespread.

It seems less shy than the trout and does not have the same need for hiding-places, and it is often found in open, wide streams. It also occurs in lakes with oxygen-rich, cool clear water. The food is the same as that of the brown trout—insects, worms and smaller fish.

The brook trout spawns in winter, from October-February. Its colours at this time are brilliant, and it is considered one of the most beautiful of the salmonid species. The eggs measure 4 mm in diameter, and they number *c.* 2,000. They are deposited in spawning sites in places with a gravel bottom and a strong current. Hatching occurs in spring. The growth is similar to that of the rainbow trout, the males mature at 2–3 years, the females at 3–4 years. It cross-breeds with both rainbow and brown trout, the latter often being called 'tiger-trout' on account of their striped appearance. Neither cross produces fertile offspring.

As a pond-fish the American brook trout is inferior to the more resistant rainbow trout, but it is an excellent game-fish for fly and spinner.

female 37 cm

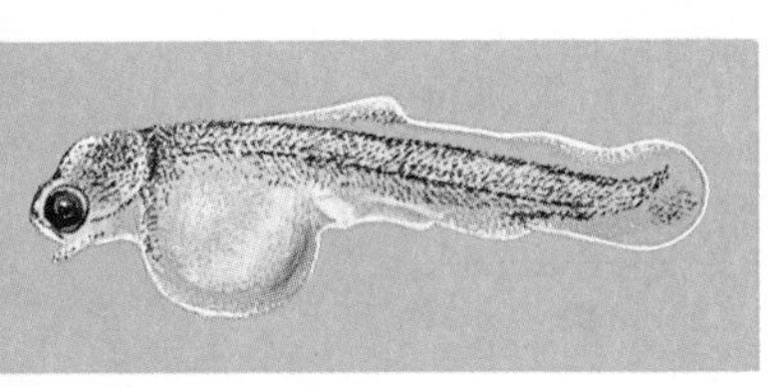

larva 13 mm

principal food:

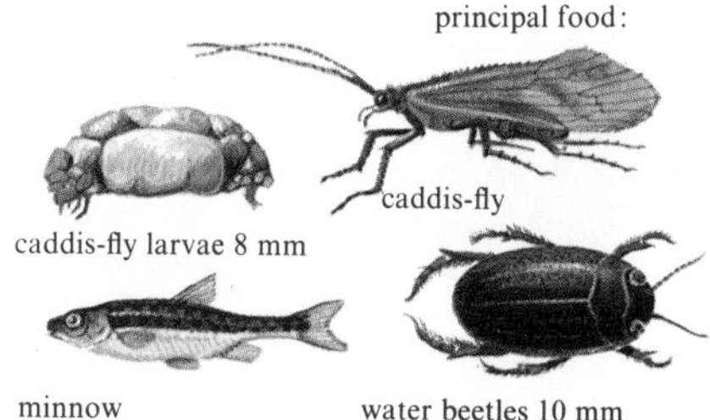

caddis-fly larvae 8 mm

minnow

water beetles 10 mm

20. AMERICAN LAKE TROUT

Salvelinus namaycush

36 cm

20. American lake trout

Salvelinus namaycush (Walbaum)

The head and body are covered by irregular hieroglyphic spots; often reaches 90 cm (7–8 kg) in size. It was introduced into, and is thriving well in several Alpine lakes (Lake Fully, Lake Barberine) in Switzerland. Not found in the British Isles.

THE WHITEFISHES

The whitefish genus, *Coregonus*, comprises slender, silvery fish, resembling the herring apart from their adipose fin typical of the salmonid fishes. The deeply forked tail-fin and the small mouth which reaches only to the level of the front part of the eye are characteristic. The teeth are small or absent. The scales are larger than in Arctic charr, the trout or the salmon. The lateral line is complete.

The species of this salmonid group are, apart from the vendace, very difficult to identify. This is due to the plasticity of the group which, even more than other salmonids, tends to form distinguishable races in response to local conditions.

Investigations in both Switzerland and Sweden now indicate that the many varieties described from western European lakes may be referred to only six species. It is probable that future research in Europe, Asia and North America will also reduce the number of species described there.

One of the most important distinguishing characters is the number of gill-rakers; however, there is no clear-cut difference between the species in this character, and the ranges of gill-raker numbers often overlap. This can therefore only be used statistically, taking a large number of fish from each population. It is only rarely possible to determine the identity of a single individual.

The whitefishes occur mainly in relatively large, deep lakes with clear, oxygen-rich water. Both migratory and non-migratory forms exist. They are also found in rivers and brackish waters.

In general, two main types of feeding exist among the whitefishes. They all, however, possess long, close-set rakers on their gill-arches, and at some time during their lives eat the small planktonic animals of the lakes. The plankton-feeders live in open water feeding on the zooplankton while the bottom-feeders eat small bottom-animals, mainly ostracods, water-slaters, larvae of midges, mayflies and caddis-flies, small snails and mussels as well as plankton. The food items are visually identified and caught singly, and for this reason whitefish eat only in the daytime. The plankton-feeding form has more numerous and longer gill-rakers than the bottom-feeding form, but intermediate types occur.

Spawning takes place in autumn or winter, on a bottom of gravel or sand at water temperatures below 7°C. Spawning usually lasts two weeks. The eggs sink to the bottom and hatch after 2–3 months into larvae with yolk-sacs which are absorbed in 3–4 days. Growth varies with food availability and population density. All whitefish types can produce dwarf forms when growth conditions are bad.

Several types have populations with an elongated, downward-turned snout—the so-called 'houtings'.

Two main groups of whitefish can be distinguished, one with a terminal mouth or a slightly projecting lower jaw, e.g. vendace, and the other in which the species have a projecting upper jaw, e.g. houting and powan.

21. Bottom whitefish

Coregonus pidschian (Gmelin)

Distinctive features: 1st gill-arch with 20 rakers (15–28); upper jaw longer than lower jaw. In the Alpine area, e.g. Lake Constance, it appears as a pale, large-eyed bottom-fish in depths of 20–140 m.
Size: Maximum *c.* 50 cm; often dwarf forms of, at the most, 30 cm.
Distribution: From Alaska through Siberia, northern Russia and Finland to northern and central Sweden. Also in the Alpine region, e.g. Lake Constance and Lake Geneva. Occurs as non-migratory or migratory forms in cold sub-Arctic rivers and lakes, and in the inner Baltic.

When young, the bottom whitefish feeds on plankton but later eats small bottom-animals. Growth varies locally. Spawning takes place at temperatures below 4°C in September-January, from 8,000–50,000 eggs being produced.

This, and the next species, are exploited commercially mainly in the northern and eastern parts of their ranges.

22. Large bottom whitefish

Coregonus nasus (Pallas)

Distinctive features: 1st gill-arch with *c.* 24 rakers (20–29).

This is a cold-water form which resembles *C. pidschian* in appearance, biology and distribution. The two species often occur in the same lakes, but varieties of the large bottom whitefish are also known from lakes in northern Germany and in Poland.
Size: In Siberia, maximum 86 cm (10 kg); generally only 50 cm (1 kg).

The food consists of small bottom-animals, and growth is slow. Spawning is from October-December, and 10,000–135,000 eggs are produced, 4 mm diameter. In Siberia maturity occurs at 7 years.

principal food of the *Coregonus* group:
(*see also page 75*)

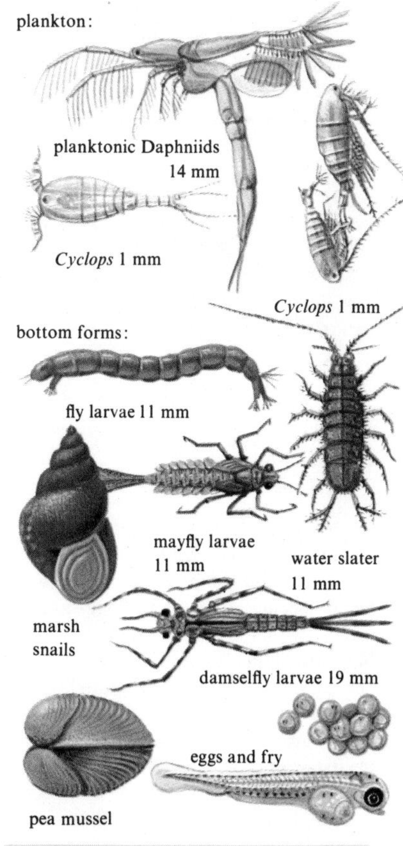

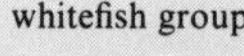

23. Powan

Coregonus lavaretus (L.)

Distinctive features: 1st gill-arch with 30–34 rakers (25–39). The species is very variable. A long-snouted type is found in the Baltic basin.
Size: Maximum *c.* 70 cm, 10 kg in weight. In small lakes with scanty food, dwarf forms, 10–20 cm long, often occur.
Distribution: England (Haweswater, Ullswater, Red Tarn—the schelly); Scotland (Loch Lomond, Loch Eck—the powan); Wales (Llyn Tegid—the gwyniad); Alpine lakes. Migratory in the Baltic, Swedish and Finnish lakes, and Northern Russia. Non-migratory dwarf forms in many Siberian rivers and lakes.

Most populations feed mainly on planktonic crustaceans. The migratory forms in the Baltic ascend the rivers to spawn from September-December. The dwarf forms produce only 1,000–6,000 eggs.

Fishing for powan was at one time of considerable commercial importance in Lake Constance.

24. Houting

Coregonus oxyrinchus (L.)

Distinctive features: 1st gill-arch with *c.* 40 rakers (35–44). Like the powan this species is very variable. Stunted, dwarf forms occur as well as long-snouted forms.
Size: Maximum 50 cm, *c.* 2 kg.
Distribution: Northern Europe and northern Asia. Also a migratory form along the North Sea coast, from which it wanders up the rivers. Also found in Alpine and Swedish lakes.

Small houtings feed on plankton, as do oceanic shoals, although the larger fish also feed on small bottom-animals.

The population is for the most part stationary, but throughout the area of distribution migratory shoals are known to ascend the rivers to spawn in the autumn.

25. Northern whitefish

Coregonus peled (Gmelin)

Distinctive features: 1st gill-arch with 44–68 rakers.
Size: Maximum *c.* 70 cm, 8 kg. Dwarf forms occur as in other whitefish species.
Distribution: Arctic; the most abundant whitefish from northern Siberia to Finland; scattered in the rivers of northern Sweden (Skellefte, Pite, Ume and Angermanälven); possibly in Jutland.

Non-migratory stocks exist in rivers and deep lakes, and migratory ones in the lower reaches of Russian and Siberian rivers. The migratory forms move higher up in the rivers in summer. Spawning occurs from October-November on a bottom of gravel, at below 4°C, and produces 5,000–125,000 eggs.

The smaller forms feed on planktonic crustaceans.

This species is the most important commercial fish in the lower reaches of the Siberian rivers.

♦ 24. HOUTING
Coregonus oxyrinchus

♦ 23. POWAN
Coregonus lavaretus

46 cm

26. Vendace
Coregonus albula (L.)

Distinctive features: A pronounced projecting lower jaw (the opposite to the general rule in the larger whitefish); 1st gill-arch with 36–52 rakers.
Size: Generally *c.* 20 cm; up to 45 cm, 1 kg, in Lake Ladoga, U.S.S.R.
Distribution: From north-western Russia, and in lakes of the upper Volga, to the inner Baltic and all countries around the Baltic. Also in south-east Norway (Mjøsen, Storsjöen); in north Germany in most larger lakes east of the Elbe, and introduced into Wagingersee, Bavaria. In Scotland, England and Ireland (Loch Maben, Derwentwater, Bassenthwaite—vendaces; Loughs Neagh, Erne, Derg—pollans).*

The vendace is a shoaling surface fish, living mainly in the open waters of large, cool lakes, feeding on planktonic crustaceans (copepods, water-fleas). A migratory form in the Baltic ascends rivers to spawn in September-December; 700–8,000 eggs are deposited on a sandy bottom at 1–5°C. The larvae hatch in early spring.

Growth is highly variable, most rapid in Lake Ladoga, where the fish reaches 25 cm at an age of 3–4 years. Becomes mature at 2–4 years.

Caught in seines and traps especially during the migration from the Gulf of Finland into the Neva river. Also fished for in several lakes. It is tasty, and often sold smoked.

**Editor's note:* The recognition of these British forms as species (or subspecies) serves no practical purpose although it has been fashionable since Regan introduced these names in 1908.

27. Smelt

Osmerus eperlanus (L.)

Distinctive features: Small, slender salmonid with large eyes and a projecting lower jaw; the pelvic fins are placed below the origin of the short, high back fin; incomplete lateral line, and 60–70 scales along the side of the body. Live smelts are rather transparent. A cucumber-like smell is characteristic.

Size: Non-migratory freshwater forms often grow to only 10–15 cm (2–3 years), rarely 20 cm (7–9 years). Migratory forms, mainly in brackish water, reach 15–18 cm (3–4 years), rarely 30 cm (*c.* 10 years).

Distribution: There is only one European species; a closely related species is found in Siberia and North America.

The smelt is known most commonly as an inshore marine and estuarine fish which migrates into rivers to spawn in freshwater. The inner Baltic has a large migratory stock. It is also found in freshwater, landlocked in cool, deep lakes which formerly communicated with the sea, but in general it is a surface-living shoaling fish.

Its food consists of planktonic animals: water-fleas and shrimp-like mysids (see page 75), the latter found as relicts from the last glacial period in several North European lakes and along the sea-shores. It also takes small bottom-animals and, with increasing size, fry of fish.

In Scandinavia spawning occurs at the time of the ice-melting, from March-May, in British rivers usually in April. The migratory smelt enter the estuaries of rivers, while the lake smelt seek shallow water or enter the tributaries for spawning. The eggs are shed on a sandy bottom usually where plants are present, and many of the adults die after spawning. Number of eggs: 9,000–40,000. These are yellow, 0·6–0·9 mm in diameter and have a sticky outer membrane which bursts and turns inside out to form a stalk, fixing the egg for some time. Often the egg breaks loose and floats downstream with the membrane as a 'parachute', Hatching occurs after 3–5 weeks. The larvae are very long bodied, and feed on small planktonic organisms. Growth is slow, fastest in the females. The lake forms mature at 1–2 years when 8–10 cm in length, the brackish water forms not until 3–4 years and 15–18 cm. In general the migratory stocks grow most rapidly, spawn most eggs and live longest. These large, long-lived fish feed mostly on other fish.

Smelt show large and irregular stock fluctuations ('smelt years'), due to differences in survival of the young in 'good' or 'bad' years. The migratory smelt which are locally numerous are particularly exploited. They are used for meal and oil but are, in places, eaten both fresh and smoked. Mainly captured with push-net, drift-net, herring trawl and fixed gear.

26 cm

♦ 26. VENDACE
Coregonus albula

principal food of the *Coregonus* group:

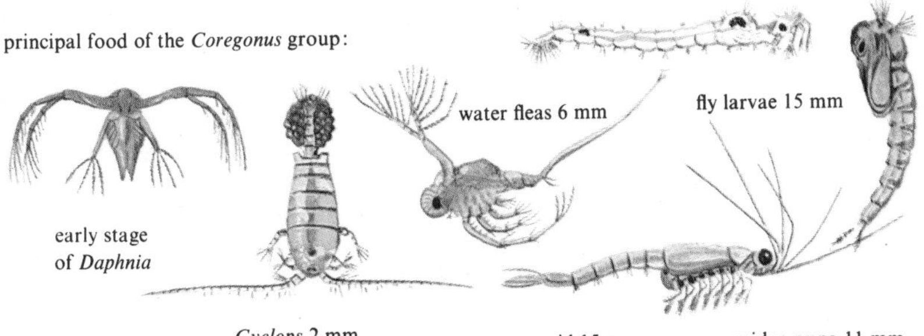

17 cm

♦ 27. SMELT
Osmerus eperlanus

larva 24 mm

28. Grayling

Thymallus thymallus (L.)

Distinctive features: Salmonid with a small mouth and pointed head, characterised by a high and long back fin, largest in the male. The marked lengthwise arrangement of the scale rows is very noticeable. The name *Thymallus* refers to the thyme-like scent of the fish.

Five other species occur in northern Asia and America.

Size: About 30 cm (250 g) at 3–4 years old, rarely over 50 cm (1 kg) at 7–14 years; maximum *c.* 60 cm (2–3 kg).

The grayling is a river fish living only in clear, cool, well-oxygenated water with strong currents, such as are found below the charr region of the mountain streams. A river bed with deep holes, large stones or excavations in the banks is preferred, but the grayling may also occur in more open unsheltered reaches. In central Europe this part of the river is named the grayling region. Downstream it is replaced by the barbel region, characterised by the river barbel and a more uniform and moderate current. In Sweden, Norway, Finland and northern U.S.S.R. the grayling is found also in lakes, as it is occasionally in the British Isles. In the Swedish and Finnish skerries it occurs, too, in brackish water. It often forms small shoals.

It feeds mainly on insect larvae, especially sedentary caddis worms, larvae and pupae of midges which it grazes from the stones on the river bed. It will eat the eggs of salmon and trout where these become exposed and, when older, may eat young fish. Flying insects are also taken.

Spawning takes place just after the spring thaw from March-May. In the spawning season the male has generally, but not always, darker colours, and the back fin is radiantly reddish-purple with dark spots. The skin becomes thick on the back and the sides of the tail. Spawning takes place on a bottom of gravel or sand in 50 cm of water, in rivers, lakes, and in the brackish Baltic skerries. During spawning a pit is formed in the bottom, and there the female covers the eggs with sand by vigorous strokes of her tail. The number of eggs varies with the size of the female, from 600 to 8,000, and they are yellow and measure 3 mm. They hatch in 3–4 weeks depending on the temperature (180–200 day-degrees C).

The yolk-sac is not large and is consumed in a few days. Some weeks later the young disperse. Growth is rapid in the first year, when a length of 7–12 cm is reached. At 2–3 years the males become mature, and the females generally at 3–5 years, when at a length of *c.* 30 cm. Growth varies considerably from one locality to another.

Although the grayling is a highly esteemed table fish in Europe, it is not of great importance as it cannot be transported alive and its special flavour is lost a few hours after death. It is also considered a good game-fish with fly and spinner in Europe, but it is not widely regarded as a sport-fish in Britain.

Unfortunately, the grayling is very sensitive to pollution and increased temperatures, and the grayling region is, for technical reasons, most suitable for hydroelectric development schemes—often resulting in the complete destruction of the population. In France, methods have been developed for hatching and rearing grayling until the young fish stage. As the fish rarely matures in ponds and is very difficult to transport alive, the stripping of eggs and their fertilisation in a dish must take place at the river-bank, after the capture of wild ripe fish. The eggs are carried to the hatchery and the very delicate fry are reared in ponds with running water and plentiful live food, e.g. larvae of midges. After one year the young, 8–12 cm long, can be released in suitable streams.

♦ 28. GRAYLING
Thymallus thymallus

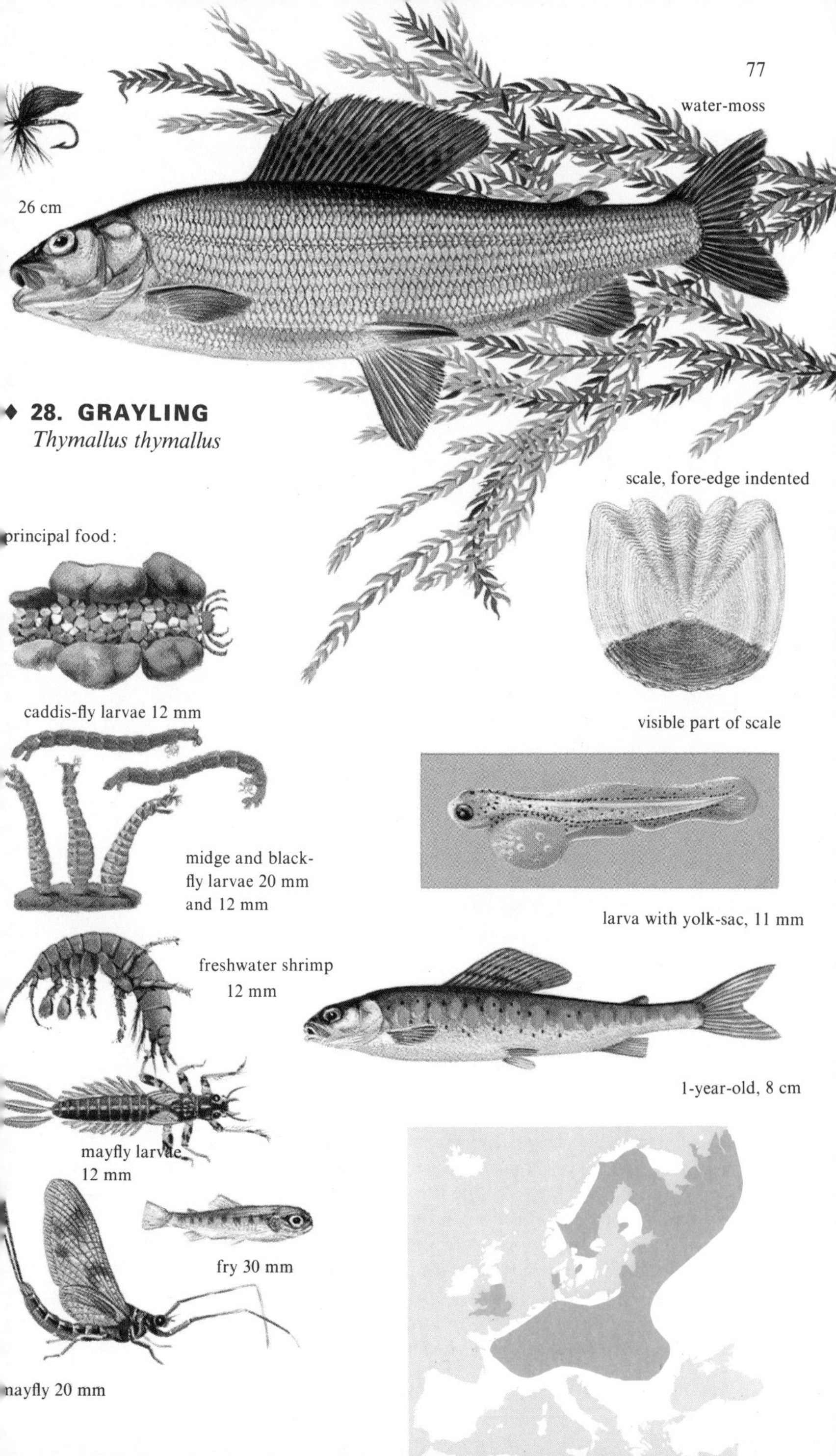

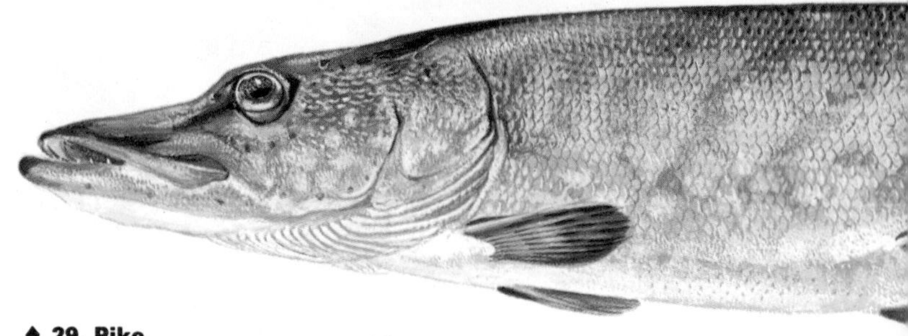

♦ 29. Pike

Esox lucius L.

Distinctive features: Flat and broad snout, elongated body, the back parallel to the belly outline; dorsal and anal fins similar in shape and sited far along the body; colour variable, those living in brackish water are yellowish, those from densely weeded lakes greenish. The young are heavily marked with light bars and spots, but old pike turn dark, often brownish or greyish.

Size: Males do not grow as fast as females, and attain maturity at an age of 2–3 years, 25–40 cm long (0·5 kg). The males occasionally reach 90–100 cm (5–8 kg) at 10–14 years. Females generally mature at 3–5 years, 40–55 cm long (0·5–1 kg). The largest pike are always females. In mainland Europe pike are known of 1·5 m (*c.* 35 kg) and aged more than 30 years. In the British Isles these maximum measurements are considerably lower.

Pike (family Esocidae) occur in all kinds of lakes, except where the water is very acid or poor in oxygen. They also occur in running water, especially in the slow-flowing parts of rivers (the bream region), and will enter brackish water as, for example, is found in the low salinity areas of the Baltic. Pike live in the well-weeded waters, usually close to the bank or just outside the weeds. However, the large pike in large lakes and in the Baltic often stray into the open, deeper water. Tagging experiments have shown that the species is rather stationary, and particularly so while immature.

Its food after the first year consists almost completely of fish: dace, roach, rudd, perch and, in the Baltic, herring. In ponds with no larger food animals it also eats the larvae of insects, and the water-slater (*Asellus*). Once past its earliest stages, the pike is a cannibal. On a number of occasions two pike of almost equal size have been found dead, the smaller jammed into the mouth of the larger, for the backward-pointing teeth do not permit it to disgorge too large a prey. It appears that a pike can eat a prey of half its own weight, although its food items are usually much less than this.

The pike lies in wait for its prey, motionless and well camouflaged in the vegetation between water-lilies or in the edge of the reeds and, with a powerful stroke of the tail it overtakes its prey. Over longer distances it is, however, a poor swimmer.

Spawning occurs at temperatures of 2–12°C from the end of March into May, and in the northernmost part of its range right into July. It usually takes place in quite shallow water, often only 20 cm deep. In lowland rivers pike spawn in the water-meadows inundated with springtime floods, elsewhere they spawn close inshore on water-plants, and they use the same spawning places year after

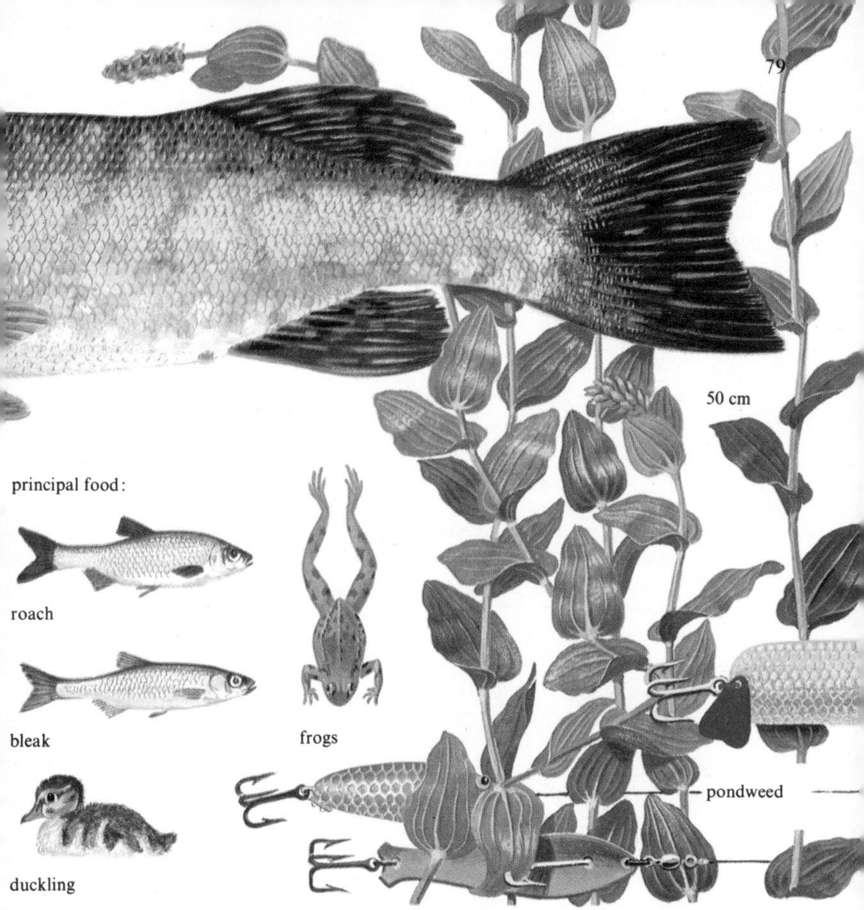

50 cm

principal food:

roach

bleak

frogs

duckling

pondweed

year. The males arrive first, the females later, and when mating their usual reflexes towards food or danger are almost completely suspended. Frequently one female is accompanied by two or three males.

Spawn is shed in several portions over 3–4 weeks. The number of eggs depends on the size of the female and can roughly be estimated at 15–20,000 per kg. A female of 5 kg, for example, spawns *c.* 90,000 (*c.* 1 litre), while large females may spawn over half a million. The eggs measure 2·5–3 mm; they are adhesive and stick to plants, and as the spring floods die down large numbers may be stranded in the water-meadows. Normally, the larvae hatch after 10–15 days (110–130 day-degrees C are needed) and are 9 mm long. The mouth is not fully formed, and the larva remains attached to plants by organs in the front of the head until the yolk-sac is consumed; only then does it become free-swimming. At 12 mm long the mouth is fully formed, and

after a few days the larva rises to the surface to fill its swim-bladder with air. At first it feeds on small planktonic animals. From a length of 25 mm it resembles the adults, and when 4–5 cm long begins to prey on the summer's hatch of smaller fish (rudd, dace, bream, etc.). A substantial amount of aquatic insect larvae and crustaceans is also eaten.

Growth rate varies but as a rule is very fast. After 1 year the pike is 9–20 cm or more, and at 2 years many males become mature, while females normally mature 2 years later. A weight of 1 kg is normally reached in 4–6 years, sometimes in 2–3 years.

Sport fishermen in particular repeatedly comment on the varying eagerness of the pike to take a bait. Immediately after spawning, during which it hardly eats, it is exhausted, hungry and very eager to rise to the bait. During summer, however, it seems less eager but whether this is because of the abundance of young fish which fall an easy prey, or due to other circumstances, is not clear. Many factors are said to be involved, including the weather, and every serious pike angler has his own pet theory. For further information ask any sport fisherman.

The pike is a valuable fish—especially as a game-fish—but like other predatory fishes it is the large ones that take a heavy toll of good fish in a well-cultivated fishing water. Young pike convert food at the ratio of 3–5 kg food to 1 kg pike meat, but at greater age, when growth is slower, have a conversion ratio of 10–30 kg food to 1 kg meat. In round figures this could mean that a 12 years-old pike, 1 m long and weighing 8 kg, consumed 2,500 fish, with a weight of 175 kg, during its life.

The expression 'like a pike in a carp-pond' is in frequent use in central Europe and has an obvious meaning. Nevertheless, pike are often deliberately introduced into carp-ponds to remove unwanted fish (e.g. crucian carp, roach, poor-growing carp). Great care has, however, to be exercised in introducing pike of the correct size and in removing the largest pike as they grow, as otherwise all but the largest stock fish would disappear.

Spinners, or hooks inserted into small dead fish, are used for pike-fishing while sometimes traps or nets are employed in commercial fisheries. Most countries in Europe have local minimum sizes and preservation measures, but despite these the pike is over-fished in many regions. The total annual European catch is over 10,000 tons, most of this in inland Europe.

30. Mud-minnow

Umbra krameri Walbaum

Distinctive features: Small, brownish fish with the dorsal fin origin over the pelvic fin and ending above the anal fin. The head has scales both on the sides and above.
Size: 5–7 cm, maximum 12 cm.

Lives in overgrown ponds, swamps and streams, and feeds on the bottom-living larvae of insects, water-slaters, worms and molluscs. It spawns in spring, about 150 eggs being deposited in a hollow which the female guards and keeps clean. This species is very tenacious of life and is sometimes kept in aquaria.

31. Eastern mud-minnow

Umbra pygmaea (De Kay)

Distinctive features: Resembles the common mud-minnow but has a dark lower jaw and a dark spot at the base of the tail-fin. The sides have light longitudinal stripes.
Size: Maximum in Europe *c.* 10 cm.

Introduced from America as an aquarium fish. It now lives wild in several—mostly German waters (Schleswig-Holstein, Lower Saxony), and is also found locally in France and Holland.

Its biology is similar to that of the native mud-minnow.

29. Pike

principal food for larva and young fish:

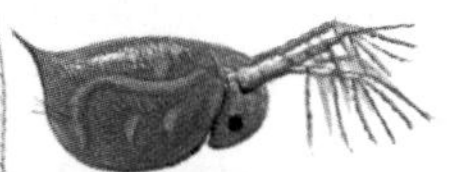

Daphnia 1 mm

Cyclops 2 mm

fry

tadpole

larva 10 mm

larva 13 mm

12 cm

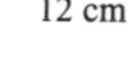

7.5 cm

30. MUD-MINNOW

Umbra krameri

8 cm

31. EASTERN MUD-MINNOW

Umbra pygmaea

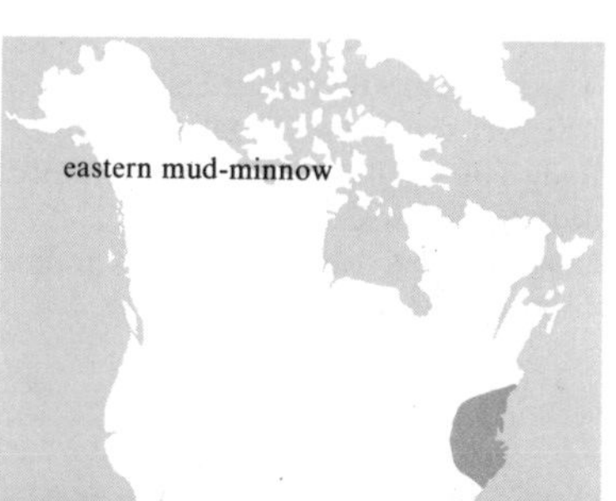

THE CARP FAMILY

There are many species in the carp family, all having a single dorsal and one anal fin. The mouth is toothless but the lower pharyngeal bones have strong teeth which crush the food against a horny plate (the 'carp-stone') in the roof of the gullet.

Hearing in this group is well developed. Sound can be transmitted through the air-bladder which is connected with the labyrinth of the ear by means of several small bones (Weberian ossicles). The air-bladder has two chambers.

At spawning time males develop a rash of usually light-coloured spawning tubercles, particularly on the head and the front of the body.

1 Dorsal fin at least twice as long as anal fin, with more than 16 rays **2**
  Dorsal fin not twice as long as anal fin, with fewer than 16 rays **3**

2 Two long and two short barbels; edge of tail-fin distinctly concave .... ***Carp,** p. 136
  No barbels; tail-fin only slightly concave. 30–35 scales in the lateral line; 23–33 gill rakers on first gill-arch .... ***Crucian carp,** p. 132
  No barbels; tail-fin only weakly concave. 25–31 scales in the lateral line; 35–48 gill-rakers on first gill-arch .... **(*) Goldfish,** p. 134

3 Barbels present around the mouth **4**
  No barbels **9**

4 2 barbels, scales small or moderate **5**
  4 barbels, scales distinct and moderate **6**
  4 barbels, scales absent (Dalmatia only) .... **Dalmatian barbel-gudgeon,** p. 112

5 Body with small scales; the fins all broadly rounded; the tail-fin weakly concave .... ***Tench,** p. 104
  Small, slender fish with distinct scales; tail-fin distinctly forked with pointed lobes .... ***Gudgeons,** p. 112

6 The longest ray in the dorsal fin spine-like with a serrate hind edge 7
The longest ray in the dorsal fin not spine-like 8

7 but serrate, or only weakly serrate in the middle third . . . .
55–65 scales in the lateral line; the rear barbels just reach the hind edge of the eye . . . . ***Barbel,** p. 114

8 66–72 scales in the lateral line; the rear barbels can reach beyond the hind edge of the eye; body and unpaired fins spotted with black (Italy only) . . . . **Italian barbel,** p. 116

48–56 scales in the lateral line . . . . **Southern barbel,** p. 116

46–51 scales in the lateral line (Iberian peninsula only) . . . . **Iberian barbel,** p. 116

9 Base of anal fin the same length as dorsal fin base (or at most 1–3 rays longer) **1**

Base of anal fin clearly longer than dorsal fin base but not more than twice as long **18**

Base of anal fin at least 3 times as long as dorsal fin base **25**

10 Lateral line complete **11**
Lateral line incomplete, sometimes absent; small fishes **17**

11 Mouth ventral; the lips hard with cutting edges . . . . **Nases,** p. 108
Otherwise **12**

12 Well-developed scales on body **13**
Body covered or partly covered with thin, rudimentary scales (Dalmatia, Bosnia, Albania) . . . . Paraphoxinus, p. 90

13 Pelvic fins well in front of a vertical line from the origin of the dorsal fin . . . . ***Rudd,** p. 100

Pelvic fins sited below the origin of the dorsal fin **14**

14 Jaws equal; lateral line orange-yellow, a dark violet stripe above it from eye to tail-fin (Alpine regions and northern Italy) .... **Soufie (Fr.),** p. 96

Otherwise **15**

15 Slender, rounded body with large black-edged scales forming a network pattern; the edge of the anal fin rounded; 44–46 scales in the lateral line .... ***Chub,** p. 94

These characters, but not combined **16**

16 62–67 scales in the lateral line; slender, rounded body (Upper Danube-system and the Black Sea region) .... **Black Sea roach,** p. 88

54–60 scales in the lateral line; slender, body somewhat compressed .... **(*) Ide,** p. 96

48–53 scales in the lateral line; slender, almost cylindrical body; lateral line sometimes weakly black-edged .... ***Dace,** p. 92

44–49 scales in the lateral line; slender, somewhat compressed body (Northern Italy, tributaries of the Upper Danube) .... **Danube roach,** p. 88

42–45 scales in the lateral line. compressed, sometimes deep bodied. Eye reddish (in Italy with faint, lead-grey stripes) .... ***Roach,** p. 86 (also Southern European roach p. 88

N.B. For Spain and Portugal, see .... Iberian species of roach, p. 90
For Dalmatia and Albania, see .... Dalmatian roaches, p. 90
and .... Albanian roach, p. 90

17 Scales small, barely visible; body elongate, dark-coloured, or barred with transverse bands .... ***Minnow,** p. 98

Scales distinct; body rather deep, sides silvery .... **(*) Bitterling,** p. 130

18 Lateral line incomplete; silvery scales are easily rubbed off; anal fin with 15–17 rays; small fishes ... **Moderlieschen (Ge.),** p. 90

Lateral line complete **19**

19 Lower jaw longer, its tip fitting into a hollow in upper jaw **20**

Lower jaw shorter than the upper jaw; more or less deep bodied **22**

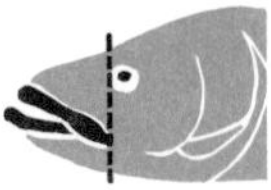

20 The upper jaw-bone extends to below the front of the eye; 15–18 anal fin-rays . . . . **Asp (Sw.),** pp. 102–3

The upper jaw-bone does not reach to the edge of the eye; 18–24 anal fin-rays; slender, silvery fish with upward-turned mouth **21**

21 46–53 scales in the lateral line; 18–23 anal fin-rays . . . . ***Bleak,** p. 118

44–48 scales in the lateral line; 13–18 anal fin-rays (Italy, Dalmatia, Albania) . . . . **Italian bleak,** p. 118

60–67 scales in the lateral line; 20–24 anal fin-rays (Danube basin) . . . . **Danube bleak,** p. 118

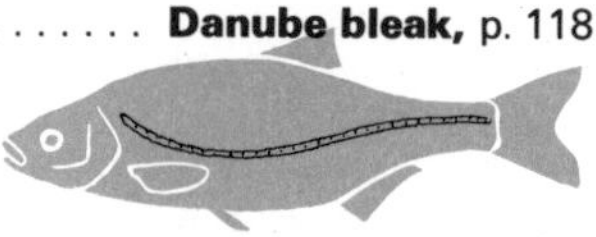

22 Lateral line curving downwards and edged with black; often a dark longitudinal band from gill-cover to tail-fin; 18–20 anal fin-rays . . . . **Schneider (Ge.),** p. 120

Lateral line not edged with black; 20–28 anal fin-rays **23**

23 Snout often dark, conical and projecting over the mouth; rather slender bodied . . . . **Zahrte (Ge.),** p. 128

Snout not projecting noticeably in front of the mouth; deep-bodied species **24**

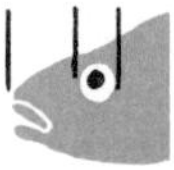

24 Pectoral and pelvic fins dark; eye diameter less than snout length . . . . ***Bream,** p. 122

Pectoral and pelvic fins reddish; eye diameter almost equals snout length . . . . ***White bream,** p. 120

25 Slender, deep-bellied but back straight, lateral line undulate. Belly sharp edged; at least 100 scales along the side . . . . **Ziege (Ge.),** p. 128

Deep-bodied, compressed; lateral line almost straight; 49–52 scales in the lateral line . . . . **Danube bream,** p. 126

Deep-bodied, compressed; lateral line almost straight; 66–73 scales in the lateral line . . . . **Zope (Ge.),** p. 126

32. Roach

Rutilus rutilus (L.)

Distinctive features: Eyes reddish; pelvic fins below the front rays of the dorsal fin; the body-edge between the pelvic fins and the vent not sharp-keeled as in the rudd. 42–45 scales along the lateral line; pharyngeal teeth in a single row, the hindmost ones only weakly serrate. The shape of the body varies to a considerable extent both with age and with environment, good feeding conditions generally producing more high-backed fish than poor ones.
Size: Very dependent on the local conditions. In overcrowded small lakes and even large ones, the roach often reaches a maximum of only 10–15 cm in length. In good conditions, however, a length of 25 cm (200 g) at 7–12 years may be attained. From British waters, Sweden and the Black Sea region records exist of roach over 40 cm long and *c.* 1 kg in weight.
The roach is one of the most common and numerous fish in lakes and slow-flowing rivers, where it occurs in shoals close to the vegetation belt. The largest individuals live farthest from the bank. In turbid (eutrophic) lakes it is found over the whole area. In the Black Sea region, Lake Aral, the Baltic estuaries and skerries it enters brackish water, and these local populations regularly migrate into freshwater for wintering and spawning.

It feeds partly on animal food: larvae and pupae of insects, snails, and crustaceans; and partly on vegetable matter: leaves of water thyme, milfoil, duckweed, stonewart, or growths of algae which are grazed from reeds, submerged woodwork or stones. In brackish water, *Corophium* and the larvae of midges are important food items. In winter, feeding is much reduced and the wintering shoals live in deeper water.

The roach spawns from April-June, when the water temperature has reached at least 10°C. Spawning occurs in quite shallow water near the bank, on a stony bottom or over dense submerged weeds. The migratory brackish-water roach of the Baltic spawn in the lower parts of the rivers, and those of Lake Aral may even do so in salt water. The males arrive on the spawning places a few days before the females, and develop, during this season, a characteristic heavy 'rash' of small grey-white spawning tubercles on the head and back (see p. 15); a similar but less well-developed rash may occur on the females.

After the females arrive, spawning continues for about a week, often with conspicuous and boisterous mating play. The males often remain at the spawning places for some time following spawning.

The number of eggs is generally 5,000–100,000 (in the migratory forms up to 200,000 per female). The eggs are *c.* 1 mm in diameter, slightly adhesive and stick to plants and stones. Hatching takes place in from 4 to 10 days, depending on the temperature. The newly hatched larvae measure 4·5–6·5 mm, and live attached to the vegetation for 2–5 days until the yolk is consumed. After this they stay in shallow water feeding on planktonic plants and animals, chiefly small crustaceans. The scales are formed at a length of *c.* 30 mm. Females appear to grow a little faster than males, but growth is always slow. Maturity is reached after 3 years, for females, or two years for males.

By its very abundance the roach is an important fish in the economy of freshwaters. It preys on smaller animals and plants, and is itself preyed on by larger, more valuable fish, such as pike, zander, perch and to some extent eels. However, the economic value of the roach to the European commercial fishing industry is small. Locally it is used as a cheap food-fish, e.g. in eastern Europe, and in the Black Sea region it is sold fresh, smoked or salted. It is caught in seines, stake-nets and traps. Its chief value in western Europe, particularly Britain, is as a sport-

20 cm

♦ 32. ROACH

Rutilus rutilus

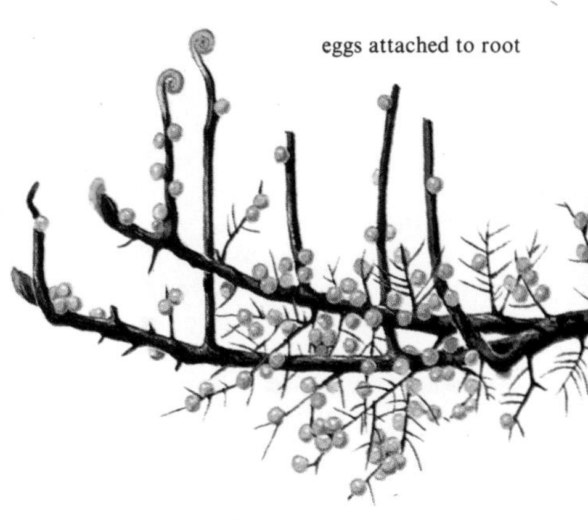

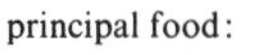

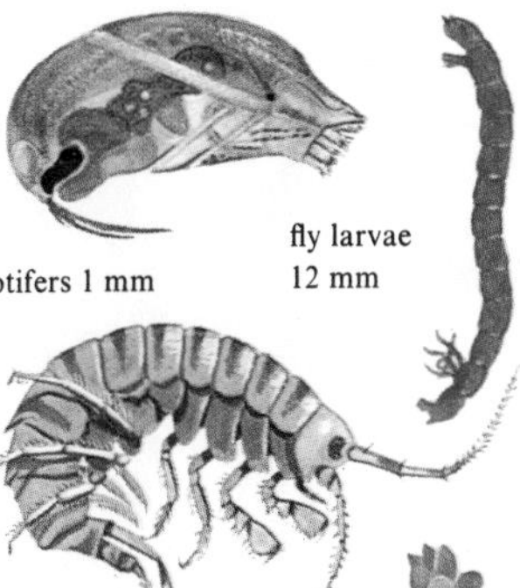

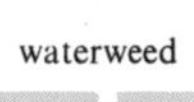

larva 9 mm

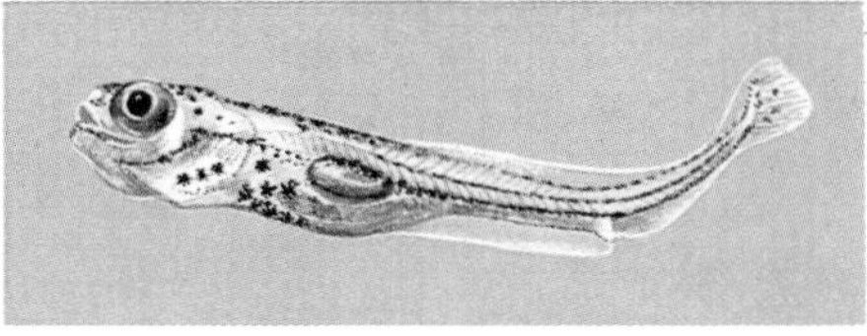

enemies:

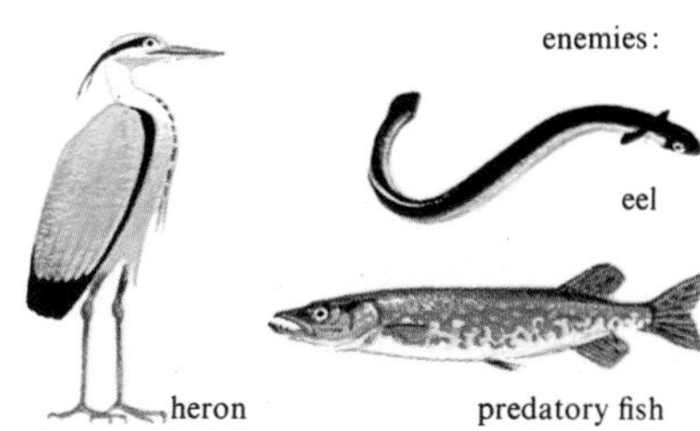

ing fish. Its abundance and tolerance of pollution mean that it is widely available to anglers. It makes good bait for predatory fish, but is difficult to keep alive and is rather fragile.

33. Danube roach

Rutilus pigus (Lacépède)

Distinctive features: Slender, somewhat compressed body; head small, 44–49 scales along the lateral line.
Size: Generally 20–30 cm (*c.* 250 g), rarely 40 cm (1 kg).
Distribution: The subspecies *R. pigus virgo* lives in the River Danube in deep water with slow currents; its food consists of small bottom-animals. Another subspecies (*R. pigus pigus*) occurs in northern Italy.

Spawns from April to May. At this time males develop more vivid colours and a rash of spawning tubercles on head and back. The females deposits 40,000–60,000 sticky eggs on stones and plants.

34. South European roach

Rutilus rubilio (Bonaparte)

Distinctive features: Similar to the common roach, but often with narrow, greyish longitudinal stripes on the sides of the body.
Size: Maximum *c.* 30 cm.
Distribution: The species replaces the common roach in lowland waters around the Adriatic basin.

A shoaling fish with a biology resembling that of the roach.
Editor's note: Recent studies of the European roaches have shown that such differences as can be discerned between these 'species' are probably only variations caused by environment. There is little evidence to support the view that the last two species (and Iberian forms) are specifically distinct from *Rutilus rutilus*.

35. Black Sea Roach

Rutilus frisii (Nordmann)

Distinctive features: Slender bodied, nearly round in cross-section; 62–67 scales along the lateral line.
Size: Generally 40–60 cm (1–2 kg), rarely 70 cm (6 kg).
Distribution: The subspecies *R. f. meidingeri*, the 'pearlfish', inhabits the following German and Austrian lakes and their tributaries: Chiemsee, Traunsee, Attersee and Mondsee, all in the Danube basin. The species is otherwise found in the Black Sea region.

Its life-history is not well known. It lives mostly in shallow water feeding on the larvae of insects, worms, small snails and mussels, crustaceans, and fish fry. Plant remains are often found in the

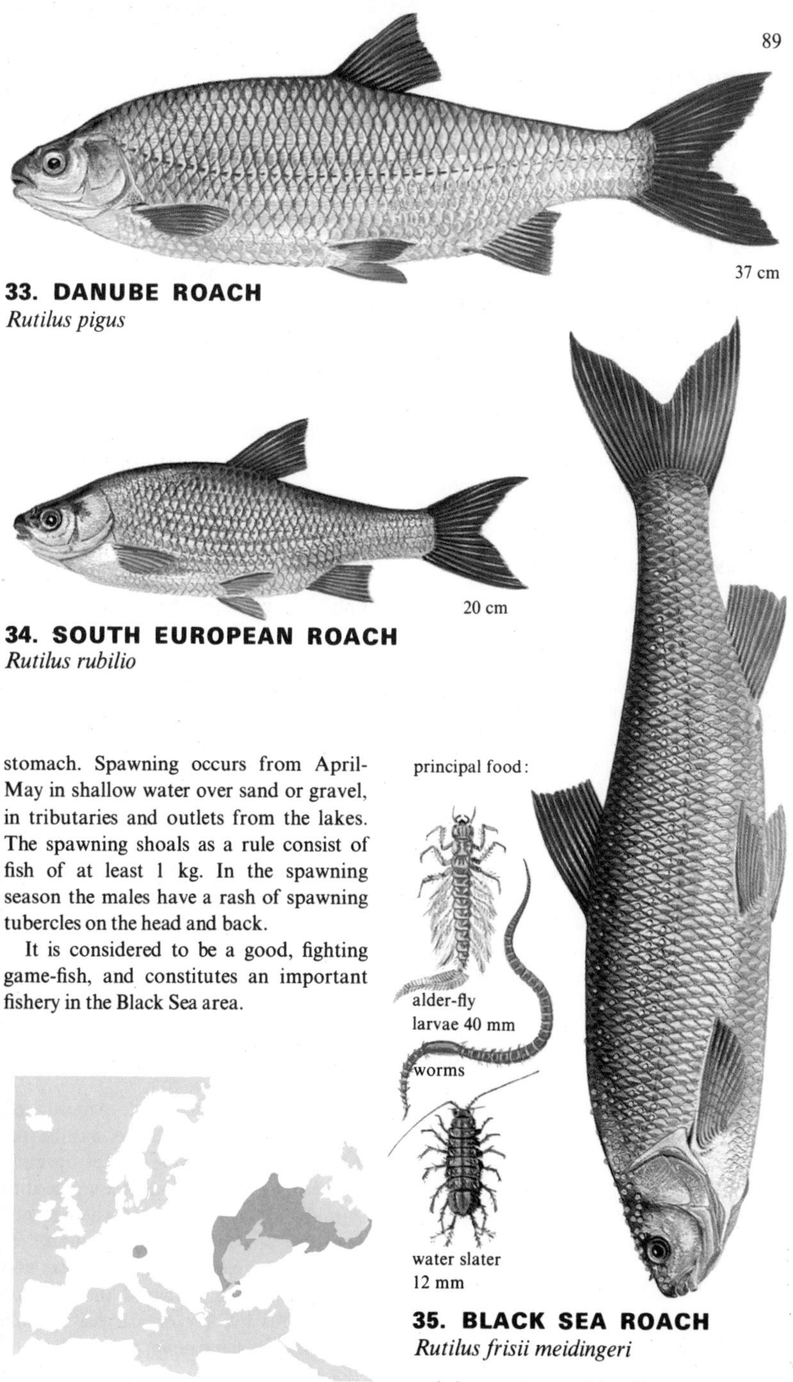

33. DANUBE ROACH
Rutilus pigus

34. SOUTH EUROPEAN ROACH
Rutilus rubilio

stomach. Spawning occurs from April-May in shallow water over sand or gravel, in tributaries and outlets from the lakes. The spawning shoals as a rule consist of fish of at least 1 kg. In the spawning season the males have a rash of spawning tubercles on the head and back.

It is considered to be a good, fighting game-fish, and constitutes an important fishery in the Black Sea area.

35. BLACK SEA ROACH
Rutilus frisii meidingeri

male in spawning condition 54 cm

Iberian Peninsula Roaches

The common roach is replaced in the waters of Spain and Portugal by four so-called species. These are: *Rutilis arcasii*, the Portugese *R. macrolepidotus,* as well as *R. lemmingii* and *R. alburnoides,* all described by Steindachner in 1866. These forms are not well known and may be no more than local populations distinguished more by their environment than by morphological characters.

They are small (15–25 cm) with only 9–10 rays in the dorsal fin, and a dark band along the lateral line. They are shoaling fish and, like the roach, omnivorous. Little is known about their biology.

Genus *Paraphoxinus*

A number of minnow-like fish from Dalmatia and Lake Ohrid are described under this genus. They are, however, very inadequately known, and the group as a whole requires close and detailed study.

Most species are small, growing to about 10 cm. *P. alepidotus* (Heckel) (no. 36) is naked apart from a row of scales along the lateral line. *P. epiroticus* Steindachner is covered by thin fragile scales, and both *P. adspersus* (Heckel) (no. 37), *P. croaticus* (Steindachner) and *P. pstrossi* Steindachner have rudimentary scales. *P. ghethaldii* Steindachner has no scales on the back and the lower caudal peduncle.

These fish live in shoals, feeding on all kinds of small animals, but their mode of life is not at all well known. They have no economic importance.

Phoxinellus hispanicus (Steindachner), a small roach-like fish, is known only from the river Guadiana, southern Spain. It lives mainly in small streams and its biology is said to be similar to the minnow.

38. Albanian minnow

Pachychilon pictum (Heckel & Kner)

Distinctive features: A slender, small roach-like fish, with very thick lips. The back has scattered small, brown dots.
Size: 15–16 cm.

It has been found only in northern and south-eastern Albania (Skutari and Lake Ohrid regions). It is a shoaling fish, feeding on various small animals. Its biology is not well known.

39. Moderlieschen (Ge.)

Leucaspius delineatus (Heckel)

Distinctive features: A small fish with large silvery scales, and an inconspicuous intense silvery band along each side. The lateral line is incomplete and extends only to 7–13 scales; the anal fin is longer than the dorsal fin; the mouth turns upwards; the lower edge of the body between the pelvic fins and the vent forms a sharp keel; and the scales are very loosely atttached and come off if the fish is handled.
Size: 6–10 cm long at 2 years. The females are the largest. Maximum size *c.* 12 cm.

It is a shoaling fish living near the surface, in peat-pits and other small ponds, more rarely in larger lakes. It also occurs in the bream region of rivers. Its sudden appearance in small ponds often seems to be unaccountable, and its German name 'Moderlieschen' means motherless because it seems to appear 'by itself'. It feeds on planktonic animals and algae, as well as small flying insects.

Spawning is from June to August, and at this time the female has a tube-like fold of skin around the genital opening, by means of which the eggs are placed in spiral bands on the stems of water-plants. The eggs are deposited in a number of spawnings spread over several weeks and the male is said to guard them. Some populations live for only 2 years, while others live for a maximum of 4 years.

9 cm

36. *Paraphoxinus alepidotus*

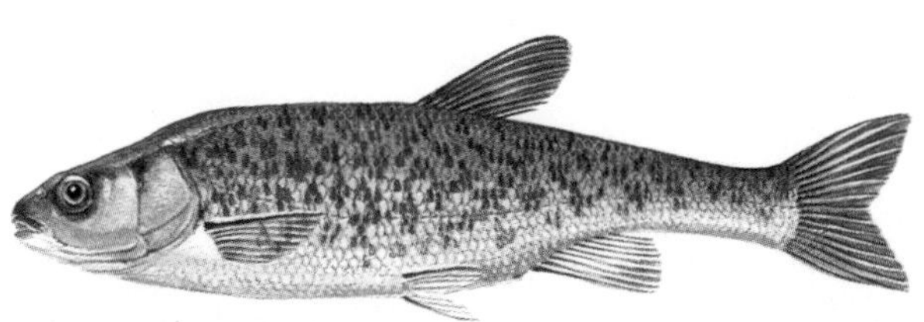

37. *Paraphoxinus adspersus*

8 cm

8 cm

38. ALBANIAN ROACH
Pachychilon pictum

principal food:

Cyclops 2 mm

rotifers ½ mm

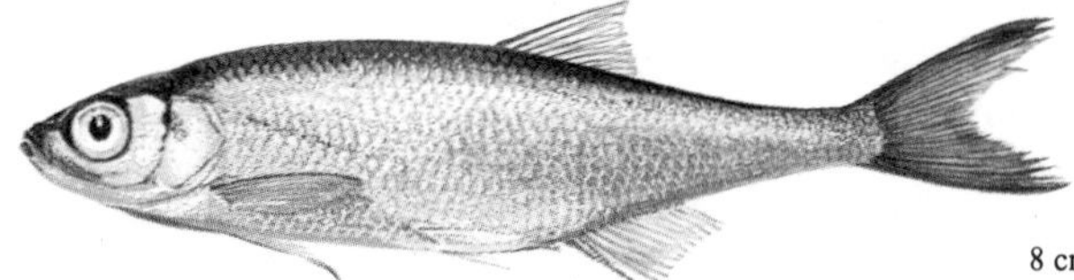

8 cm

39. MODERLIESCHEN
Leucaspus delineatus

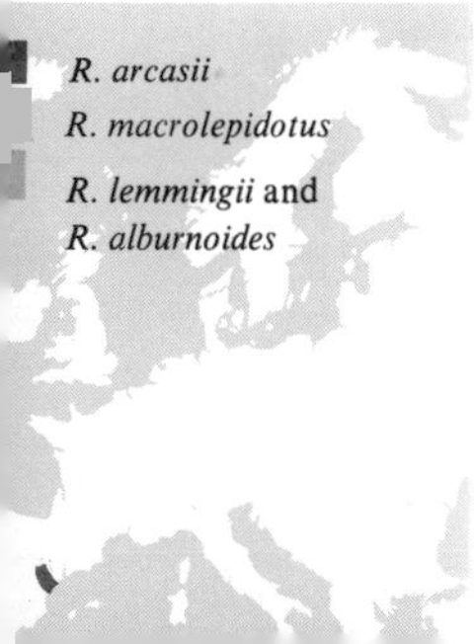

R. arcasii
R. macrolepidotus
R. lemmingii and
R. alburnoides

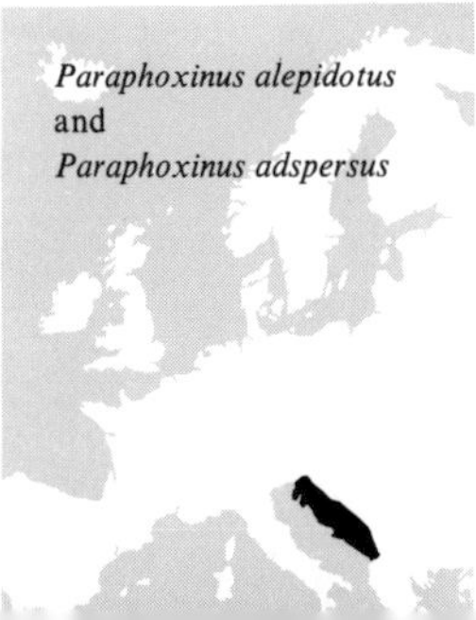

Paraphoxinus alepidotus
and
Paraphoxinus adspersus

Moderliesche
Albanian roac

It is sometimes kept in aquaria, and can be used as anglers' bait.

40. Dace

Leuciscus leuciscus (L.)

Distinctive features: Resembles the roach, but more slender. The eyes are yellowish, never red, and the iris has small dark spots. 47 to 54 scales in the lateral line; edge of anal fin concave; the pharyngeal teeth in two rows.

Size: Generally 15–20 cm at 2–3 years old; rarely over 25 cm and 200 g, at *c.* 10 years. A few records of over 30 cm. exist.

Distribution: Several forms can be distinguished in different parts of Europe.

Lives in cool, running water and in lakes, and even in brackish water near the mouths of rivers. It feeds on water insects, and flying insects of all kinds, worms, small snails, also parts of plants.

The dace spawns in streams on a sandy or stony bottom from March-May, and the males have spawning tubercles over the whole body during these months. The shoals spend two or more weeks on the spawning beds before returning down the streams. Egg number: 3,000–27,000. The large eggs (2 mm in diameter) are deposited on the bottom. The young at 1 year old measure 6–7 cm, at 2 years 10–20 cm, and maturity is reached at 3–4 years.

The dace is a bony fish and for this reason, and its small size, is not eaten. The Siberian subspecies, however, has some importance as a food-fish, and is caught with fixed gear, seines or on hooks.

The dace rises willingly to a fly but is of little importance as a game-fish, although the capture of large dace requires considerable angling expertise. It is good rather tough bait-fish.

DALMATIAN AND CROATIAN DACE-LIKE FISH

Six relatives of the dace have been described from Dalmatian and Croatian rivers and lakes. Very little is known about them, and they are difficult to identify, —it is very likely that some are merely local races. All are shoaling fish like the dace, rarely growing over 25 cm. The following species may be noted:

41. *Leuciscus svallize* (Heckel & Kner)

48–49 scales along the lateral line; the anal fin has 13 rays. Dalmatia and southern Albania.

42. *L. illyricus* (Heckel & Kner)

49–54 scales along the lateral line; body rather high, compressed.

43. *L. ukliva* (Heckel)

The snout is curved; 62–64 scales along the lateral line; a faint dark, longitudinal band.

44. *L. turskyi* (Heckel)

70–72 scales along the lateral line; body with a broad, dark, longitudinal band.

45. *L. microlepis* (Heckel)

73–75 scales along the lateral line; body sometimes with a dark, longitudinal band.

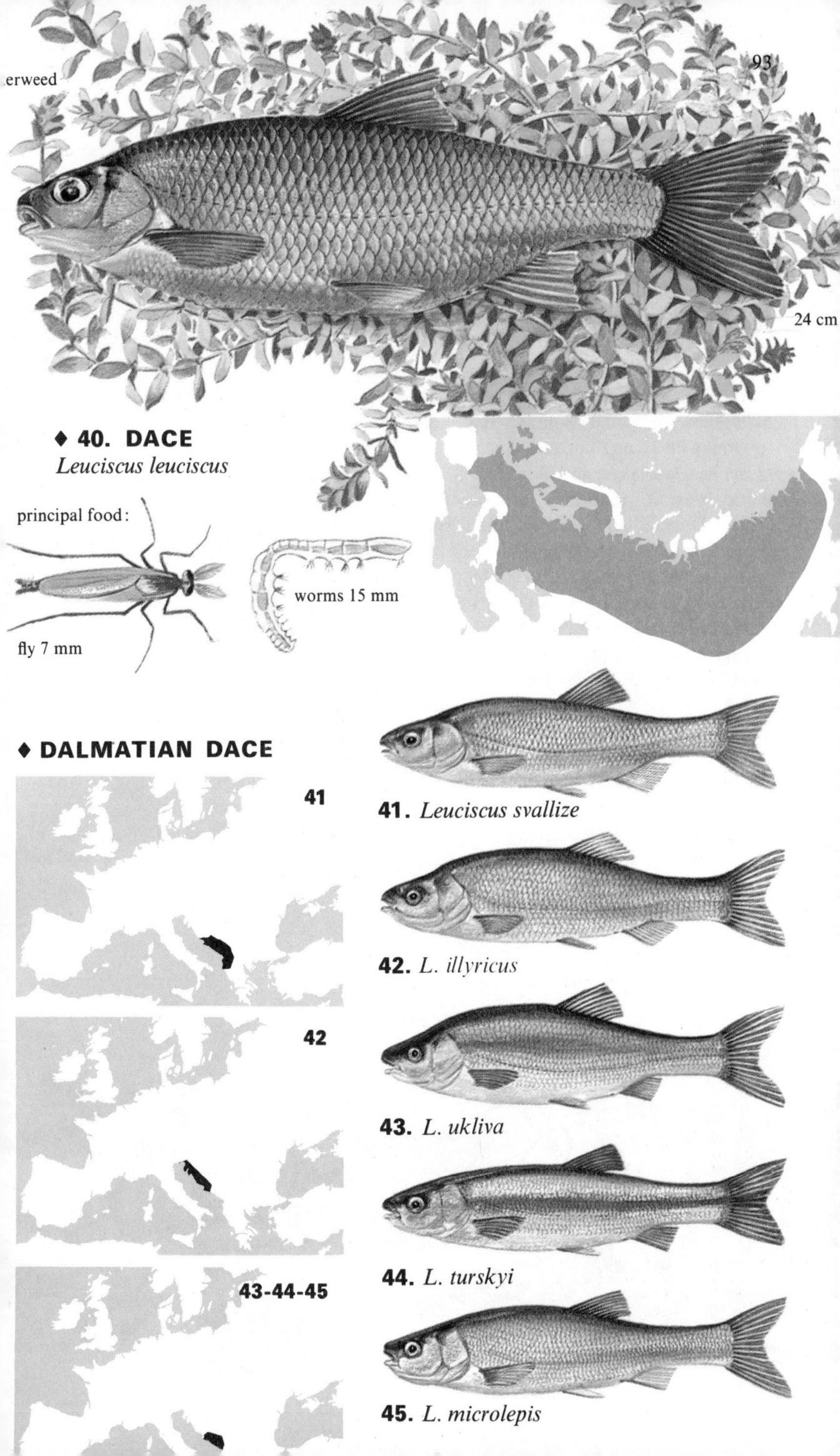

♦ 40. DACE

Leuciscus leuciscus

♦ DALMATIAN DACE

41. *Leuciscus svallize*

42. *L. illyricus*

43. *L. ukliva*

44. *L. turskyi*

45. *L. microlepis*

46. Chub

Leuciscus cephalus (L.)

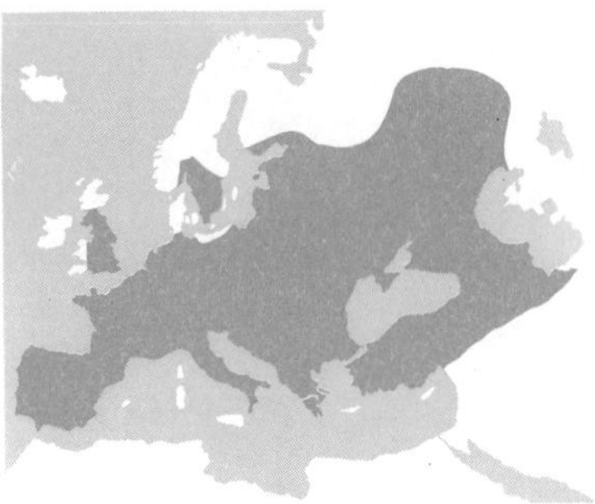

Distinctive features: Resembles the ide but the head is broader, and the scales are black-edged and large; 44–46 scales in the lateral line. The hind edge of the anal fin curves outwards (i.e. it is convex), most clearly seen in older fish.

Size: 30–40 cm (600–1,000 g) at 7–10 years, rarely growing to 60 cm (*c*. 4 kg).

The chub is a river fish often found near the surface in large shoals. The largest individuals are usually solitary. It prefers streams with strong currents but may be found in a few lakes, and along the North Baltic coast it penetrates into brackish water. During winter it migrates into deeper water in rivers and lakes, but returns to the shallow water in spring.

Its food is composed of flying insects, all kinds of water insects, worms, molluscs, fish eggs, and often plants and seeds. With increasing size the chub feeds on larger animals, particularly fish, trout fry and minnows, frogs, etc.

Spawns from April-June. At this time the males have small spawning tubercles on head and body. The eggs number 100,000–200,000 with a diameter of 0·7 mm. They stick to stones, pieces of wood or plants and hatch in about a week. Growth is slow, and the males mature at 3–4 years, the females at 4–5 years, when *c*. 22 cm long.

The chub is exceptionally bony and is not eaten. On the other hand it is considered to be a fine sporting fish which fights well when hooked on fly or spinner.

47. Black Sea chub

47. *Leuciscus borysthenicus* (Kessler)

Distinctive features: Dark, grey-green back; resembles the dace, but the anal fin is square cut.

Size: Maximum 40 cm.

Lives in the lower reaches of the rivers entering the Black Sea. Moves in shoals.

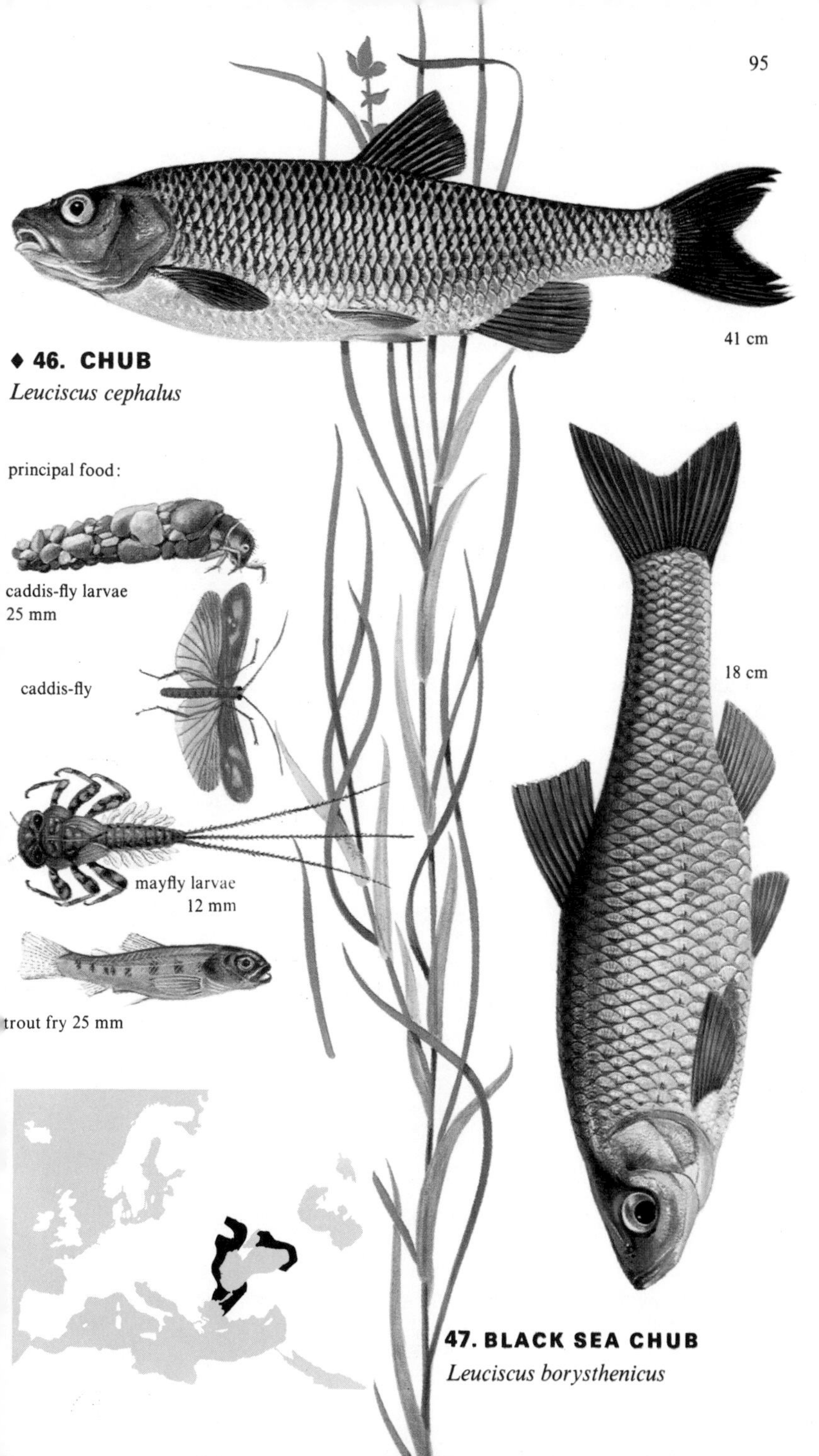

♦ **46. CHUB**

Leuciscus cephalus

47. BLACK SEA CHUB

Leuciscus borysthenicus

48. Soufie (Fr.)

Leuciscus souffia Risso

Distinctive features: The male has a bright, violet band along the sides, especially noticeable in the breeding season. This band is fainter in the female. The lateral line is orange-yellow.
Size: Generally 12–17 cm, maximum 24 cm.

Lives in running water on a bottom of stones and gravel in the grayling region. Also found in some lakes. In the Alps up to an altitude of 850 m. Its food consists of all kinds of insects including flying ones such as gnats and mayflies. In lakes it forms shoals which feed on small planktonic and bottom-living animals. It is a spring spawner (March-May), and deposits its eggs in water with strong currents on gravel bottoms. The eggs number 6,000–8,000.

It is of no direct economic importance but can be used as a bait. Its flesh is said to make excellent eating.

49. Ide

Leuciscus idus (L.)

Distinctive features: 55–61 scales along the lateral line; the eyes are yellow, pelvic and anal fins red. Distinguished from the chub by the straight hind edge of the anal fin.
Size: 30–40 cm long (700–1,200 g) at 6–9 years. Rarely reaching 60 cm (*c.* 4 kg).

The ide is a migratory fish, living in brackish water, rivers and in isolated stocks in a few lakes. In freshwater its food consists mainly of insects, in brackish water mainly of mussels, snails and crustaceans. The larger individuals also eat roach and bleak.

From March-April the ide moves into the streams to spawn on stony and sandy beds where the temperature is at least 7–8°C. The males reach the spawning place a few days before the females. Spawning occurs in shallow water with a great deal of splashing and leaping and continues for *c.* 3 days. The slightly sticky eggs, numbering 39,000–114,000 and 1·5 mm in diameter, are deposited on vegetation or stones. After spawning the ide migrate downstream in dense shoals. The larvae hatch in 10–20 days, and seek calmer water. At first they feed on planktonic animals, and at 1 year measure *c.* 13 cm; after 2 years *c.* 18 cm. At 5–6 years the males mature, while the females mature 2 years later. Ide over-winter in deep water.

Over-fishing and pollution have reduced the stocks, but locally, for example in the northern U.S.S.R, the ide is the object of a considerable fishery with seines, floating nets and stake-nets. The meat is said to be tasty. The ide is tenacious of life and can be kept for some time in suitable submerged boxes. As a sporting fish it is taken on a spinner.

A yellow variety, the golden ide, or orfe, is kept as an ornamental fish in aquaria and fish-ponds, from whence it sometimes escapes into our rivers.

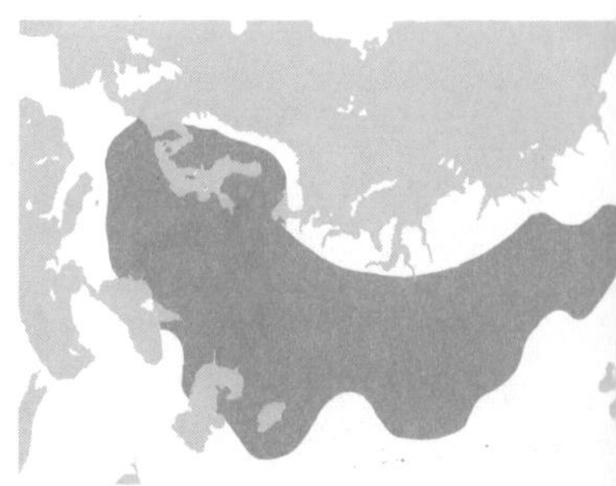

14 cm

48. SOUFIE
Leuciscus souffia

principal food:

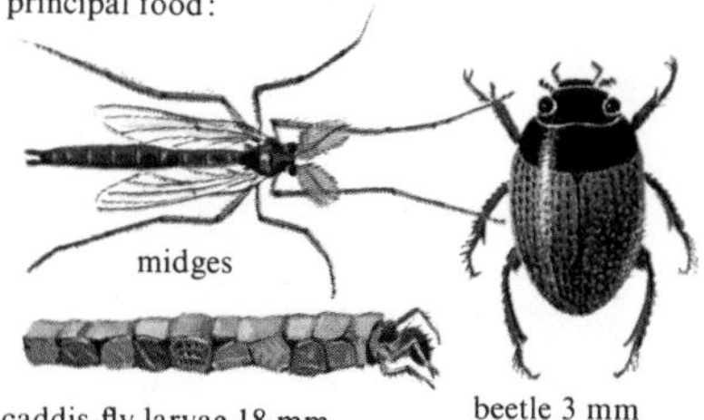

midges

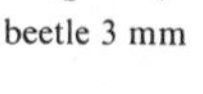

caddis-fly larvae 18 mm

beetle 3 mm

38 cm

(◆) 49. IDE
Leuciscus idus

principal food in fresh water:

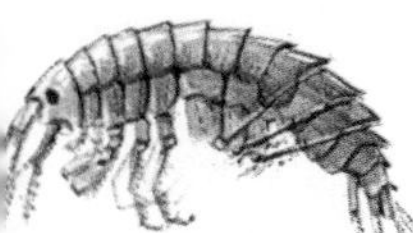

freshwater shrimp 15 mm

caddis-fly larvae 20 mm

golden ide

principal food in brackish water:

freshwater limpet 7 mm

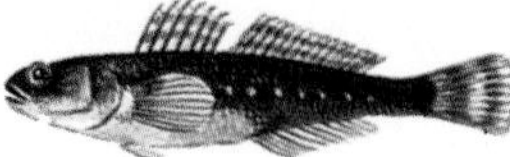

goby

50. Minnow

Phoxinus phoxinus (L.)

Distinctive features: A small, dark coloured fish, with a blunt snout and small scales (85–100 along the lateral line).
Size: Up to 9 cm, very rarely 12 cm. The females are the largest.

The minnow belongs to the upper regions of rivers with cool, fresh, running water, and a sandy or stony bottom (the trout region). Rarer in lakes. In the northern Baltic it lives in brackish water. It is usually found in small shoals, often with trout or salmon parr of an equal size, and feeds on small bottom-animals, fish fry and flying insects. Minnows are often eaten by larger fish, e.g. perch, pike, trout and chub. In streams where both species are present it competes with young trout for food. Sometimes it makes a nuisance of itself by eating trout eggs.

From June-July the minnows gather in large spawning shoals. The male's belly, pectoral and pelvic fins turn reddish, the back and front of the body dark. According to their size the females spawn 200–1,000 eggs, in several batches. The eggs, 1–1¼ mm in diameter are deposited in clumps between stones in running water. They hatch after 5–10 days, and the larvae stay between the stones until the yolk-sac is absorbed. Minnows mature at 1 year and a length of 35–40 mm.

In some areas, such as northern U.S.S.R., the minnow has direct economic importance, and is caught with seines or in fine-meshed traps. On account of its abundance the minnow has considerable indirect economic value, both as food for better fish and as a competitor. It makes a good bait-fish.

Being easy to obtain and keep alive for long periods, the minnow has often been used as a laboratory animal, including von Frisch's famous experiments on the hearing of fishes (see p. 13).

There are 10 species in the genus *Phoxinus* in eastern Europe and northern Asia.

51. Swamp-minnow

Phoxinus percnurus (Pallas)

Distinctive features: Closely resembles a young minnow, but does not have the large, lateral blotches. In their place the sides are irregularly spotted. The body of the adult is stout, rather similar to that of the young tench. Several subspecies are known in eastern Europe.
Size: Generally 5–9 cm, maximum 12 cm.

It is particularly common in overgrown ponds and lakes, where it lives in small shoals. It feeds on small crustaceans, the larvae of insects and flying insects. The eggs are deposited on water-plants.

9 cm

♦ 50. MINNOW

Phoxinus phoxinus

male in spawning colours

principal food:

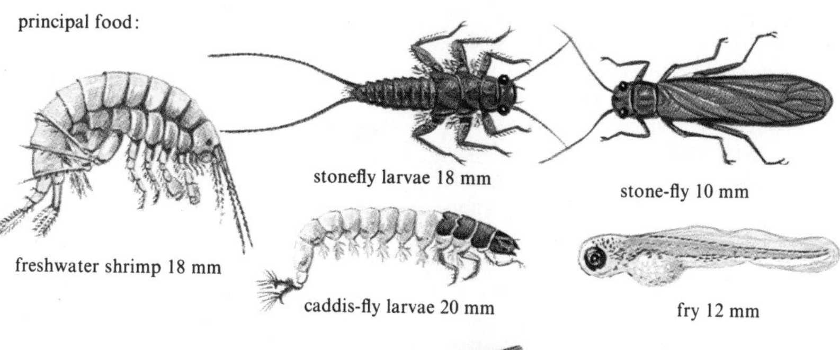

freshwater shrimp 18 mm

stonefly larvae 18 mm

stone-fly 10 mm

caddis-fly larvae 20 mm

fry 12 mm

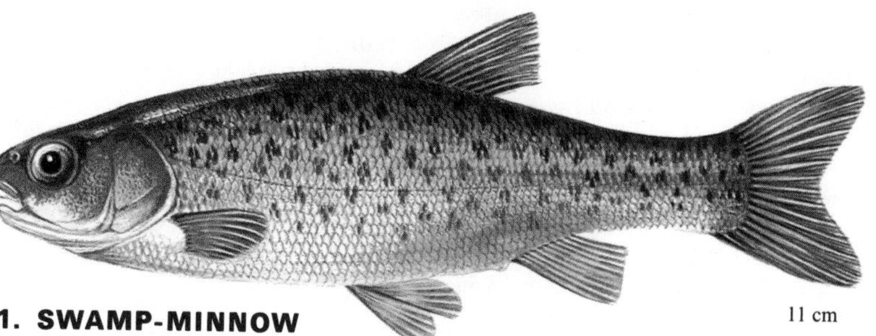

11 cm

51. SWAMP-MINNOW

Phoxinus percnurus

principal food:

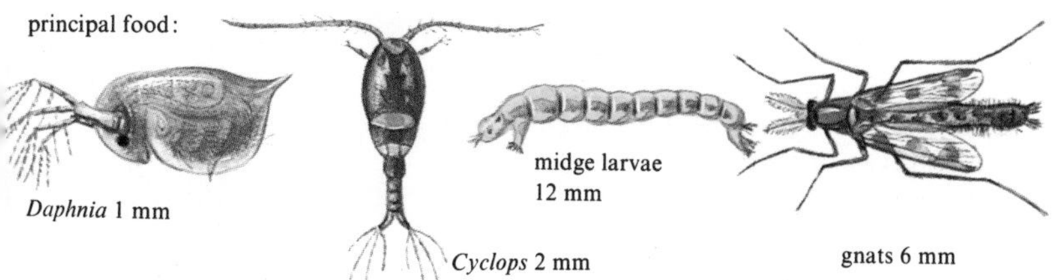

Daphnia 1 mm

Cyclops 2 mm

midge larvae 12 mm

gnats 6 mm

52. Rudd

Scardinius erythrophthalmus (L.)

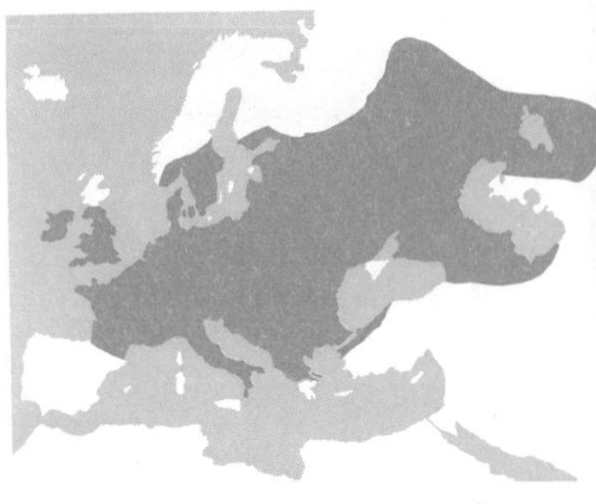

Distinctive features: The extremities of the pelvic, anal and tail-fins are bright red; eyes yellow to orange; the body deep and compressed, with 40–43 scales along the lateral line. The pelvic fins are sited in front of the origin of the dorsal fin.
Size: Generally 20–30 cm, (200–400 g) at *c.* 10 years. Rarely 30–35 cm (0·5–0·8 kg). Maximum 45 cm (1·7 kg).

The rudd lives among vegetation in shallow, warm lakes or slow-running water in the bream region of rivers. It over-winters in deeper water. It keeps in small shoals, sometimes together with other fish of the carp family, feeding on the leaves of pond-weed, water-milfoil, stonewort and other plants, as well as on insects, snails and occasionally fish eggs. Growth is slow and it matures at 2–3 years. Spawning is in May-June, and in southern Europe as early as April. The eggs number 100,000–200,000, *c.* 1·5 mm in diameter, very sticky, and deposited on water-plants. They hatch in 3–10 days, depending on the temperature. The fry remain passively attached to the plants until the yolk-sac is consumed. In the succeeding weeks they feed on animal plankton.

The rudd is well known for its habit of joining in the spawning of other species, and hybridises with bream, roach, white bream, and bleak. It is a popular sporting fish among anglers, and takes a bait readily. It has no value as human food, but as it is tenacious of life it makes a good bait-fish.

A peculiar subspecies of the rudd (*S. e. racovitzai* Müller) is found only in warm springs in western Rumania (Baile Epicopesti). It has become adapted to life in high temperatures (28–34°C) to such an extent that temperatures below 20° C are lethal. This subspecies reaches a length of only 9 cm and matures at 1–2 years old. It spawns from February-March, and the adults die after spawning.

Its food consists of filamentous algae and diatoms.

53. Greek rudd

Scardinius graecus Stephanidis

Distinctive features: Similar to the common rudd, but the body is more slender. The greatest depth is well in front of the dorsal fin, which is placed with a little behind the middle of the body. The profile of head and anterior body is often concave.
Size: Usual length 25–35 cm.

It is known only from southern Greece and probably should be considered as a race of the common rudd, which it resembles in biology.

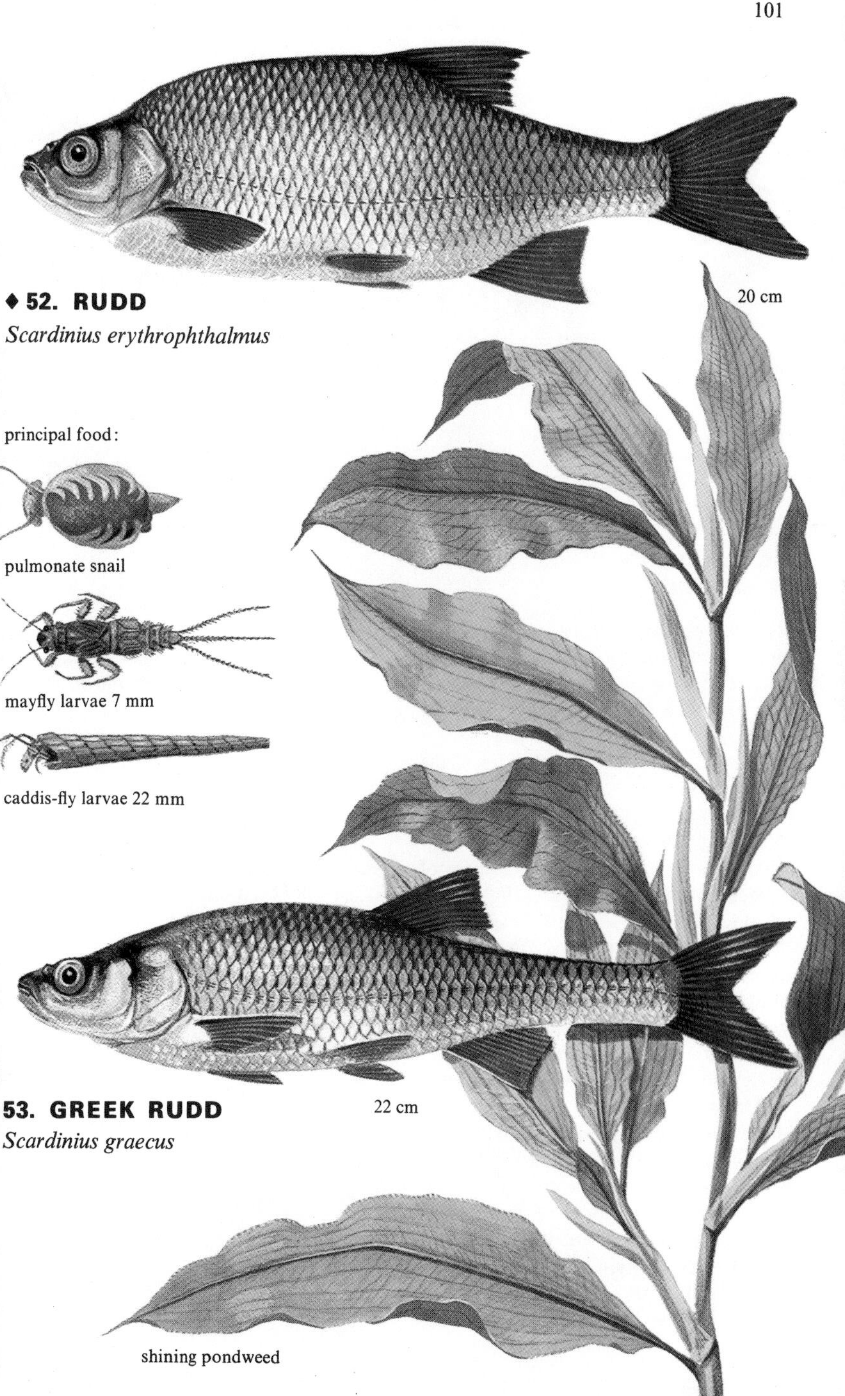

♦ 52. RUDD
Scardinius erythrophthalmus

53. GREEK RUDD
Scardinius graecus

54. ASP

Aspius aspius

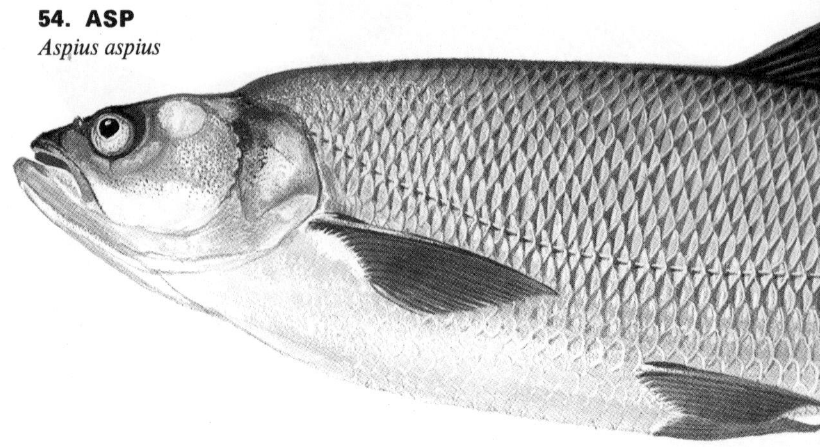

54. Asp (Sw.)

Aspius aspius (L.)

Distinctive features: Elongate body with small scales, 60–70 along the lateral line; eyes small, mouth large, the lower jaw the longer. A sharp keel between the pelvic fins and vent. The males have a large number of whitish tubercles in the spawning season.

Size: 50–55 cm (2–3 kg) at 4–5 years. Maximum 120 cm (9 kg).

The asp lives in the middle reaches of lowland rivers (barbel region). In the area of the Black Sea and the Caspian Sea it is partly a migratory fish, moving into brackish water to feed. The adults live as solitary predators, hunting shoals of bleak, roach, and dace; frogs and ducklings are also eaten. Spawning is from April-May, sometimes continuing into June, beginning in March in the south, at temperatures of 4·5–14·5°C. The spawning shoals move upstream in the rivers to find a bottom of stone or gravel and a strong current. Depending on the size of the female, 58,000–480,000 eggs are deposited, and they develop between the stones in 10–17 days (8·5–12·5°C). The fry move downstream, and at first feed on planktonic animals, but at an age as early as 2–3 months begin eating young fish. At 1 year it measures 10 cm. It over-winters in the deep parts of the rivers.

Its flesh is considered tasty, especially in winter. Fisheries are found mainly in south-eastern Europe, employing seines, stake-nets, traps and hooks.

It is also well-thought-of as a sporting fish in Europe. Minimum length rules (generally 28–35 cm) are enforced in some areas. It can be caught on baited hook and on a spinner.

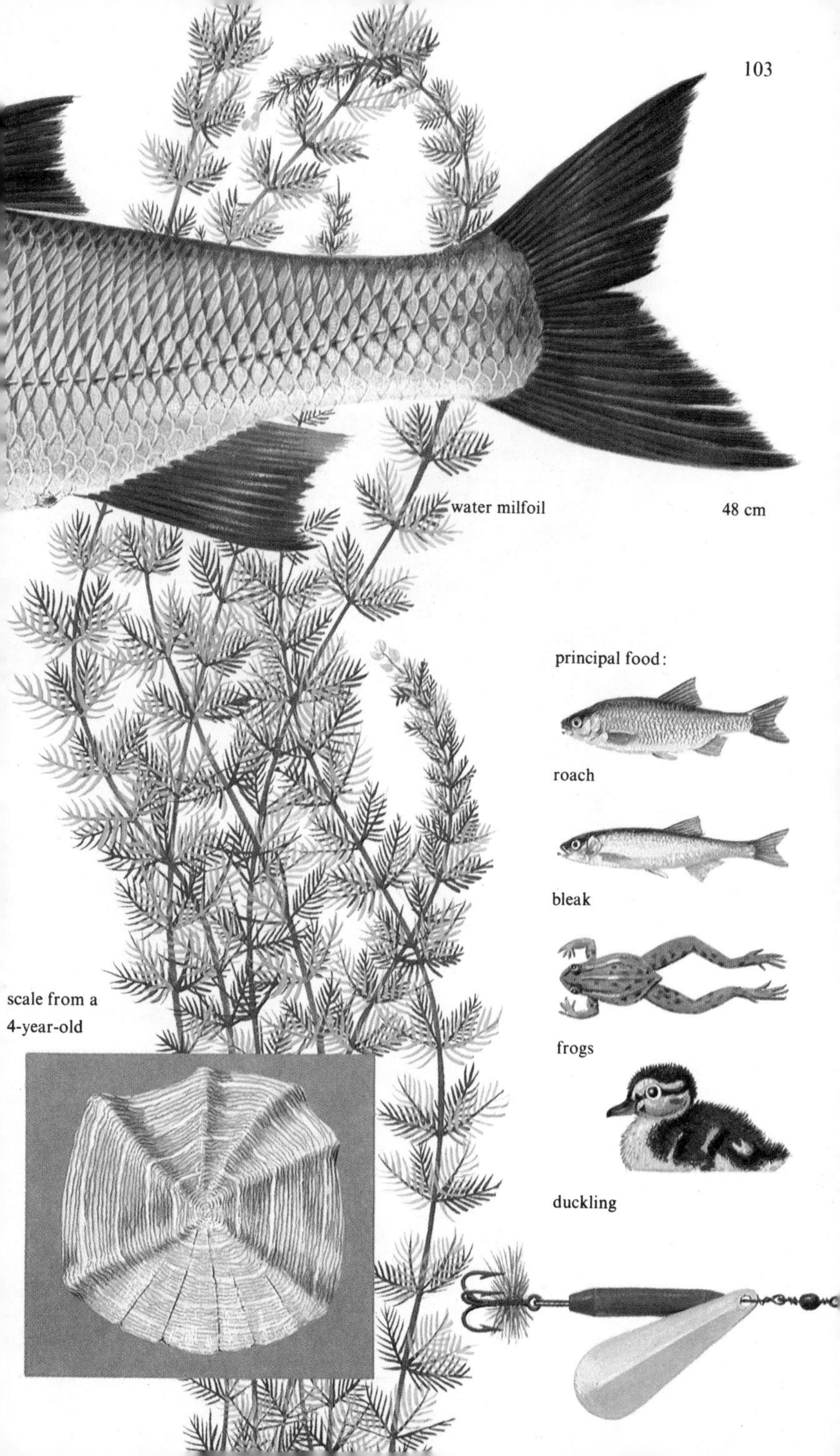
water milfoil
48 cm
principal food:
roach
bleak
frogs
duckling
scale from a
4-year-old

amphibious bistort
water buttercup

♦ 55. TENCH
Tinca tinca

male 36 cm

55. Tench
Tinca tinca (L.)

Distinctive features: The body, including the tail-peduncle, is deep; all fins have smoothly rounded margins, and the body is blackish-green or dark brown with a bronze lustre. There are 95–120 small scales along the lateral line, and the skin is thick and very slimy. At each corner of the mouth there is a thin barbel. From an age of 2 years (*c.* 12 cm) males can be recognised by the second

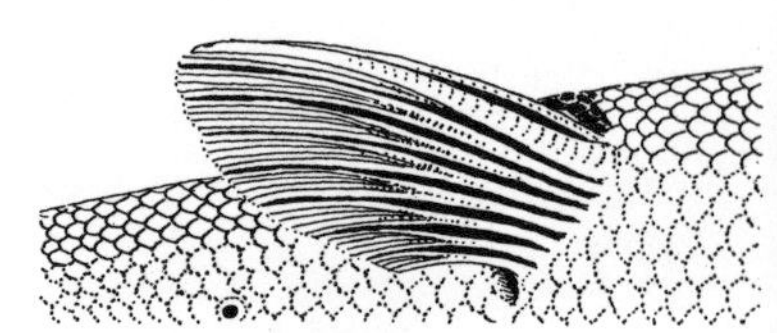

yellow water lily
hornwort
newly hatched larva 5 mm

ray in the pelvic fins being much thickened (see fig. on p. 104).

Size: 25–30 cm long (*c.* 250 g) at 3–4 years; rarely over 50 cm (*c.* 2 kg). Some old records from south-eastern Europe note a maximum size of 70 cm (*c.* 8 kg).

The tench is a rather shy bottom-fish living in slow-flowing water (the bream region of rivers), in lakes and in bog-ponds with a rich vegetation and a soft bottom. It occurs also in weak brackish water, for example in the eastern Baltic.

It feeds on the larvae of insects, mostly midges, small pea-mussels, orb-shell cockles and snails. Feeding is intensive only during summer; in winter the tench hibernates in a passive state. The tench is even more resistant than the carp and can endure a low oxygen content better than most other fish species. It can stay alive for a long time when taken out of the water.

Spawning takes place in shallow water with a dense vegetation and at temperatures of 19–20°C. In a warm spring spawning may start in May, otherwise in June. The number of eggs for a female of 500 g is *c.* 300,000, while the maximum is *c.* 900,000. The eggs measure 0·8–1·0 mm and are deposited on plants or on the bottom in clumps, in separate spawnings at about 2 week intervals over a period of 2 months. The eggs hatch in 3–6 days depending on temperature (100–120 day-degrees C are necessary). The larvae are 4–5 mm in length, and have organs of attachment enabling them to hang passively on plants for the first few days. 10 days after hatching the yolk is consumed, and the fry at first eat small planktonic animals, and later larvae of midges, ostracods, young snails and mussels.

Growth is slow:
1st summer, 4–8 cm, 5–10 g;
2nd summer, 10–15 cm, 40–100 g;
3rd summer, 20–30 cm, 200–300 g.

In the second year the external differences between the sexes become pronounced, and in the third or fourth year the tench spawns for the first time. In spite of its slow growth, it is often stocked with carp in fish-ponds and removed before they can breed at 3 years old. In heavily fertililised ponds growth is accelerated, and the tench can attain a weight of 800 g in 3 years.

Tench-ponds succeed best if they are shallow and sunny, but with deeper sections and a good vegetation of Canadian pondweed (*Elodea*), water-milfoil (*Myriophyllum*), hornwort (*Ceratophyllum*) and water-soldier (*Stratiotes*). An annual yield of 20–80 kg per hectare is considered to be normal.

The tench is in many places a popular angler's fish, which is caught on the bottom with hooks baited with worms or water-insects. Its flesh is soft but tasty, and especially in Germany fetches a high price. A muddy flavour can be avoided by keeping the tench alive in clear water for some time after capture.

An orange-yellow or reddish variety, the golden tench, is kept in parks as an ornamental fish.

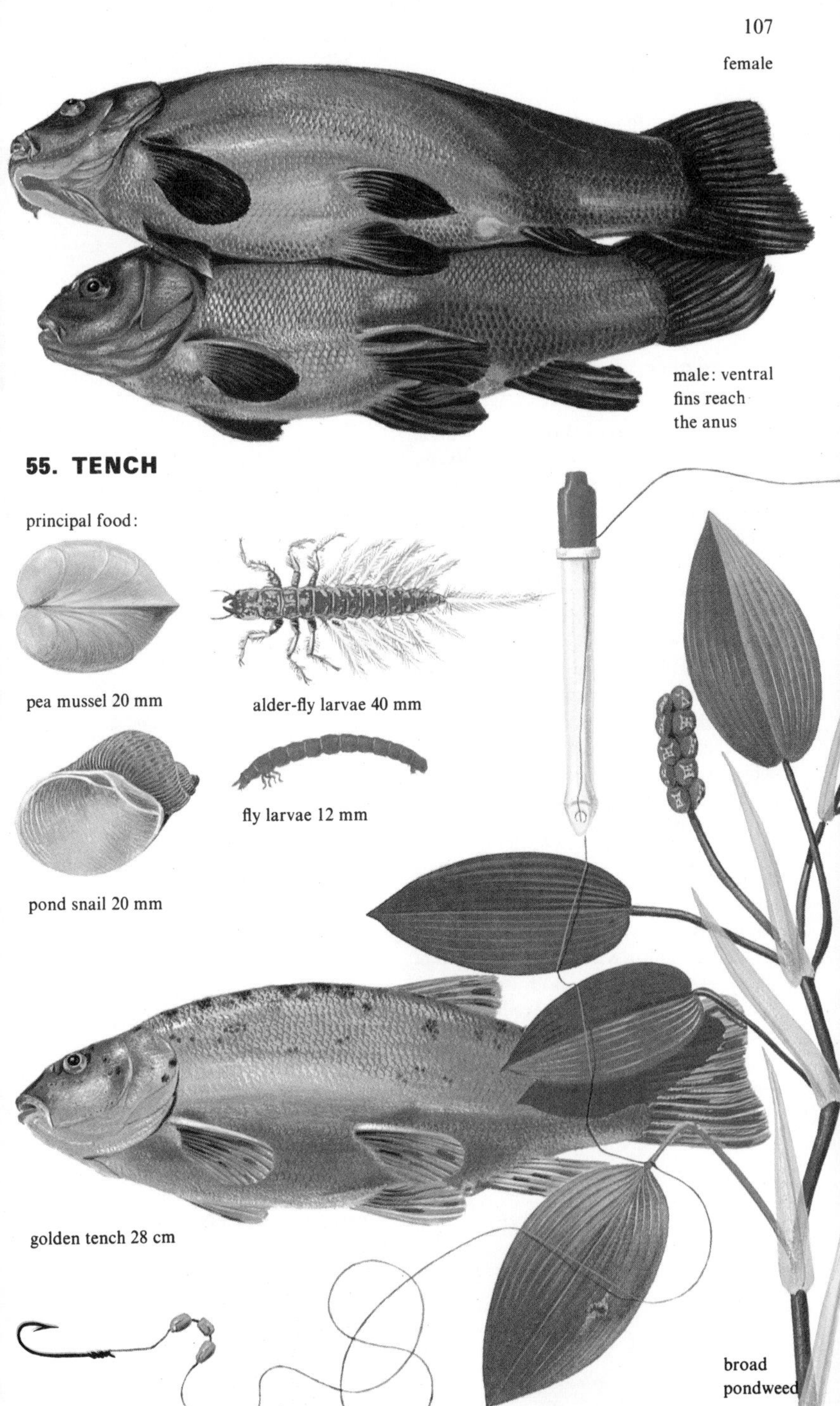
female
male: ventral
fins reach
the anus
principal food:
pea mussel 20 mm
alder-fly larvae 40 mm
pond snail 20 mm
fly larvae 12 mm
golden tench 28 cm
broad
pondweed

55. TENCH

THE NASES

The snout projects and the mouth is ventral. The lips are horny with sharp edges and are used to scrape algae and small animals from stones and plants. The pharyngeal teeth are knife-shaped.

There are seven species, six of which live in southern Europe.

56. The nase

Chondrostoma nasus (L.)

Distinctive features: Prominent, blunt snout and ventral jaw with transverse mouth; the lips have sharp edges. 57–62 scales along the lateral line. Peritoneum is black.
Size: 25–40 cm, rarely 50 cm (1·5 kg).

The nase lives in the middle reaches of rivers (barbel region), and prefers moderately deep water with a fair current and a stony or sandy bottom. It is often found in the deeps below dams and waterfalls, or where tributaries carry edible debris into the river. It feeds mainly on algae which it grazes from stones and submerged wood, but also on the larvae of insects, worms and other small animals living among the algae. In winter it forms large shoals in deep holes or in the lee of stones. It always spawns in spring and by March-May moves upstream or into small tributaries to spawn in a strong current on a gravel bottom. Both sexes have spawning tubercles on the head and front part of the body. The eggs, 2,000–100,000 in number, measure 1·5 mm. The nase becomes mature at 2–4 years.

In the Danube and the Rhine it is often caught in traps. It is used mainly as food in trout-farms, but locally it is also eaten smoked, fried or pickled. It is difficult to catch on hooks.

57. South European nase

Chondrostoma genei Bonaparte

Resembles the common nase in mode of life, and is found as a bottom-fish in the middle reaches of the rivers (barbel region). It spawns in March-May, but its biology is little known. It is too rare to play any commercial role.
Size: Generally 15–20 cm.

58. South-west European nase

Chondrostoma toxostoma Vallot

Distinctive features: The mouth is small and arched, horse-shoe shaped. 57–62 scales along the lateral line.
Size: 25–30 cm.

Its biology is like that of the common nase. In the Rhône basin, where both species live, it appears to be replaced in many places by the common nase. It is of no importance to commercial fisheries or angling.

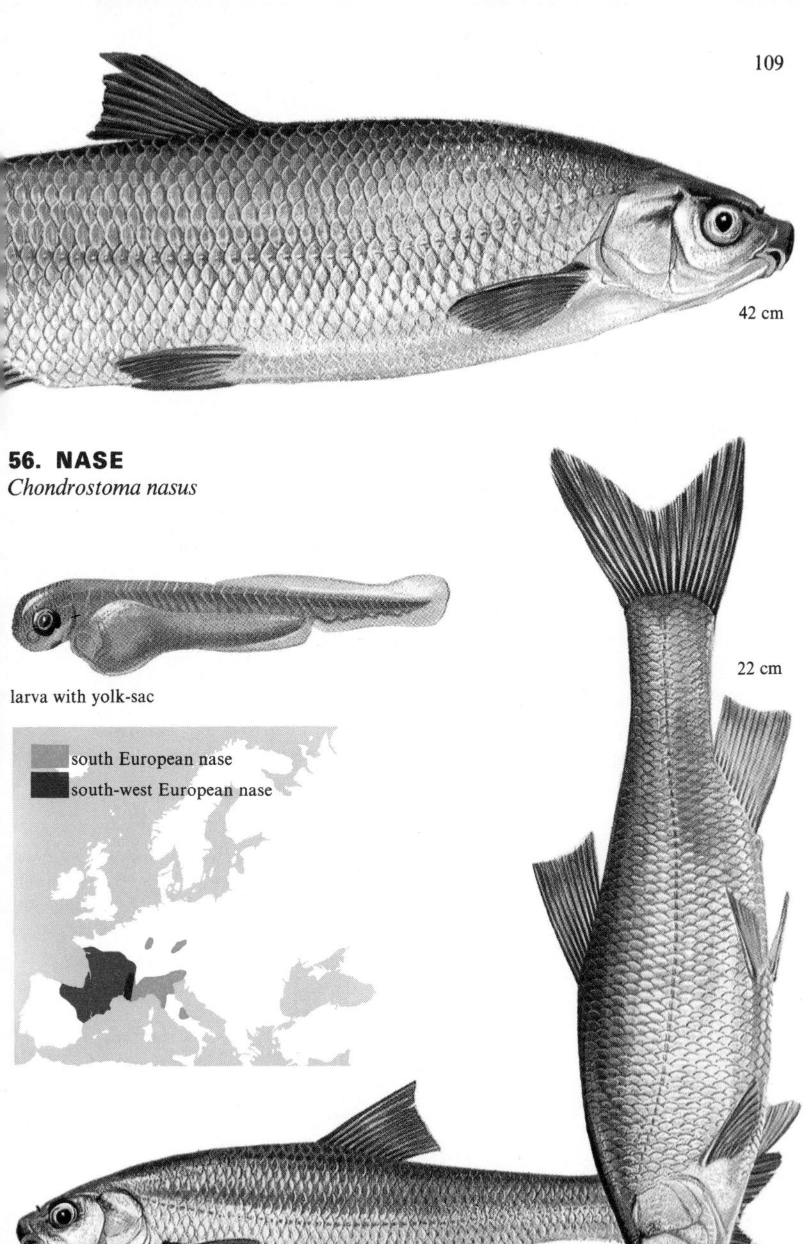

56. NASE

Chondrostoma nasus

57. SOUTH EUROPEAN NASE

Chondrostoma genei

58. SOUTH-WEST EUROPEAN NASE

Chondrostoma toxostoma

59. Italian nase

Chondrostoma soetta Bonaparte

Distinctive features: This species has a deeper body than the common nase. The fins are dark, sometimes having a yellowish or reddish tint.
Size: Grows to 45 cm.

Like the other species of this genus it lives in shoals in the middle regions of rivers, feeding on bottom-living animals, and partly on plants. In the rivers of northern Italy it is of local importance as a commercial fish, and is caught in traps and nets.

60. Iberian nase

Chondrostoma polylepis Steindachner

This species is small and has a more rounded snout than the common nase. It is the only member of the genus occurring in Portugal, and in the Spanish rivers running to the Atlantic. It is *c.* 25 cm in length, and lives in shoals like the other nase species. Its biology is not well known and it is of little value as a commercial fish.

61. Dalmatian nase

Chondrostoma kneri Heckel

Closely similar to the South European nase, it has the same semi-circular mouth but only 52–54 scales along the lateral line. However, it has six pharyngeal teeth on each side, in contrast to the South European nase which has five teeth each side. Grows to 20 cm.

62. Minnow-nase

Chondrostoma phoxinus Heckel

An interesting form living in Dalmatia and Bosnia (near Livno). It is distinguished by its very small scales (88–90 along the lateral line) and its compact form in which it resembles the minnow. It lives in shoals in rapidly running water.

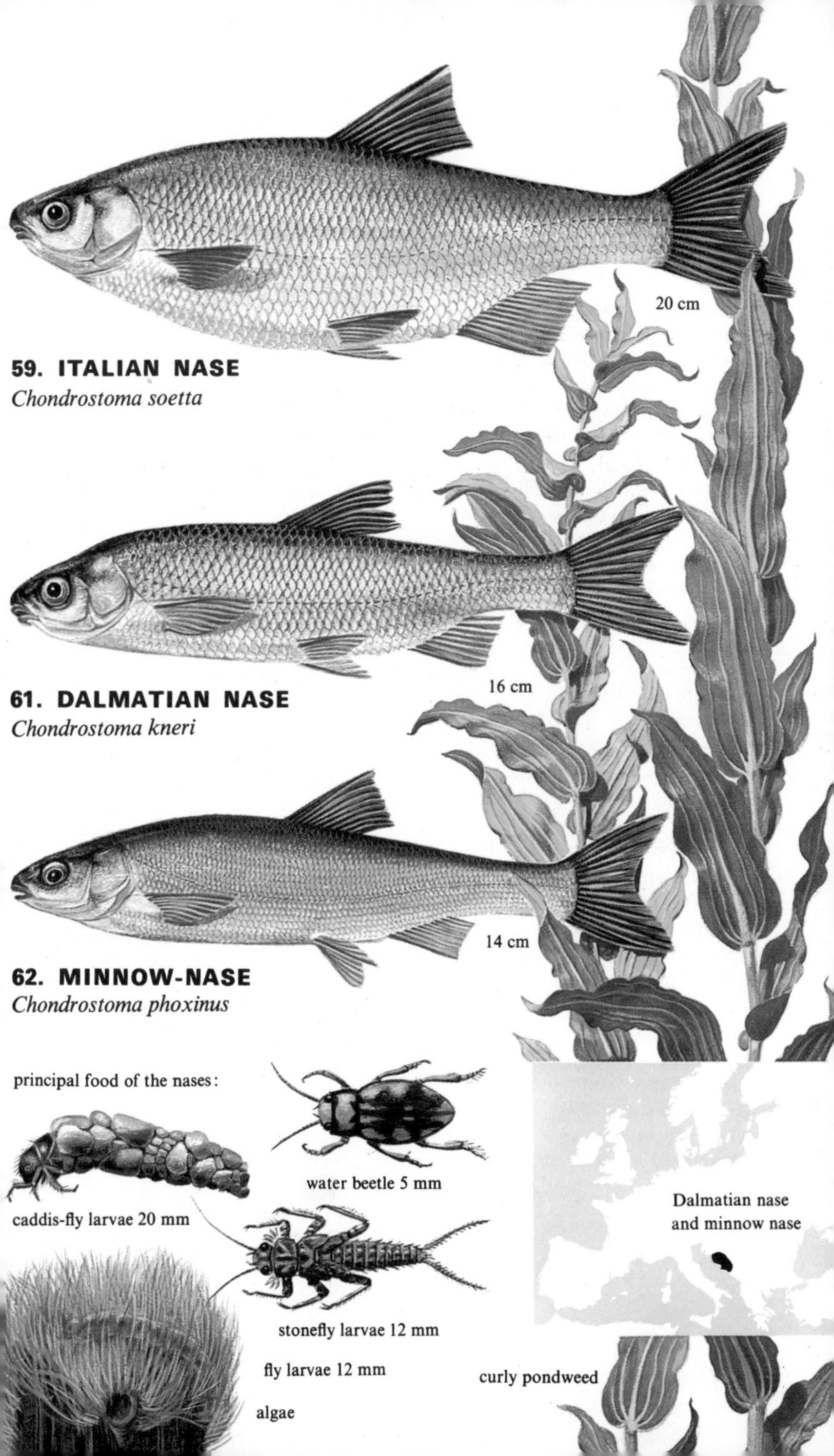
20 cm
59. ITALIAN NASE
Chondrostoma soetta
16 cm
61. DALMATIAN NASE
Chondrostoma kneri
14 cm
62. MINNOW-NASE
Chondrostoma phoxinus
principal food of the nases:
water beetle 5 mm
caddis-fly larvae 20 mm
stonefly larvae 12 mm
fly larvae 12 mm
algae
curly pondweed
Dalmatian nase
and minnow nase

GUDGEONS

Small bottom-living fish with ventral mouths and two barbels, living in rivers and lakes.

63. Gudgeon

Gobio gobio (L.)

The gudgeon lives in rapidly running water on sand and gravel (grayling region) on the continent, but is also found in slow-flowing lowland streams. Also occurs in lakes with clear water, sand or stone bottoms, at shallow depth. Sometimes in brackish water. During summer it forms small shoals in shallow water, in winter it retires to deeper places. The gudgeon is wholly a bottom-fish, feeding on the larvae of insects, worms, crustaceans, and occasionally fish eggs, sucked in by its protractile mouth. It feeds in winter as well as in summer.

Size: Generally 8–14 cm, at 2–3 years, maximum *c.* 20 cm.

Spawning takes place from May-June. At this time the males develop a rash of spawning tubercles on the head and front of the body. Spawning often occurs in water only a few cm deep, the eggs being deposited on stones or plants. The 1,000–3,000 eggs are shed in series, at intervals of several days. They measure 1·5 mm and hatch after 10–30 days, depending on the temperature. The young live in shoals at the bottom near the spawning place. The gudgeon probably reaches a maximum age of 3 years in some waters, although 6- and 7-year-old fish have been found.

The gudgeon is occasionally angled for, and in France it is a highly esteemed table fish. It can be used as a bait-fish but is rather fragile and not tenacious of life.

DANUBIAN GUDGEONS

In addition to the common gudgeon, the tributaries of the River Danube have three other kinds: the white-finned gudgeon, *Gobio albipinnatus* Lukasch, with no spots on the dorsal fin and the tail-fin and is distributed in the Volga and Don basins; *G. kessleri* Dubowski, with barbels reaching the hind margin of the eye and bands of dark spots on the dorsal and the tail-fins, living both in the estuary of the Danube and in a number of tributaries. In the tributaries of the upper Danube the third species, *G. uranoscopus*, is widespread.

64. Danube gudgeon

Gobio uranoscopus (Agassiz)

Distinctive features: A long barbel is present in each side of the mouth, and which can reach the hind margin of the eye. The caudal peduncle is cylindrical.

Size: 10–15 cm.

Lives in rapidly running water (trout region) with a bottom of gravel or stones. Like the common gudgeon it feeds on all kinds of small larvae of insects, on worms and crustaceans. It spawns from May-June; breeding biology resembles common gudgeon. It has no value commercially or as an angler's fish.

65. Dalmatian barbel-gudgeon

Aulopyge hugeli (Heckel)

Distinctive features: Long snout, projecting lower jaw and four short barbels; skin scaleless, the lateral line undulates but runs from head to tail. The female is considerably deeper in the body than the male. A bottom-living fish in running water.

Size: Maximum 13 cm.

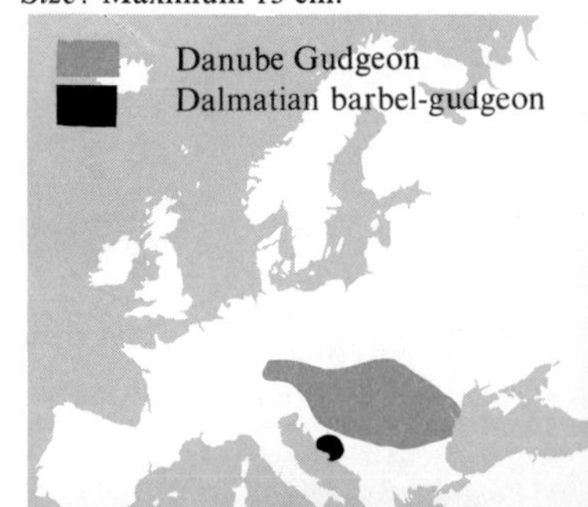

female 12 cm

63. GUDGEON

Gobio gobio

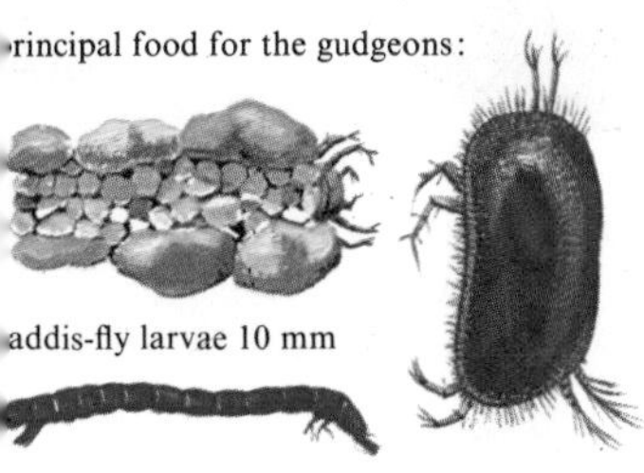

›rincipal food for the gudgeons:

addis-fly larvae 10 mm

ly larvae 12 mm

ostracods 2 mm

fish seen from above

10 cm

›4. DANUBE GUDGEON

Gobio uranoscopus

emale 11 cm

65. DALMATIAN BARBEL-GUDGEON

Aulopyge hugeli

BARBELS

The barbels are distinguished by their inferior mouths which have four barbels. Very many species are found in Asia and in Africa, living in rapidly running, clear water, which must not be too cool (the barbel region of the rivers).

Besides the barbels mentioned below two other species occur in Europe: *Barbus graecus* in the River Aspropotamos, Greece, and the south-eastern species *B. cyclolepis* in the rivers Struma and Maritza, in the Crimea and western Transcaucasia.

66. Barbel

Barbus barbus (L.)

Distinctive features: A total of 4 barbels on the upper lip; the longest ray in the dorsal fin is ossified and like a spine with a serrate hind edge. Dorsal and anal fins short; 55–65 scales along the lateral line: colour variable. Several subspecies have been described.

Size: Mean length 30–50 cm, maximum *c.* 90 cm (8·5 kg). The barbels in the River Dnieper can attain 16 kg.

The barbel is a bottom-fish moving in small shoals in the middle reaches of rivers which have clear water and rapid currents (barbel region). During daylight it remains in the current, often near waterfalls and weir-pools or around the heads of piers. In the dark hours the shoals disperse for feeding. Its food consists of snails, mussels, insects, worms and sometimes plant debris. The adults also take small fish. It has been noticed that barbel are often attracted to the effluent from slaughter-houses where this enters the river. The winter is spent in a kind of hibernation with small groups gathered in deep parts of the rivers, in holes in the banks or below stones, wooden piles, etc.

In the spawning season, from May-June, the males develop whitish spawning tube cles in length-wise rows on the head an back. The barbel gather in large shoal moving upstream to a bottom of gravel stones where spawning takes place. Th females spawn 3,000–9,000 eggs. Th powerful race in the R. Dnieper (*B. barbu borysthenicus*) produces 15,000–32,0C eggs. The roe is slightly poisonous an was at one time used in folk medicine as a emetic. The 2 mm-diameter yellowish egg stick to stones, and most are washed dow by the current between the stones, whe they hatch in from 10–15 days. When th yolk is finally consumed the young sta to move about, feeding on small botton animals. In 4–5 years the barbel is mature

Fished for with seines, traps and hook The flesh is very bony, but tasty, especial in big fish. Its commercial importance i however, only small although large catch are often made during the spawnin migrations. It is a popular anglers' fis fighting bravely, and is most often caug in early morning and late evening. A countries have minimum sizes, as a ru between 25 and 35 cm; all fish below the lengths must be returned to the water.

34 cm

♦ 66. BARBEL

Barbus barbus

principal food:

caddis-fly larvae 22 mm

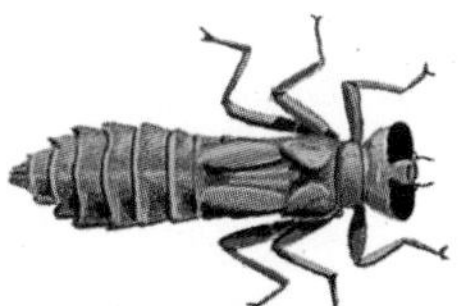

dragonfly larvae 35 mm

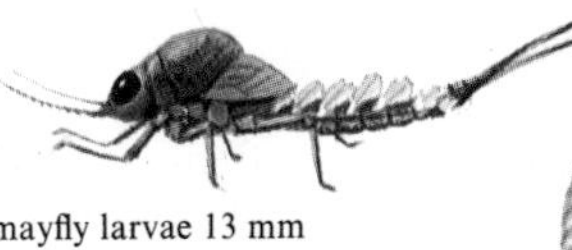

mayfly larvae 13 mm

young gudgeon

pea mussel 8 mm

arrowhead

67. Italian barbel

Barbus plebejus Valenciennes

Distinctive features: Body and vertical fins covered with small, irregular dark spots. This species may only be a variety of the common barbel.
Size: Mean length 25–30 cm.

Like other barbels it prefers rapidly running and clean water. It is an omnivorous bottom-fish, and locally has some value as a game-fish. It is also caught in nets and traps.

68. Southern barbel

Barbus meridionalis Risso

Distinctive features: The back is more strongly arched than in the common barbel, and the hind edge of the spiny ray in the dorsal fin is not serrate. The back and sides have irregular, reddish-brown spots; similar spots are present on the fins, often arranged in bands; 48–55 scales in the lateral line.
Size: Generally 20 cm (*c.* 150 g); maximum 40 cm.

The Mediterranean barbel is spread over southern and eastern Europe, forming several subspecies. It has been suggested that it is a relict from the warm period before the glacial age. A subspecies *B. m. petenyi,* the semling, lives in the Danube area. The Albanian barbel, *B. albanicus* is possibly a variety of the southern barbel.

Lives in rapid, flowing water as do the other barbels.

69. Iberian barbel

Barbus comiza Steindachner

A small species with only 50 scales along the lateral line. Known from the southwestern part of the Iberian peninsula (the rivers Tagus, Jarama, Guadiana, Guadalquivir). Its biology has not been studied in any detail.

28 cm

67. ITALIAN BARBEL
Barbus plebejus

68. SOUTHERN BARBEL
Barbus meridionalis

22 cm

18 cm

SEMLING
Barbus meridionalis petenyi

70. Bleak
Alburnus alburnus (L.)

Distinctive features: A slender fish with an enclosed lower jaw; the base of the anal fin is longer than that of the dorsal fin; 46–53 scales along the lateral line.
Size: generally 12–15 cm, rarely 18–20 cm (40 g).

The bleak is usually found in open waters near the surface. It lives in shoals in a broad band along the shores of lakes or slow-flowing streams. It shuns turbid water and very dense vegetation, and is often numerous in dammed-up lakes. It winters in deeper water than the other cyprinid fishes.

Its food consists of water-fleas, pupae of gnats and flying insects.

Spawning occurs in very shallow water with a hard bottom from May-June (occasionally July). The eggs, numbering *c.* 1,500, are shed in 3 portions. They stick to branches or stones, and hatch in a week. The young feed on planktonic animals, and growth is slow, reaching only 3–5 cm in 1 year. Maturity is attained at 3 years. Hybrids with other cyprinid fishes occur.

The bleak is an important food for perch, pike, zander and large trout. It can be used as bait, and anglers take them by various means (including on flies), often in competitions where the quantity of the catch is more important than the quality of the fish. Where bleak are numerous their fragile scales are used to make pearl essence (*essence d'orient*). The brilliant silvery guanine crystals are washed from the scales, and 4–5,000 fish yield 100 g essence. Locally in Europe, bleak may be used as pig-fodder.

71. Danube bleak
Chalcalburnus chalcoides (Güldenstädt)

Distinctive features: Elongate body with 60–67 scales along the lateral line.
Size: 15–25 cm, rarely over 30 cm.

The subspecies *C. c. mento* is found in the Danube system and in other rivers of the Black Sea. Other subspecies occur in brackish water and migrate into rivers for spawning.

It feeds on plankton, aquatic insects, small molluscs and worms. Spawns from May-June over a bottom of gravel where 20,000–40,000 eggs are deposited. In the spawning season the males have distinct tubercles on the head and the front of the body. Locally it is very numerous. In the eastern part of its range the migratory forms have some commercial importance.

72. Italian bleak
Alburnus albidus (Costa)

Distinctive features: Distinguished by the anal fin which has only 13–18 rays, in contrast to 18–23 in the common bleak.
Size: Maximum 20 cm.

A little-known species which may not be distinct.

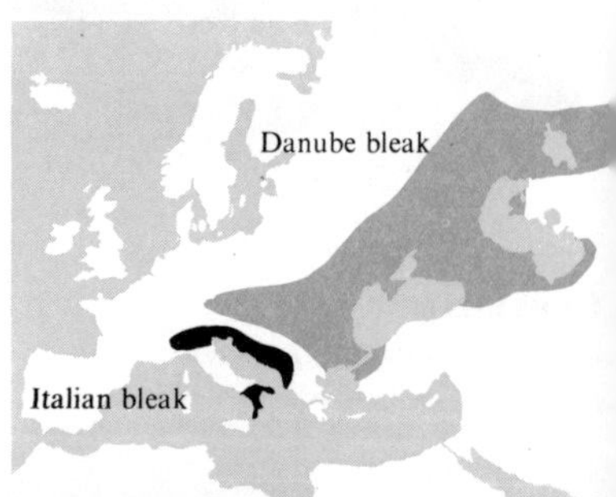

♦ 70. BLEAK 17 cm
Alburnus alburnus

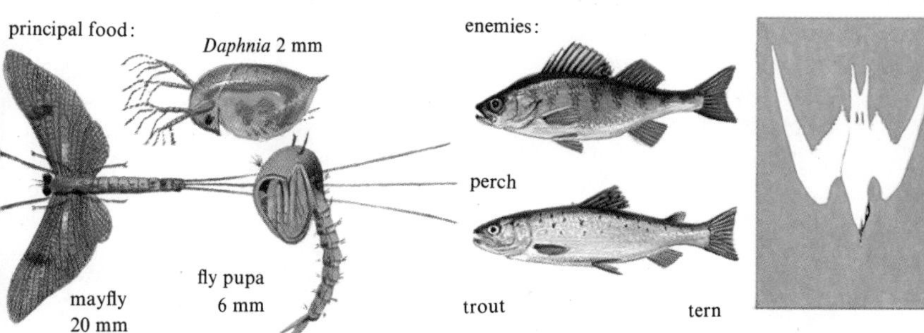

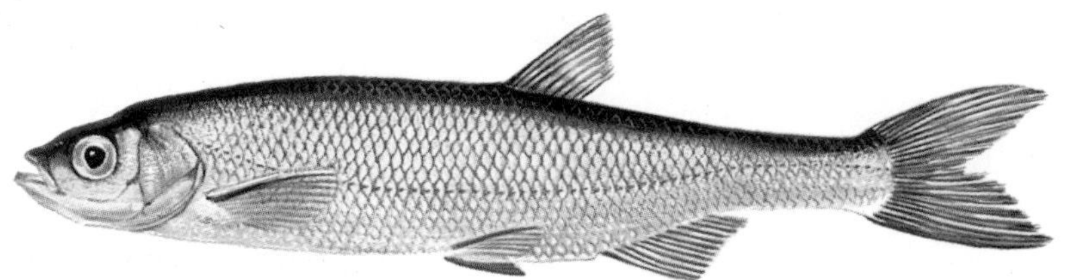

71. DANUBE BLEAK 23 cm
Chalcalburnus chalcoides

72. ITALIAN BLEAK 16 cm
Alburnus albidus

73. Schneider (Ge.)

Alburnoides bipunctatus (Bloch)

Distinctive features: Has a deeper body than the bleak; terminal mouth with almost level jaws; 47–51 scales along the lateral line. In the spawning season has a dark band along the side of the body from eye to tail-fin; appears to have lengthwise stripes due to the dark edges to the scales.
Size: 9–13 cm, rarely over 16 cm.

It lives in shoals in clear, running water close to the bottom, and is sometimes found in lakes. Feeds on small bottom-animals, also on flying insects. Spawns from May-June in running water over a bottom of stones and gravel.

Sometimes used as bait. It can be kept in aquaria.

Size: Generally 20–30 cm (up to 500 g). Rarely 35 cm.

Prefers shallow, warm lowland lakes with dense vegetation, and the lower reaches of rivers (bream region). It is usually found close to the vegetation near the shore, feeding on larvae of midges and other insects, small snails and worms. Occasionally it eats plankton, and appears to be less exclusively a bottom-feeding fish than the common bream. It over-winters in deeper water.

Spawns in May-June, sometimes in July in Scandinavia, and at this time the males have a rash of spawning tubercles on the head and front of the body. The spawning shoals seek shallow water with plentiful submerged vegetation to which the sticky, light yellow, 2 mm diameter, eggs are fastened. Spawning is accompanied by boisterous displays and splashing, as with the bream. In southern part of its range it sheds 17,000–109,000 eggs in three spawnings at intervals of a few days. The young are found close to the shore. Growth is slow, and maturity is reached when 10–12 cm long, at 3–5 years. The females are considerably larger age for age than the males.

The white bream is a competitor for food with the common bream, perch and eels. It is caught in seines and traps used in fishing for common bream, and by anglers. Its small size, and the number of bones, decreases its value both for food and as a sport-fish.

74. Silver bream or white bream

Blicca bjoerkna (L.)

Distinctive features: Closely resembles the common bream but is distinguished by the red pectoral and pelvic fins with grey tips. The eye diameter is greater than, or as long as, the length of the snout; the anal fin has 22–26 rays; 43–55 scales along the lateral line; pharyngeal teeth are in two rows.

13 cm

73. SCHNEIDER

Alburnoides bipunctatus

principal food:

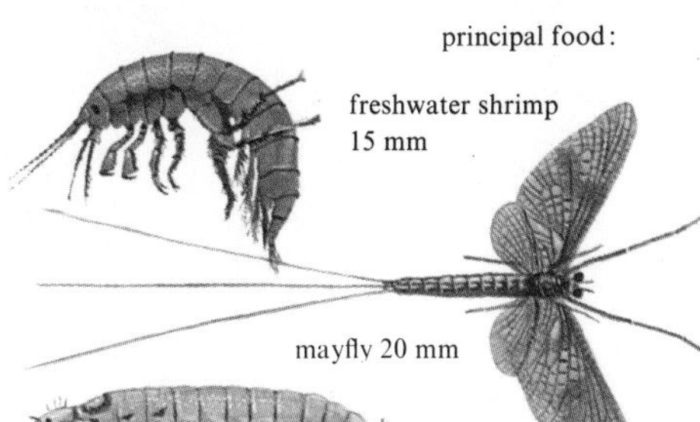

freshwater shrimp 15 mm

mayfly 20 mm

caddis-fly larvae 20 mm

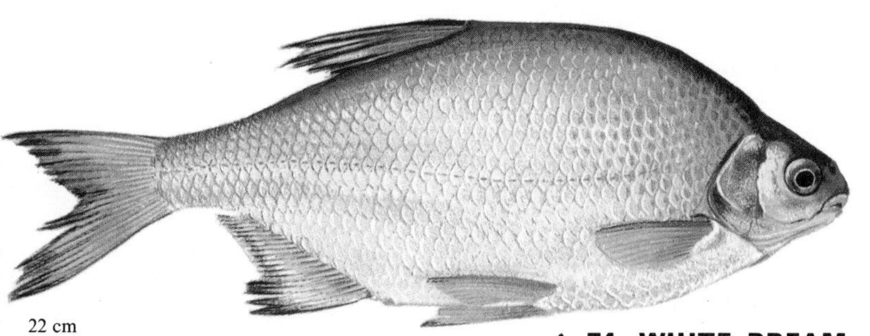

22 cm

♦ 74. WHITE BREAM

Blicca bjoerkna

principal food:

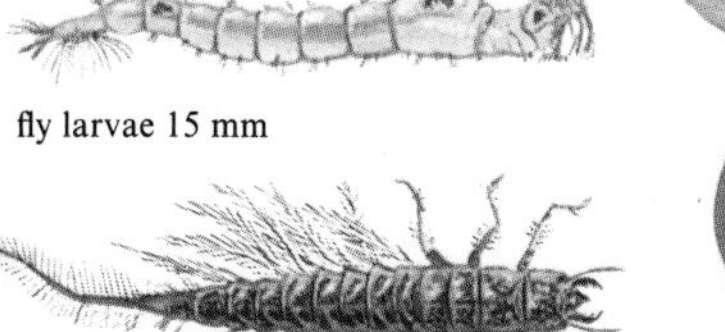

fly larvae 15 mm

alder-fly larvae 40 mm

pond snail 22 mm

♦ **75. COMMON BREAM**
Abramis brama

75. Common bream
Abramis brama (L.)

Distinctive features: Very deep, compressed body; anal fin with 23–28 rays and with a base twice the length of the dorsal fin; 49–57 scales along the lateral line; pharyngeal teeth in a single row. In the spawning season the males have numerous white or yellow spawning tubercles on head and front of body.
Size: Generally 30–40 cm, 0·5–2 kg in weight. Rarely 60 cm (3 kg). Maximum 80 cm (9 kg).

The bream is very common in stagnant or slow-flowing waters (bream region) with a clayey or muddy bottom, and is found in small lakes and bog-ponds. It occurs in brackish water in the Inner Baltic, in estuaries, and in the Aral-Caspian area. The older fish keep mainly over a clean bottom feeding on blood worms, the larvae of midges (Chironomidae), pea-mussels (*Pisidium*) and worms (e.g. *Tubifex*). At night they often move into shallow water even to the edge of the shore. In the soft mud bottom one can often see a shallow depression, 10 cm across ('bream pits') where a bream has stayed for some minutes to suck in some especially inviting food item with its protractile mouth. When feeding on the bottom the bream hovers almost at right angles to the bottom, and expels inedible plants and mud to form the pit. In turbid or over-crowded lakes bream often supplement their normal food by planktonic animals.

In winter it seeks deeper water, and in places densely packed shoals of thousands of fish gather.

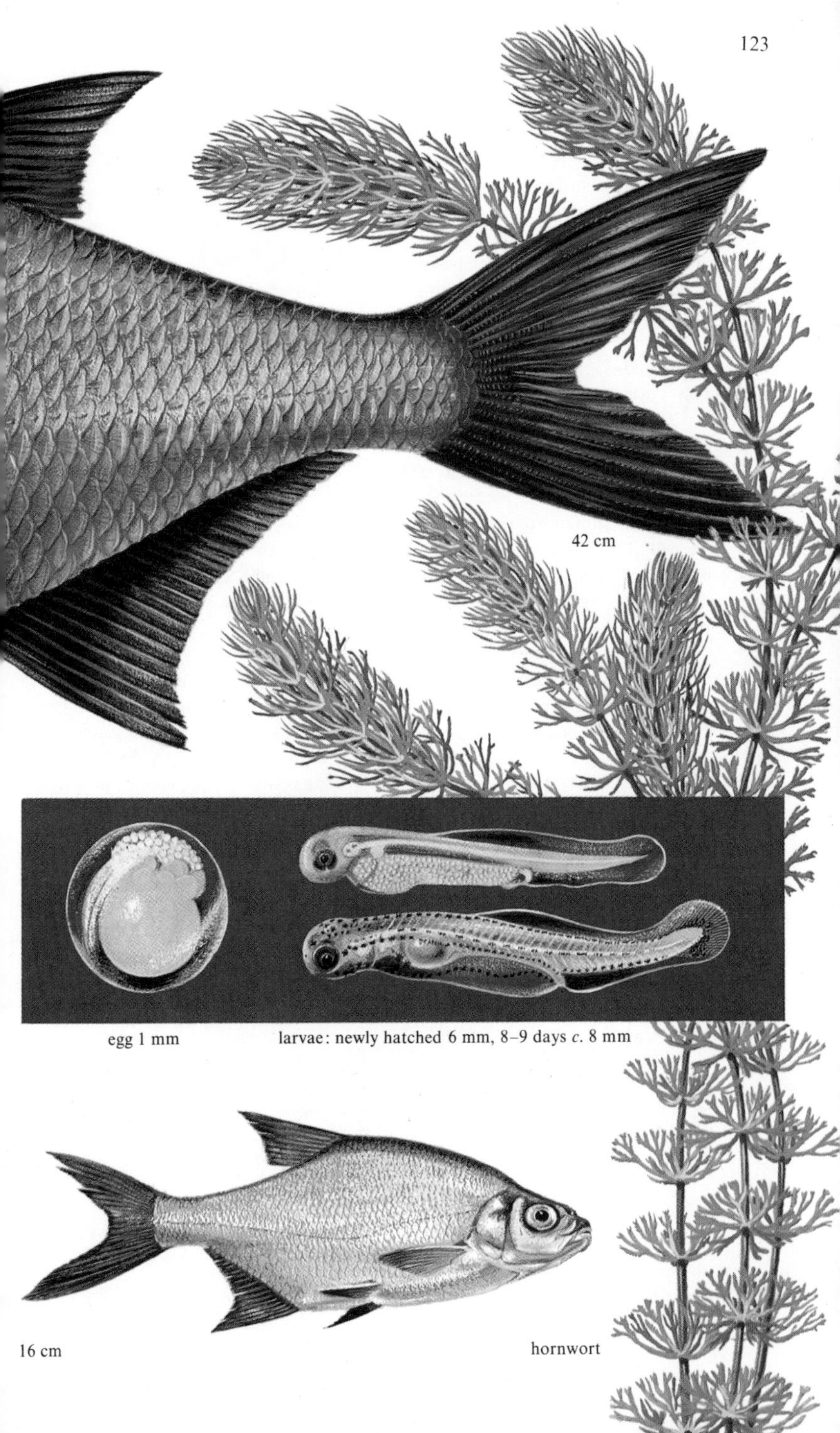
42 cm
egg 1 mm
larvae: newly hatched 6 mm, 8–9 days *c.* 8 mm
16 cm
hornwort

Spawning is from May-June, a little earlier in the south and later in the north. Spawning occurs in dense weeds in very shallow water at a temperature of over 12°C. During the 3–4 days of spawning, the males occupy small territories and defend them against other males, while the females are allowed to remain. Spawning takes place with a lot of noisy splashing, and may be repeated once or twice at weekly intervals. The number of eggs is large—92,000–338,000—and the eggs themselves correspondingly small. They stick to plants and hatch in 3–12 days, depending on the temperature.

The larvae, which measure 4 mm at hatching, remain attached to plants for a few days, until the contents of the yolk-sac are consumed. They then gather in small shoals in the shore region and feed at first on plankton. In the rivers Don and Volga the young migrate to the sea as early as July. Growth depends to some extent on competition. In heavily populated lakes, and in the northern part of its range, growth is slow, and maturity is not attained until 10 years of age and a length of 20 cm. Where food is abundant and temperature is favourable growth can be rapid. In the Sea of Azov for example, maturity and a length of 20 cm are reached in only 3–4 years, and 35 cm in 8–20 years.

The flesh of fish over 1 kg is tasty, and it is widely eaten in inland Europe. Bream are caught mainly with stake-nets, but in winter also with seines, even amongst ice where the yield may be good provided that the shoals can be found. Bream can live for some time out of water and are relatively easy to transport alive in tanks.

75. Bream

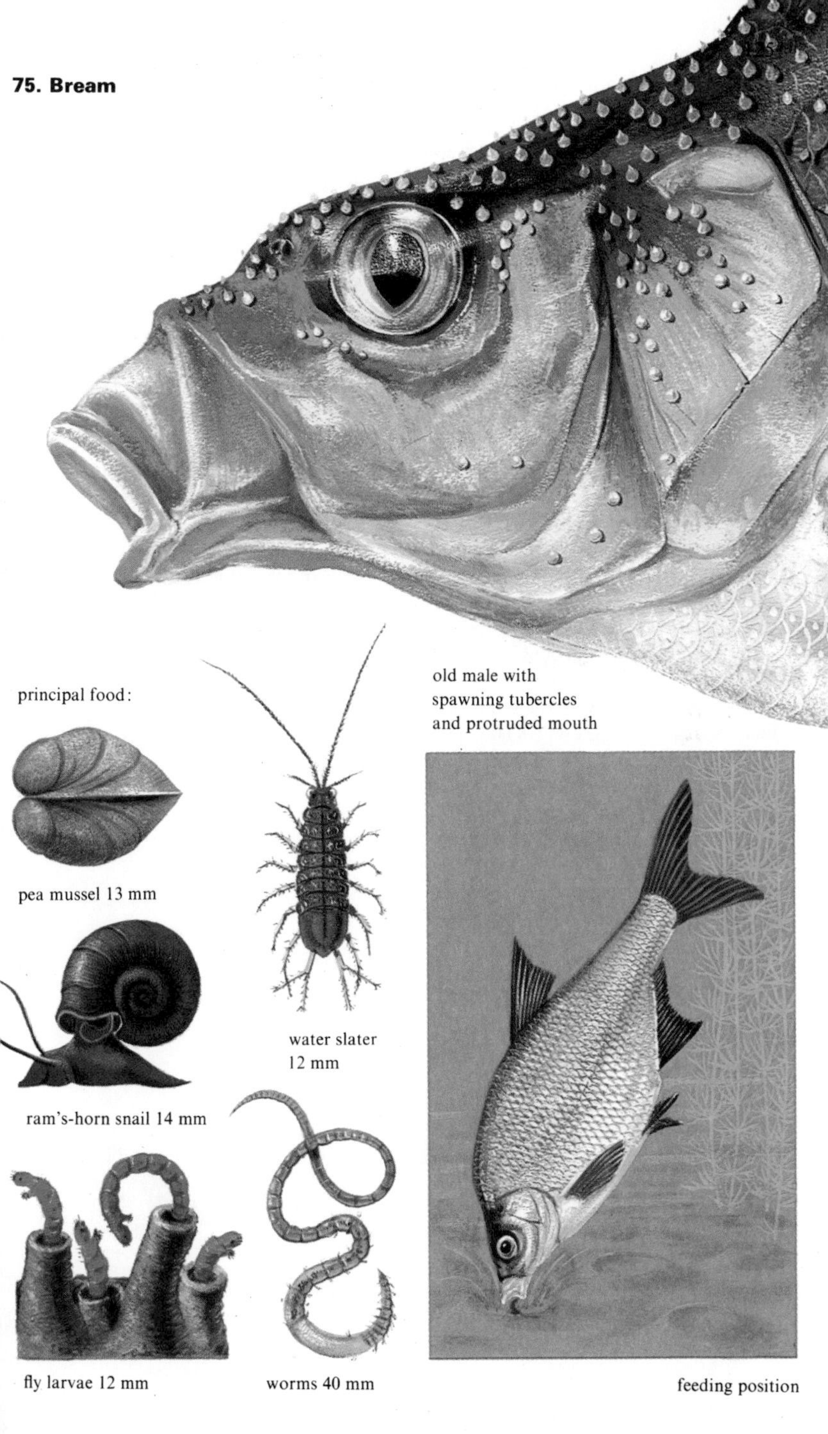

old male with
spawning tubercles
and protruded mouth
principal food:
pea mussel 13 mm
water slater
12 mm
ram's-horn snail 14 mm
fly larvae 12 mm
worms 40 mm
feeding position

76. Danube bream

Abramis sapa (Pallas)

Distinctive features: Resembles the common bream, body much compressed; snout blunt and curved, lower jaw just ventral, and large eyes. Anal fin with 41–48 rays, its base longer than in the common bream; the lower lobe of the tail-fin clearly longer than the upper; 49–52 scales along the lateral line.

Size: Generally 15–20 cm, rarely 30.

The Danube bream is a bottom-living, shoaling fish found mainly in rivers. In the Black Sea area it is migratory, feeding in brackish water but spawning and wintering in the lower reaches of the rivers. Its food consists of small mussels, freshwater shrimps and larvae of midges. Spawning is from April-May, when the males have a rash of spawning tubercles on the body and head, and on the inner surface of the pectoral and pelvic fins. Spawning takes place in running water with dense vegetation. In the rivers of the Black Sea and Aral Sea only 8,000–42,000 eggs are produced, though elsewhere *c.* 150,000 have been recorded. It grows more slowly than the common bream.

The flesh is rather fatty in the autumn, but generally bony and barely edible, though it is sometimes sold dried or smoked.

77. Zope (Ge.)

Abramis ballerus (L.)

Distinctive features: Resembles the bream, but the body is even more compressed, and the mouth is terminal. Scales small, 66–73 in the lateral line; anal fin long with 39–46 rays.

Size: Generally 20–30 cm, rarely 40 cm.

Lives in the lower reaches of rivers (the bream region) and in some lakes, mostly in open water where it feeds on planktonic animals. Over-winters in deeper water, where it shoals passively without feeding. It does not occur in brackish water.

In the spawning season, from April-May, the shoals move upstream and spawning takes place in shallow water with dense vegetation. Its biology is not well known, although the zope is abundant in places. Its growth is slow, and at 5 years measures *c.* 21 cm.

The zope has no value either as a food-fish or as an angler's fish.

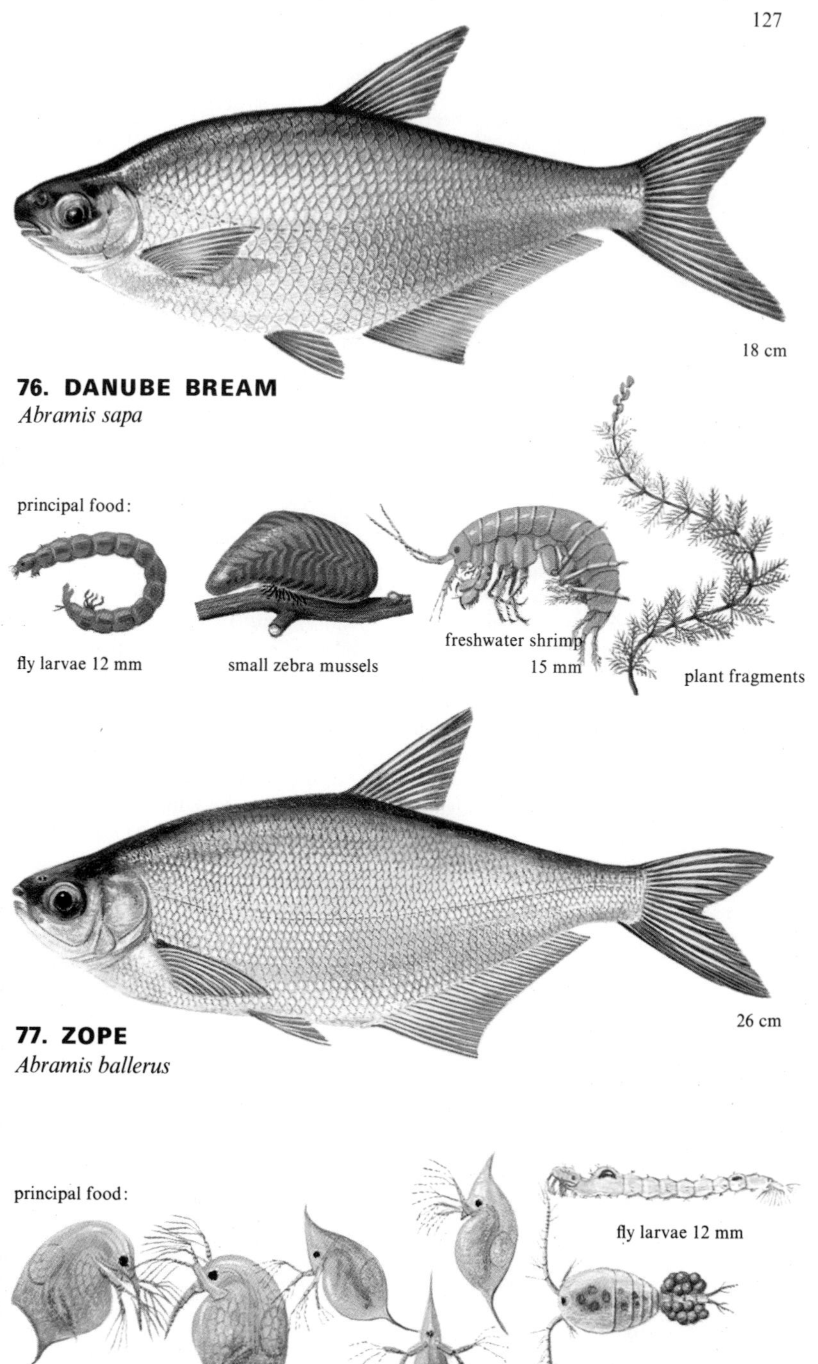

76. DANUBE BREAM
Abramis sapa

77. ZOPE
Abramis ballerus

78. Zährte (Ge.)

Vimba vimba (L.)

Distinctive features: Slender and less deep-bodied than the bream; the snout projects over the lower jaw; the anal fin is somewhat shorter than in the bream, with only 20–23 rays; 53–61 scales in the lateral line. In the spawning season the head and back are almost black, lips, throat and paired fins orange-red.
Size: 20–30 cm (90–250 g) Maximum 50 cm (over 1 kg).

The species is partly migratory, living in the lower reaches of rivers (bream region) and for part of the year in brackish water (Baltic, Black Sea, Caspian Sea). It is found also in a number of lakes. Six races are known, each with a slightly different biology. It is a fish which is found over muddy bottoms feeding on the larvae of midges, snails and worms.

In the spawning season, from March-July, the shoals move upstream in rivers and brooks to spawn on a stony bottom in shallow, well-weeded water. Both sexes have numerous spawning tubercles on the head and back. The 80,000–200,000 eggs are shed in several spawnings. They are 1·4 mm in diameter and slightly sticky, and at first adhere to plants or stones, but are washed down between the stones later. They hatch in $2\frac{1}{2}$–10 days, depending on temperature. The race in the Azov Sea basin is smaller, and lays fewer eggs than the others. The larvae have no means of attachment and lie passively between the stones until the yolk-mass is consumed. Rate of growth is little known.

Despite the very many bones the flesh is considered tasty, especially in winter, and the fish are caught in stake-nets and traps during the spawning migrations.

79. Ziege (Ge.)

Pelecus cultratus (L.)

Distinctive features: Jaws strongly angled upwards; long, pointed pectoral fins; lateral line wavy; belly has a sharp keel from throat to vent.
Size: Generally 20–30 cm at 3–4 years. Maximum 50–60 cm (2 kg).

The species is a pelagic, shoaling fish found in the lower reaches of the larger river systems. It penetrates into brackish water with a salinity of up to 12‰ (*c.* $\frac{1}{3}$ of the strength of sea water). It feeds on flying insects, the pupae of mosquitoes, crustaceans and smaller fish, and in brackish water mostly herring fry.

It becomes mature at 3–5 years, and spawns from May-June when the temperature is about 12°C. Number of eggs, 30,000. In rivers the eggs are carried by the currents until they hatch (3–4 days). Spawning also takes place in brackish water where, according to the salinity, the eggs may float. This species regularly migrates between the Sea of Azov and the river Don.

A commercial fishery exists in the Black Sea region. The fish is sold salted or smoked, but is not particularly tasty. Its scales are used to make *essence d'orient* for the artificial pearl industry.

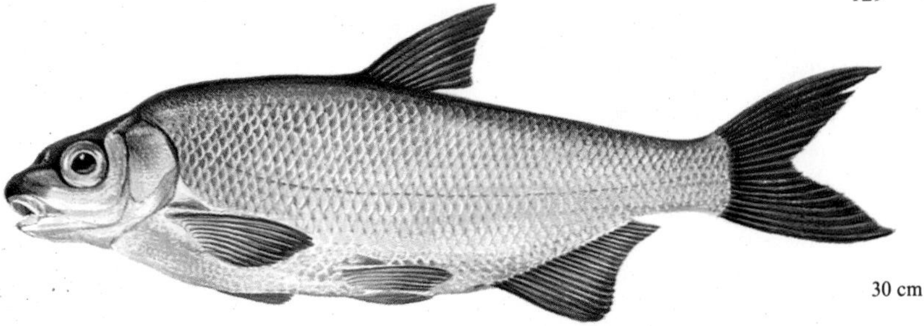

30 cm

78. ZAHRTE
Vimba vimba

principal food:

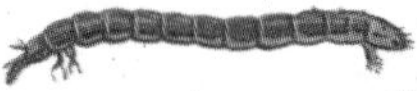

fly larvae 12 mm

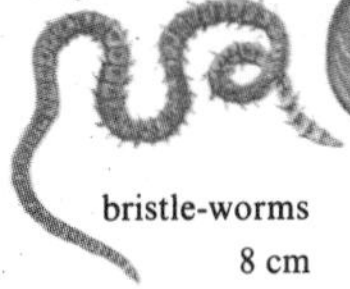

bristle-worms
8 cm

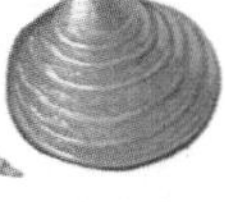

pea mussel
8 mm

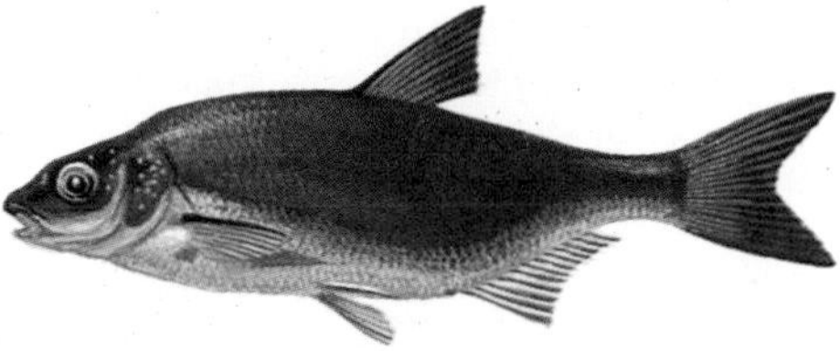

male in spawning colours

38 cm

79. ZIEGE
Pelecus cultratus

principal food in fresh water:

fly pupa 6 mm

Daphnia
2 mm

mayfly 20 mm

principal food in brackish water:

herring fry

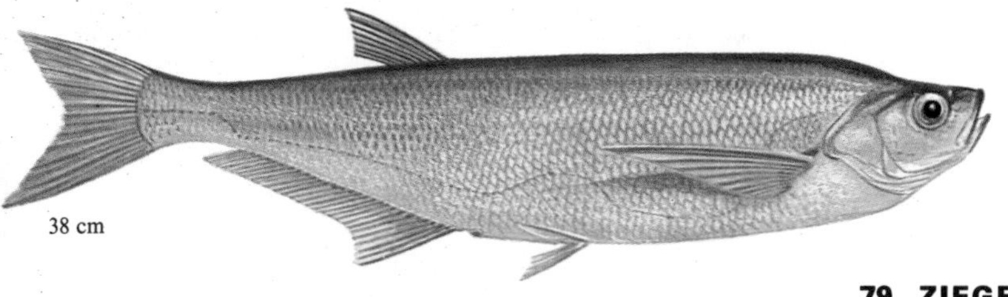

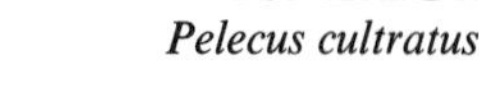

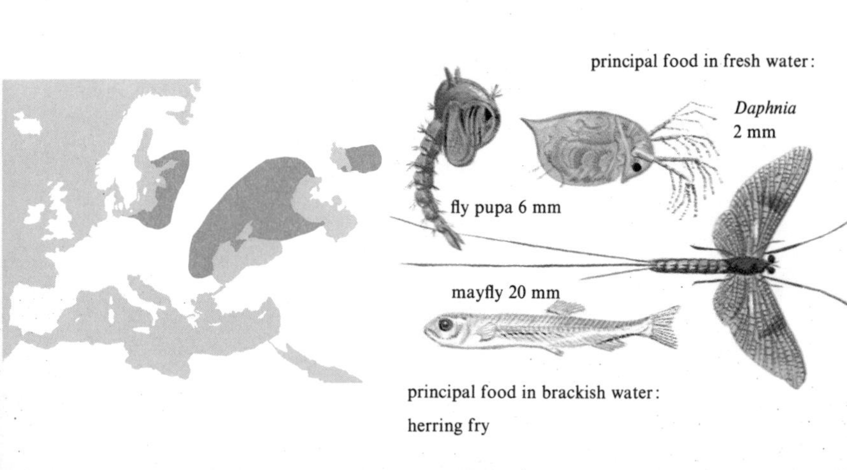

80. Bitterling

Rhodeus amarus Bloch

Distinctive features: Small fish with a deep, compressed body. Incomplete lateral line extending only on to 5–6 scales; a lateral blue-green stripe from the middle of the side to the base of the tail-fin.
Size: Generally 5–6 cm at 2–3 years. Maximum 9 cm.

It lives in the densely weeded zones in small lakes and ponds, and in slow-flowing streams; the food is mainly vegetable matter. Lifespan is, at most, 5 years.

Reproduction in the bitterling is remarkable. By April and May the males possess all the colours of the rainbow and the females develop a 6 cm-long, fleshy egg-tube (ovipositor) from the genital opening. Successful spawning depends on the passive assistance of a freshwater mussel. The mussel, as it lies half buried in the bottom, feeds on plankton which it filters from the water drawn in through a special tube between the gaping shells. The male selects a particular mussel which he guards against other males. The female then inserts her egg-tube into the mantle cavity of the mussel and places 1 or 2 eggs in its gills, to which they adhere. The male then sheds spawn close to the mussel, which draws part of it in with its respiratory water, and by this means the eggs are fertilised. The process may be repeated by the same pair of fish or the male may find another partner to use his selected mussel. A female deposits a total of 40–100 eggs. They are *c.* 3 mm in diameter, and remain well protected in the mussel until they hatch 2–3 weeks later. The young fish leave the mussel after about 2 days, when the yolk-mass has been absorbed. The mussel does not seem to be harmed in any way by acting as host to the young.

Bitterling kept in aquaria appear to develop an ovipositor or if males, their breeding colouration, only in the presence (sight) of mussels. In the absence of mussels the ovipositor shrinks.

The adoption and defence of a well-defined territory by the male and the courtship display of this species recall the behaviour of the sticklebacks, and have been object of analysis by students of animal behaviour. Their task has been made easier by the facility with which bitterling can be kept in aquaria. It is not clear what advantages are bestowed by the adoption of the bitterling's unusual breeding habits. Obviously, however, the eggs and early larvae are well protected during development. It may also be important that in drought conditions the mussels move away from the drying shore and thus preserve the eggs.

The flesh has a bitter taste, but is sometimes used as a bait.

There are several related forms with similar habits in East Asia, and the bitterling has been introduced into lakes in north-west England where it thrived for a time and may still survive.

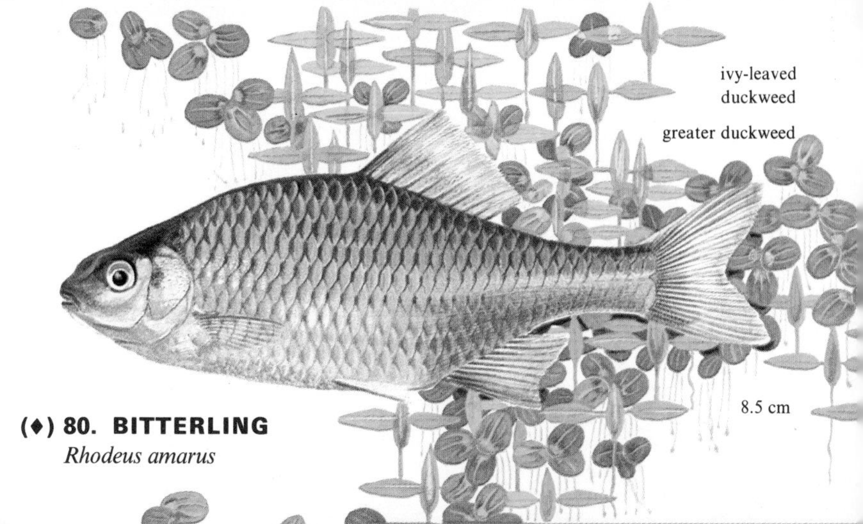
ivy-leaved
duckweed
greater duckweed
8.5 cm

(♦) 80. BITTERLING
Rhodeus amarus

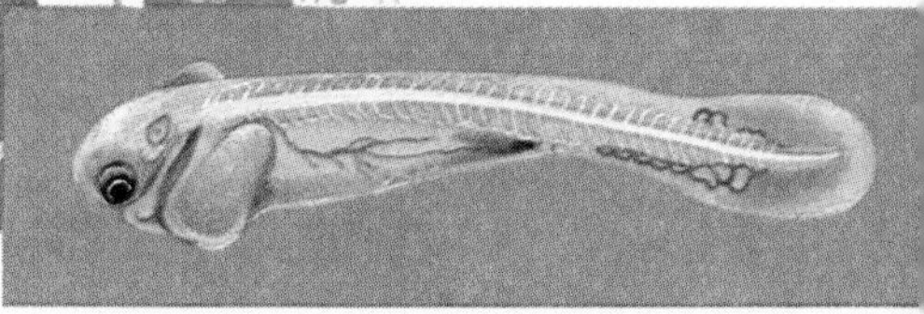

newly hatched larva 9 mm

female

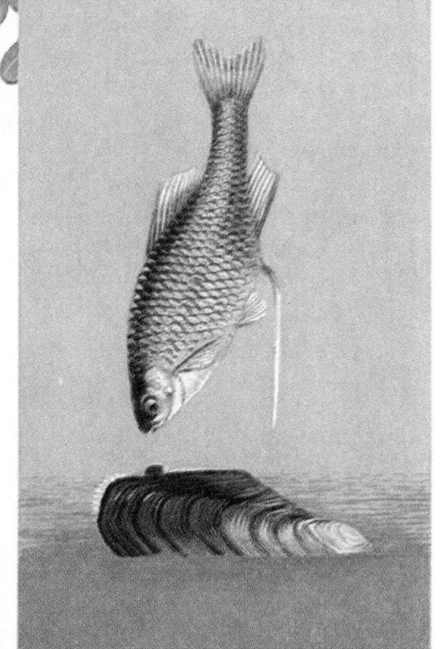

the female inspects the swan mussel the male has chosen

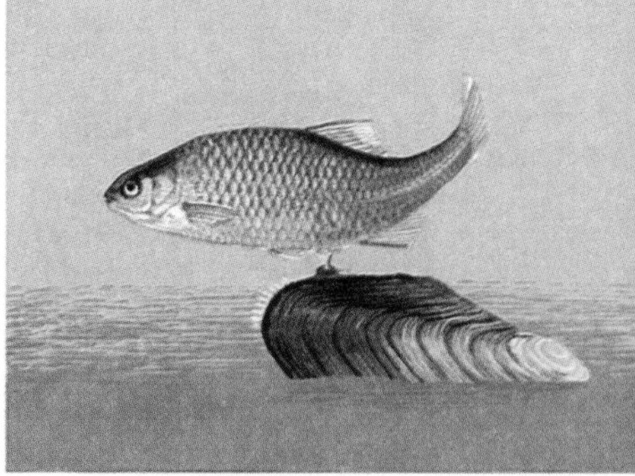

the ovipositor is inserted into the mussel

male

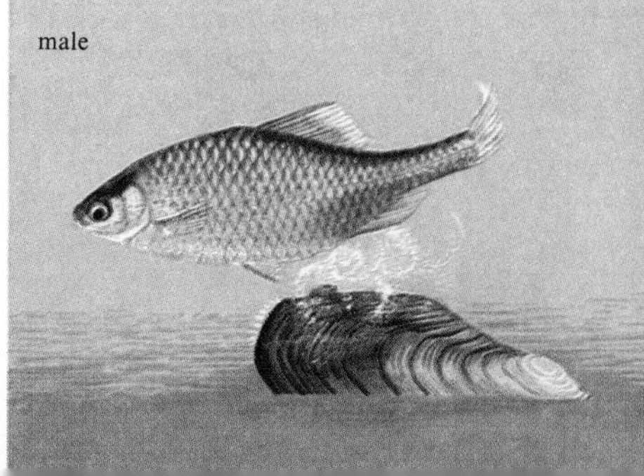

the male releases his sperm above the swan mussel's inhalent siphon

81. Crucian carp

Carassius carassius (L.)

Distinctive features: No barbels; 31–35 scales along the lateral line; first gill-arch has 23–33 gill-rakers; pharyngeal teeth in one row.
Size: Rarely over 10–15 cm at 5–6 years, maximum 45 cm (3·4 kg).

The crucian carp is characteristic of densely overgrown, swampy waters in which often no other fish can exist. In small ponds with little available food it grows very slowly, and develops into a stunted, big-headed form (*forma humilis*) which is often very numerous. With better conditions, in larger lakes where food is abundant, the fish become very deep bodied (*forma gibelio*). Between these two extremes all intermediate conditions exist.

The crucian carp can thrive under unfavourable conditions due to its remarkable hardiness. It can endure pollution, oxygen deficiency and winter cold better than most other freshwater fishes. During winter, particularly in the colder parts of its range, it often hibernates almost buried in the mud. In this way it survives the complete freezing of the water, provided the mud around it does not freeze too. Its metabolic processes almost cease and it revives only with the spring thaw.

It feeds on plants, insect larvae, especially those of midges and mayflies, and to some extent on planktonic animals.

Spawning continues for some time, as the eggs are shed in at least three portions. Spawning takes place from May-June but is dependent on a minimum temperature of 14°C, the optimum being 19–20°C. The eggs are sticky, light red, 1·5 mm in diameter, and spawned in numbers of 150,000–300,000. They stick to plants and hatch in 5–7 days (*c.* 100 day-degrees C incubation are required). The young, 4·2–4·9 mm at hatching, have attachment organs in front of the eyes and cling to the plants until the whole of the yolk is consumed in a couple of days. Growth depends considerably on the availability of food. Maturity is normally reached in 3–4 years at a length of 8–15 cm. The males mature in their third year, the females a year later, the latter growing faster than the males from the second year, and living longer.

The crucian carp is sometimes stocked as a pond-fish in central Europe, especially in ponds where the common carp will not thrive. A well-developed, deep-bodied German race 'Spechthausen' is especially fast growing and matures at 2 years, at a length of 13–15 cm. The presence of crucian carp is undesirable in carp-ponds because they compete for food with the more valuable carp, and partly because they form a 'reservoir' for parasites which affect the carp.

Hybrids between carp and crucian carp, which are intermediate in appearance between the parent species, can be produced by artificial means (see carp, p.206). They are used in south-eastern Europe partly in fish-farms and partly for stocking small waters. These hybrids have several advantages, in that being sterile they will not overfill the water with stunted fish, while they also have the hardiness and resistance to diseases of the crucian carp, and a fairly good growth-rate inherited from the carp.

In open waters the crucian carp is mainly fished in traps, and there is some interest in this species among anglers.

It is difficult to determine the original distribution of the species because for many years it has been introduced and artificially spread to many places, e.g. the British Isles, Spain, France and Norway. It is often confused with the goldfish.

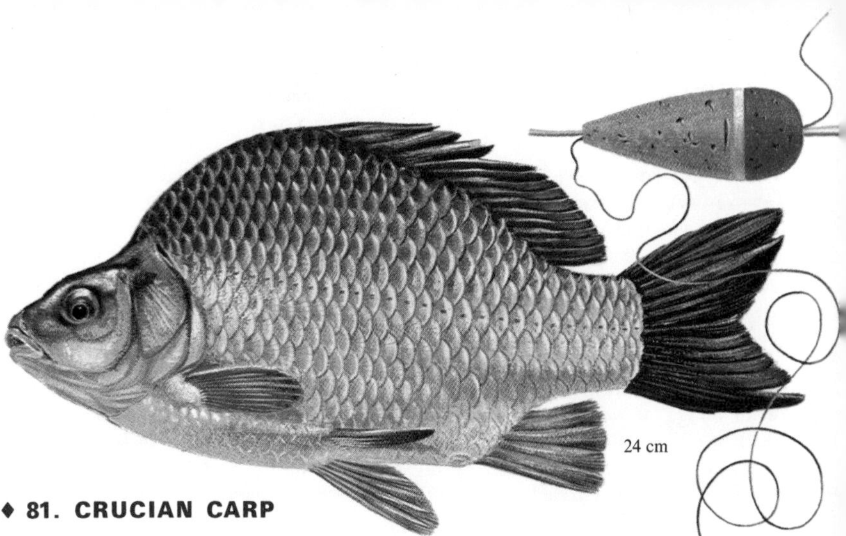

24 cm

♦ 81. CRUCIAN CARP

Carassius carassius

forma humilis

8 cm

principal food:

caddis-fly larvae 25 mm

freshwater shrimp

pea mussel
12 mm

pond snail
15 mm

The lake form of crucian carp, shown at top, is an excellent example of the incredible toughness of the true carp group. Slightly anaesthetized it lay for some 14 hours in a flat dish with a little water in the bottom. When it came round and was immediately put back in the lake it swam quietly away as though nothing had happened.

Cyclops
3 mm

Daphnia
3 mm

worms

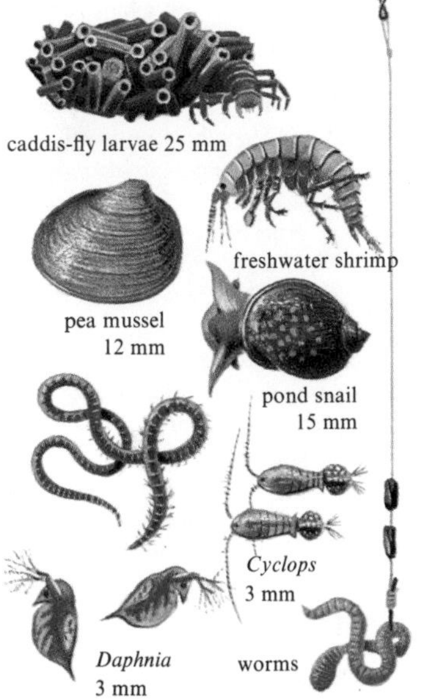

enemies:

pike

eel

82. Gibel carp: Goldfish

Carassius auratus (L.)

Distinctive features: Resembles its near relative the crucian carp, but has silvery-white sides and belly; 27–31 scales along the lateral line; first gill-arch with 35–48 gill-rakers; peritoneum black. As described, this is the feral form of the goldfish. *Size:* Rarely over 20 cm at 5–6 years, maximum 45 cm (*c.* 3 kg).

The goldfish lives in densely weeded small waters, in lakes, and in the lower reaches of several Asiatic and eastern European rivers (in the bream region). It is frequently found in these waters with the crucian carp, with which it has often been confused, and which it resembles in hardiness and biology.

Its reproductive biology has one very peculiar feature: in China and eastern Siberia approximately equal numbers of males and females are found; in many parts of Europe, however, males are not found and the whole population consists of females. These females reproduce by pairing with males of related species such as carp, crucian carp, etc. During spawning true fertilisation does not take place, for the spermatozoa penetrate the outer membranes of the eggs but perish before their nuclei combine with those of the eggs. However, the mere presence of the sperm stimulates the egg nuclei to start dividing and thus produce new individuals. The offspring produced in this way will have received only the hereditable genes of the female, and therefore can only become females. This form of reproduction is known as gynogenesis, and is extremely rare among animals.

The eggs, 160,000–380,000 in number, are spawned in 3 portions. Growth is more rapid than in the crucian carp, and the goldfish matures at an age of 3–4 years, when it measures 15–20 cm. In several places in eastern Europe it has has been used in fish-farms. When young the goldfish is grey or olive and resembles the Gibel carp. Only after several months, or even years, do the orange pigments begin to show.

The goldfish was brought to Portugal from the Far East, probably in 1611. It is now found widely in several small rivers and ponds in southern and central Europe, where it thrives. It lives too in isolated waters in southern England and in rivers, particularly where the water is artificially heated. The strange-looking aquarists' varieties do not survive long in these conditions, and stocks soon revert to the Prussian carp (wild) form and coloration.

Many varieties of goldfish are kept by aquarists and pond-keepers. These varieties, veil-tails, telescope-eyed fish, etc., have been produced by Chinese and Japanese breeders after very long-term and careful selection of breeding stock.

The original distribution of the goldfish is very difficult to establish because of the many introductions made throughout the past centuries. Fish from goldfish bowls are apparently even today tipped into nearby rivers, thus making our record-keeping all the harder.

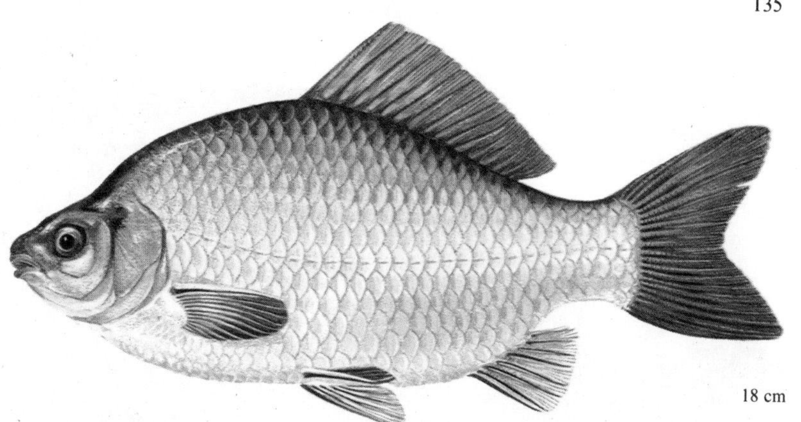

18 cm

(♦) 82. GIBEL CARP
Carassius auratus

22 cm

(♦) GOLDFISH

telescope-eyed fish

veil-tail fish

♦ **83. CARP**
Cyprinus carpio

83. Carp
Cyprinus carpio L.

Distinctive features: Upper lip with 2 long and 2 short barbels; 33–40 scales along lateral line (in those carp which are fully scaled). Stocks which have bred continuously in the wild have a more slender body than cultivated carp, which are often high-backed. The variation in scale cover of the body is due to genetic causes and 3 main types (see page 139) are recognised, one of which has two categories. Scaled carps (often known as king carps) are covered by small uniform scales; mirror-carps have either irregularly spread, large mirror-like scales of different sizes, or a linear arrangement of a series of small scales along the back and large, uniform scales along the lateral line; finally, leather-carps are almost without scales.
Size: At 3–4 years wild carp measure 20–40 cm, (300–1,000 g). Maximum rarely over 100 cm (25–30 kg) at 40 years.
Distribution: The carp was originally an Asiatic fish distributed in a broad band from Manchuria to the rivers of the Black Sea.

It has been an important cultivated food-fish for about 2,000 years and was probably introduced into Europe by the Romans, and became widely distributed, mainly between 1300 and 1500. It now occurs northwards to 60°N and has been introduced into many countries, such as the U.S.A. where it has multiplied to pest proportions. (See also the section on carp pond-farming, p. 205.)

The carp inhabits rivers and lakes in stagnant or slow-flowing waters with a muddy bottom and dense vegetation.

34 cm

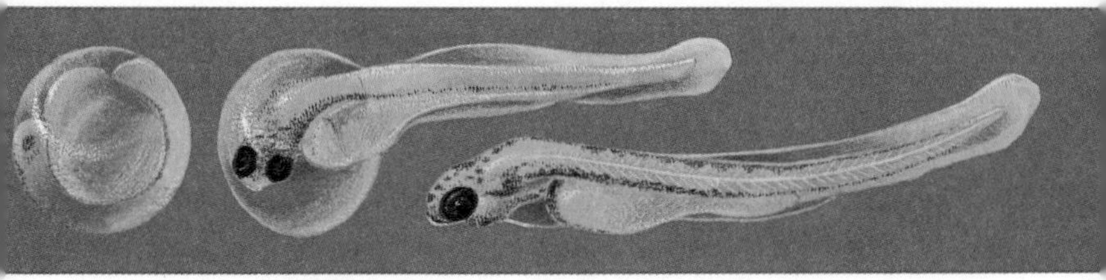

egg, 36 hours just hatching at 5 days, newly hatched larvae

principal food:

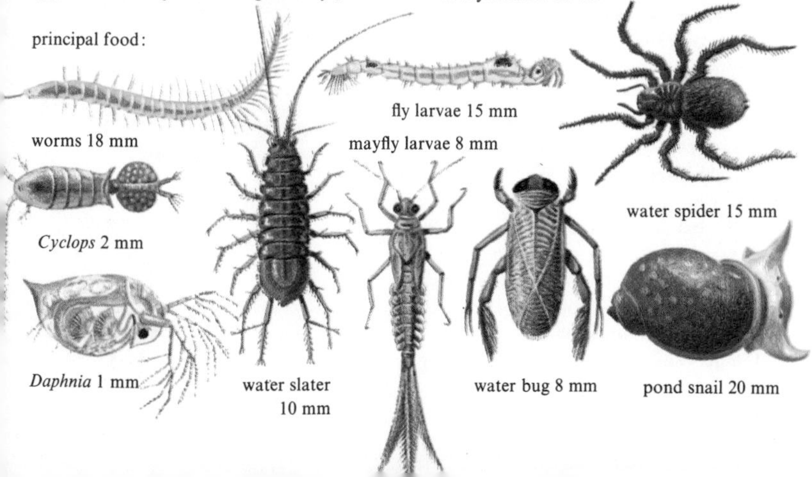

worms 18 mm

fly larvae 15 mm

mayfly larvae 8 mm

water spider 15 mm

Cyclops 2 mm

Daphnia 1 mm

water slater 10 mm

water bug 8 mm

pond snail 20 mm

It is a shy and mainly nocturnal fish. Its food consists of water-fleas, larvae of midges and other water insects, also worms, small snails and mussels. The seeds of plants and algae are widely eaten as well. Occasionally it is said to eat frogs, sticklebacks or fish fry.

Spawning takes place in quite shallow water, e.g. flooded meadows, in May, or later, when the water temperature reaches 17–20°C. This high temperature required for spawning means that wild carp only rarely breed successfully in central and north Europe. Many of the populations in the British Isles have little breeding success.

The roe can weigh up to one third of the weight of the female. Among pond-kept fish females actually spawn about 60,000–70,000 eggs per lb of the mother's weight, but more eggs are usually present in the overies. Wild carp shed their spawn in several portions at about weekly intervals. The 1 mm-diameter eggs swell in water to 1·6 mm. They are attached to plants, and hatch in 3–8 days, depending on the temperature (*c.* 100 day-degrees C are required). The newly hatched larvae have a yolk-sac, and are attached to plants or lie on the bottom for 2–3 days before floating to the surface, where their swim-bladders become filled with air. They feed on microscopic algae, rotifers and small crustaceans (water-fleas). The carp reaches maturity at 3–4 years, the males at an earlier age than the females.

Growth is variable and depends on the amount of food. In carp-ponds where natural as well as artificial food is available, a weight of 1 kg is reached in 2–3 years. Rapid growth produces the deep-bodied fish that breeeders favour. In particularly favourable areas (e.g. Caspian Sea, Lake Aral) wild carp may have very rapid growth, but it is normally slow. In the U.S.A., where the carp was introduced in 1877, it has spread considerably and now in places forms over-populated communities with small, stunted fish.

Temperature plays a role in the feeding intensity of the carp. Below 8°C it feeds very little if at all; the greatest feeding activity occurs at 20°C.

In winter it moves in shoals to deep frost-free areas, and during this season loses 5–15% of its weight. It is very resistant and can tolerate water with very little oxygen (0·5 ml oxygen per litre).

As an anglers' fish the carp is a fine 'fighter', but it is difficult to tempt with a bait and it is hard to capture even in nets, although less so in winter. When landed it is very passive and tenacious of life, and will live for several hours in or out of water and can be transported easily when packed in wet weeds or sacks.

The carp is commercially of great importance in southern and eastern Europe, mainly in the U.S.S.R., Yugoslavia, Czechoslovakia, Hungary, Poland, Austria, Germany and France. The largest total carp-pond areas are in Czechoslovakia and France, totalling 150,000 hectares (1 hectare equals 100 ares). The total commercial catch throughout the world is 200,000 tons annually. (The technique of carp-farming is described on p. 205.)

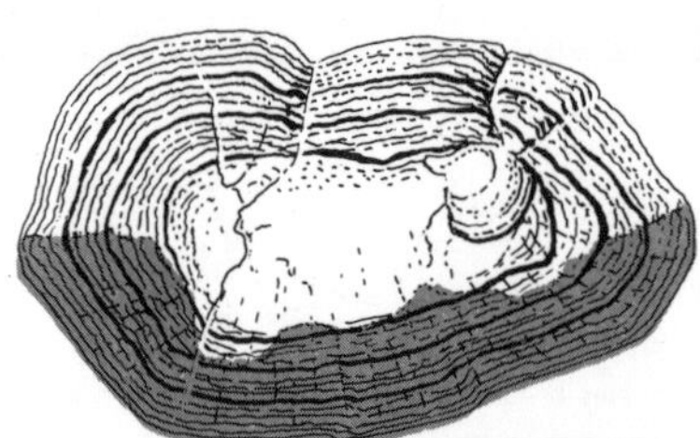

scale of mirror carp

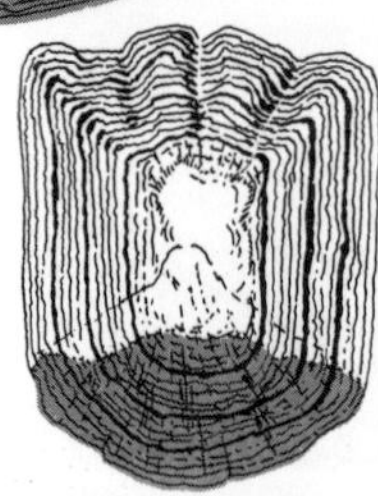

scale of king carp, both natural size

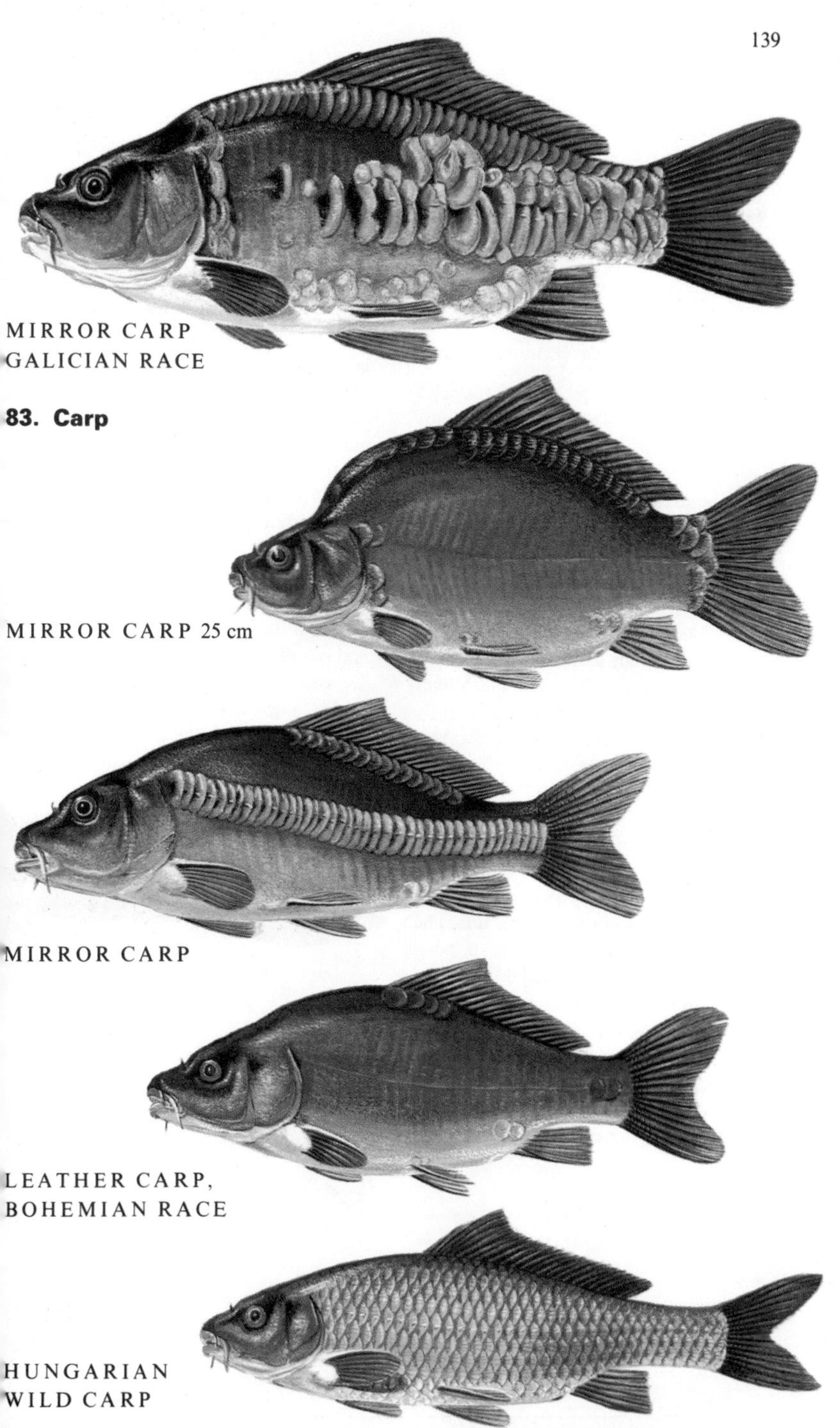
MIRROR CARP
GALICIAN RACE
MIRROR CARP 25 cm
MIRROR CARP
LEATHER CARP,
BOHEMIAN RACE
HUNGARIAN
WILD CARP

83. Carp

LOACHES

This family includes many small, elongate bottom-living fishes with several barbels around the mouth. Most of them live in Asiatic rivers and brooks with rapid currents and sandy bottoms. Three species are found in Europe.

84. Stone loach

Noemacheilus barbatulus (L.)

Distinctive features: The body is rounded in cross-section at the front; area beneath the eyes is without backward-pointing spines; 6 barbels around the mouth.
Size: Generally 8–12 cm at 2–3 years; very rarely over 15 cm. The females are the largest.

Lives in cool, clear water, in rivers and brooks, and in the shore region of clear lakes. Tolerates weak brackish water, e.g. in the German haffs and the Finnish skerries of the Baltic Sea. The loach lives very close to the bottom and is mainly nocturnal, spending the day under cover, although on dull days it may be active. It lives solitarily, and feeds on shrimps (*Gammarus*), insect larvae, worms, leeches and occasionally molluscs.

Spawning takes place from April-May, and both sexes have spawning tubercles on the inner sides of the pectoral fins. The sticky eggs are spawned in separate positions and total 500,000–800,000. In some cases it appears that they are deposited in a hollow (usually under a stone) and guarded by the female. Other observers, however, have reported that the eggs are attached to plants and stones. The stone loach reaches maturity at 2–3 years, and attains a maximum age of 6–7 years.

It makes a good angling bait-fish, and is said to have been cultivated in ponds for food, but its use, size and value are small.

85. Pond loach

Misgurnus fossilis (L.)

Distinctive features: A total of 10 barbels, 4 on the tip of the snout, 4 on the lower jaw and 1 at each corner of the mouth; small scales; slimy, eel-like body.
Size: Usually 20–25 cm at 3–4 years, maximum 50 cm (in eastern Europe). Maturity is attained at 3 to 4 years.

It lives in shallow ponds and small lakes with a muddy bottom. It is particularly well adapted to life in these potentially oxygen-poor waters, for it regularly rises to the surface to swallow a bubble of air, which passes through the intestine and out of the vent. During its passage the air comes into contact with a strongly folded, mucous lining which absorbs about half the oxygen in the air, and this passes

11 cm

♦ 84. STONE LOACH

Noemacheilus barbatulus

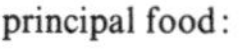

principal food:

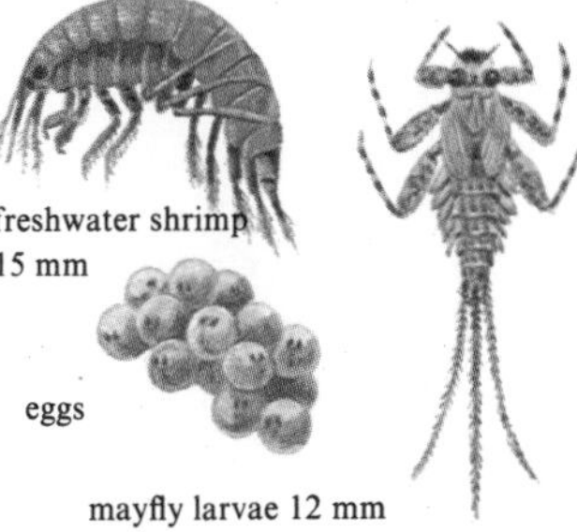

freshwater shrimp 15 mm

eggs

mayfly larvae 12 mm

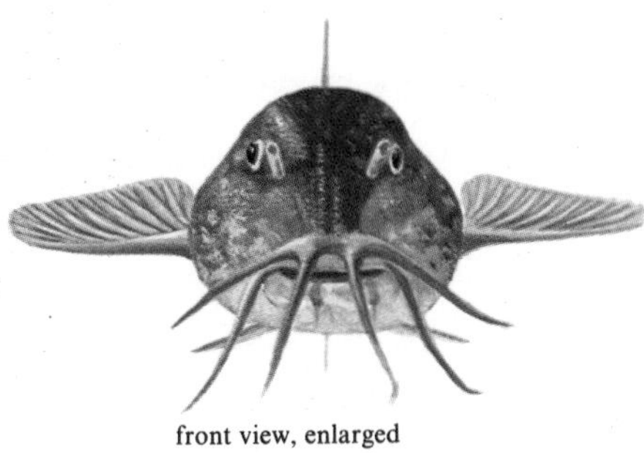

front view, enlarged about 2 times

21 cm

85. POND LOACH

Misgurnus fossilis

principal food:

larva with external gills

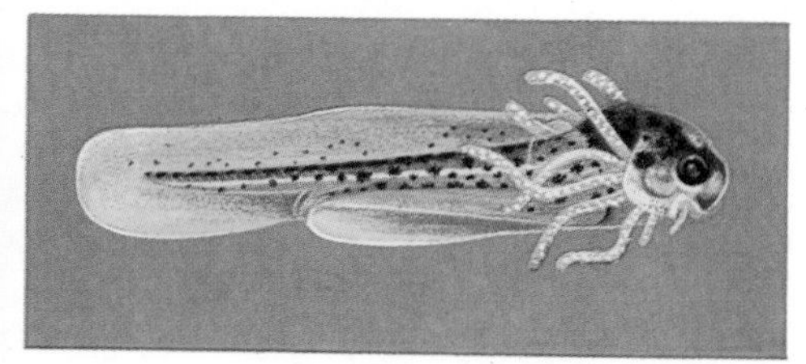

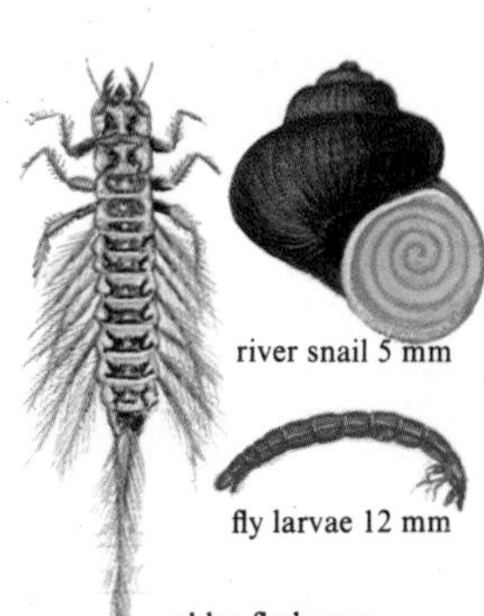

river snail 5 mm

fly larvae 12 mm

alder-fly larvae 40 mm

into the blood. In addition to this intestinal respiration the gills perform their usual function in extracting oxygen from the water. Should the pond in which it lives dry up, the loach buries itself in the mud and estivates, with all its vital functions reduced to a minimum. It is said to survive in this state for up to one year.

The pond loach eats small snails, mussels, and the larvae of insects.

It has long been known as the 'weather-fish' because it is said to react to the change in barometric pressure by restless activity before a thunderstorm.

Spawning takes place from April-June. The brownish eggs number 70,000–150,000, are 1·5 mm in diameter, and are shed intermittently over several weeks onto plants. At hatching the larvae have several thread-like external gill filaments, which later become reduced and disappear. They are presumably another adaptation enabling the loach to survive in the poor oxygen conditions that exist in small pools.

86. Spined loach

Cobitis taenia L.

Distinctive features: Head and body very compressed, head with 3 pairs of short barbels. Below each eye is a movable double spine; the 2nd ray in the pectoral fin of the male is thickened; and the sides have 1 or 2 rows of fairly regular round spots.

Size: Often 5–10 cm, maximum 12 cm.

The spined loach is a stationary bottom-living fish found in clear, running water, or on the sandy bottom of larger lakes. It is nocturnal and stays buried in the bottom during daytime. It feeds on small crustaceans (ostracods, copepods), and rotifers. Spawning occurs in spring, and the eggs which are not guarded are deposited on stones or roots.

87. Golden loach

Cobitis aurata (De Filippi)

The sides of the body have a golden lustre, and along the centre of each side is a row of large dark spots. Maximum length *c.* 14 cm. Several eastern subspecies.

88. Balkan loach

Cobitis elongata Heckel & Kner

A narrow dark line runs along the sides, passing through the large, round spots. This is a large species, with a maximum length of 16·5 cm.

89. Rumanian loach

Cobitis romanica Bacescu

Very pale and weakly spotted; the dorsal fin origin is just above that of the pelvic fins. 7–12 cm in length. Found in the upper reaches of a number of Rumanian tributaries of the Danube.

90. Bergatino loach

Cobitis larvata De Filippi

A triangle formed by 2 dark halter-like stripes in front of the eyes; two symmetrical black spots on the caudal peduncle. 5–9 cm in length. Found at Bergatino, northern Italy.

91. Italian loach

Cobitis conspera (Cantoni)

Two elongate spots in front of the dorsal fin, 3–4 spots behind the fin. No markings in front of the eyes as in the Bergatino loach. 5–9 cm in length. Occurs in the Brenta river, northern Italy.

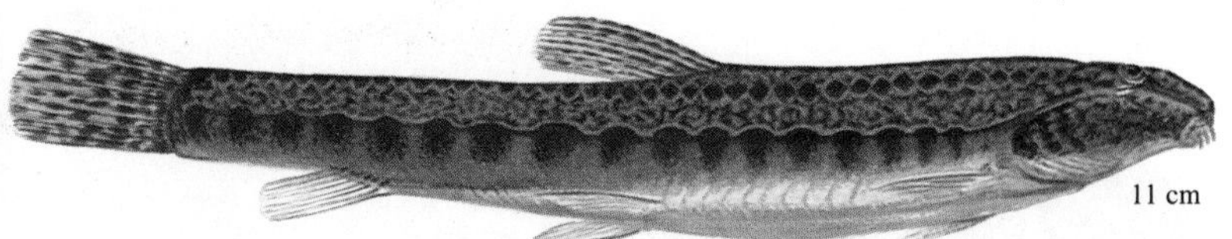

♦ 86. SPINED LOACH

Cobitis taenia

principal food:

rotifers 1 mm

Cyclops 1 mm

ostracods 1 mm

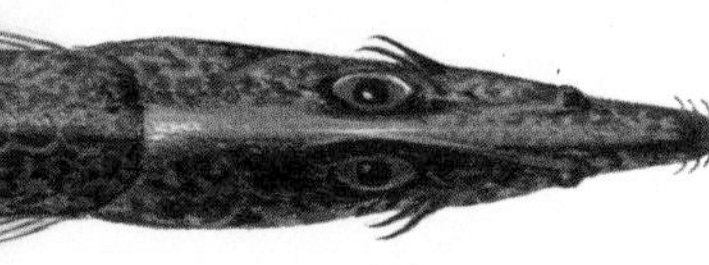

head from above, enlarged 3 times

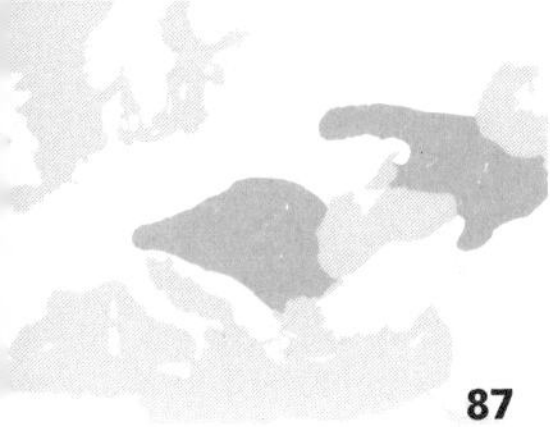

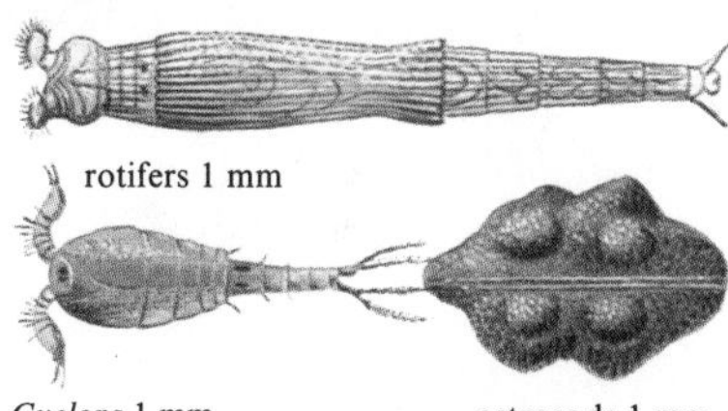

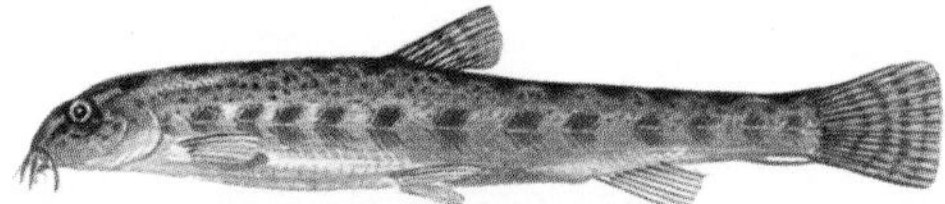

87. GOLDEN LOACH

87

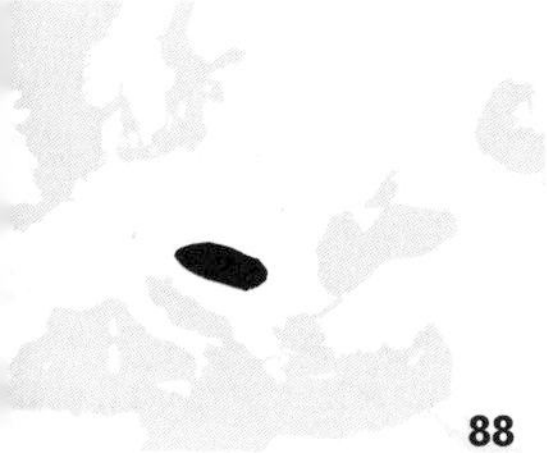

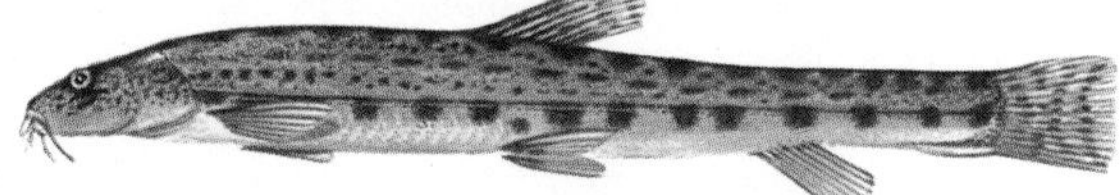

88. BALKAN LOACH

88

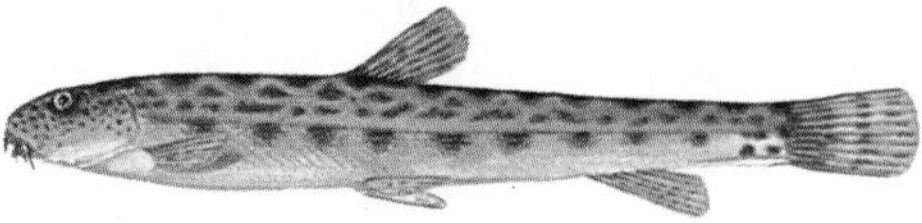

89. RUMANIAN LOACH

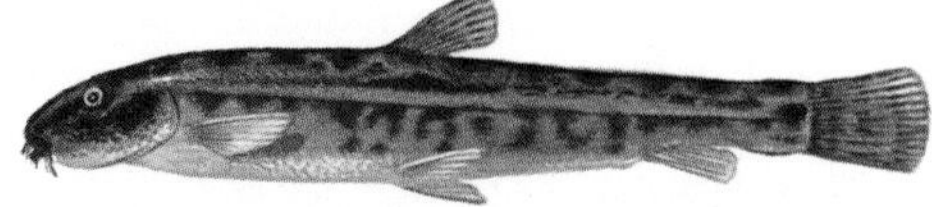

90. BERGATINO LOACH

89

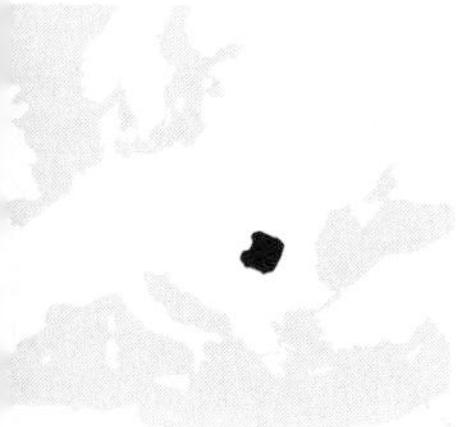

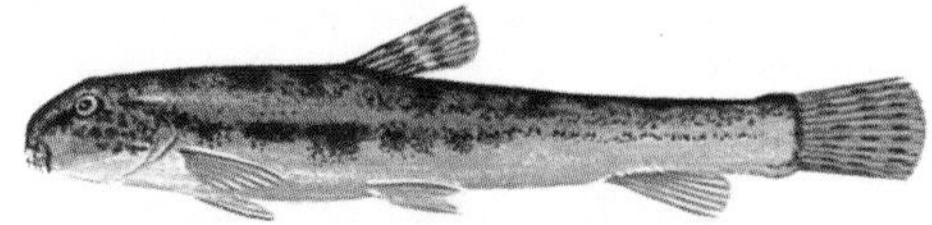

91. ITALIAN LOACH

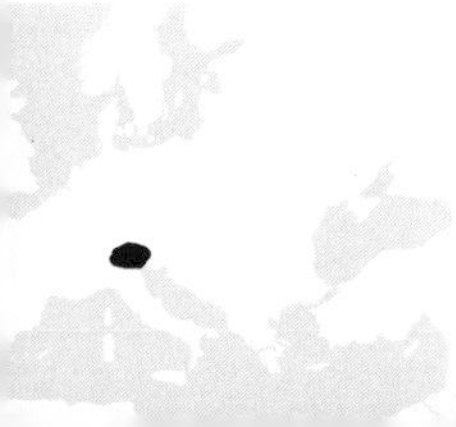

91

CATFISHES

A family with numerous species, mostly living in the tropics. The body is stout, the head flat and toad-like, the mouth broad with at least 2 pairs of long barbels. The skin is slimy and scaleless, and the air-bladder has an air-duct.

Most of the catfishes are omnivorous, bottom-living animals.

92. Wels or Sheat-fish

Siluris glanis L.

Distinctive features: Broad, flat head with a wide mouth. The upper jaw has two very long barbels, and under the lower jaw there are 4 shorter ones. Slimy body without scales; no adipose fin; anal fin very long.
Size: About 50 cm and 2 kg at 4 years. The males are a little larger than the females. Usual size 100 cm (10 kg) at 9–10 years. Maximum 3–4 m 200 kg. The largest authentic record is of a R. Dnieper fish of 5 m and 306 kg.

Wels live in lakes with a soft bottom, and in the slow-flowing reaches of larger rivers (bream region). In the Black Sea, and more rarely in the Baltic, it occurs in brackish water. It keeps close to the bottom during daylight, seeking cover in hollows, under stones or buried in the mud. It is most active at night, often in quite shallow water. It is a voracious predator, and can decimate the stock of large fish in an area. It eats mainly eels, burbot, tench, bream and roach. Crayfish and frogs are also important food items, and occasionally it takes water-voles and ducklings. Horrifying tales are told about its attacking and drowning swimming dogs and even children, but these are based more on hearsay than observation. They feed most intensively in spring and summer, eating less in the autumn and hibernating in a state of lethargy.

The wels requires a high temperature to thrive, and rarely spawn below 20°C; in central Europe spawning takes place at the beginning of June, in northern Europe from July-August. Spawning takes place close to the shore in dense vegetation, and the male excavates a shallow depression in the muddy bottom in which the female lays her eggs. A female of 2 kg spawns *c.* 60,000 eggs, which are light yellow, sticky and 3 mm in diameter. They stick together and to the vegetation in the 'nest' and are guarded by the male for about 3 days until they hatch. The newly hatched larvae measure 7 mm and already have a

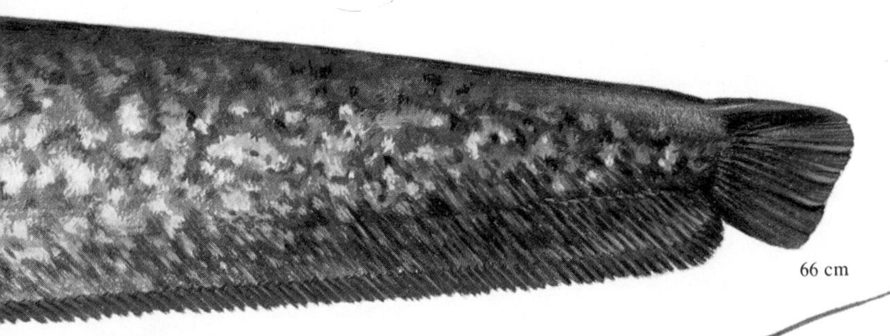

66 cm

(♦) 92. WELS
Siluris glanis

newly hatched larva 7 mm

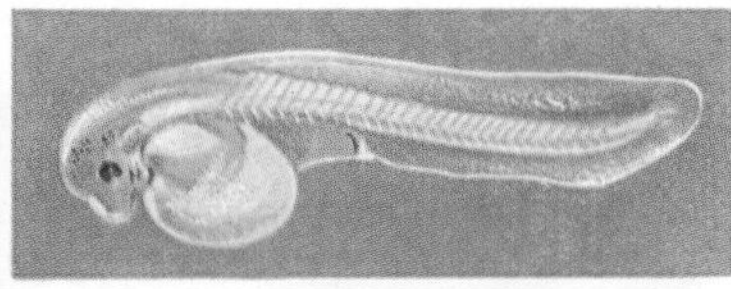

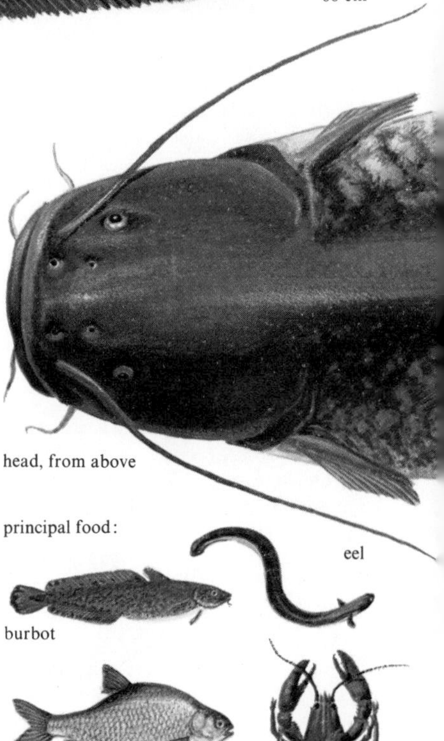

small barbel. After the yolk sac has been absorbed the young fish feed on plankton and from the age of one year mostly on other small fish. Growth is very rapid, and at one month the length is 3–4 cm and after one year *c.* 20 cm. Maturity is attained at 4–5 years, at *c.* 50 cm (2 kg).

The wels is an important commercial fish in the Azov Sea, the Caspian Sea and Lake Aral as well as in countries bordering on the River Danube. It is caught in strong stake-nets and traps, also hooks baited with light-coloured oil-cloth or other material, or with frogs and burbots. The roe is sometimes used as caviar, but

head, from above

principal food:

eel

burbot

bream

crayfish

newt

duckling

water vole

were often mixed with the eggs of sturgeon or sterlet. Glue is produced from the swim-bladder and the bones. The flesh is almost free of bones and very tasty. Fish for the table are best at weights of 3–4 kg, as the old fish are often tough. Especially in Hungary it is stocked in fish-farms and fed on fish, such as white bream, which have no value and are competitors with more valuable species. Elsewhere, the wels is considered to be an undesirable predator in properly controlled fisheries.

93. Aristotle's catfish

Siluris aristotelis (Agassiz)

Similar to the common catfish, but has only 4 barbels. Its biology is the same as that of the wels and it lives only in the Akheloos river and its tributaries, southern Greece.

94. Catfish

Ictalurus nebulosus (Le Sueur)

Distinctive features: The head is broad and flat with a total of 8 barbels; dorsal fin with a strong and stiff first ray; an adipose fin on the back behind the dorsal fin; the anal fin relatively short.

Size: Rarely over 33 cm, 245 g and 8 years. Maximum 45 cm (2 kg).

Distribution: This catfish has been introduced from North America and has spread widely in central Europe and in France. It is a bottom-living fish with nocturnal habits. It lives in swamps, lakes or slow-running rivers with a soft bottom. Its food consists of the larvae of midges and may-flies, molluscs and the eggs and young of other fish.

It spawns in shallow water at 18–20°C from June-July. A pair of fish build a flat hollow nest under an overhanging river-bank, tree-root or other shelter. The eggs, which number 500–3,500, depending on the size of the female, are shed in clumps, and hatch after 8 days. The eggs and the newly hatched young are guarded by the male.

This catfish is very tenacious of life and can therefore be kept in oxygen-poor and polluted waters, and is suitable for aquaria. It is not suitable for fish-farming because it is difficult to catch due to its habit of hiding in the mud. The flesh is orange-coloured, rather sweet, but tasty, and it should be skinned before cooking. Although it takes the hook readily it has no value as a game-fish.

Editor's note: A related American catfish *Ictalurus melas* is widespread in Italy and has been found elsewhere in northern Europe. It has often been confused with the above species in the past.

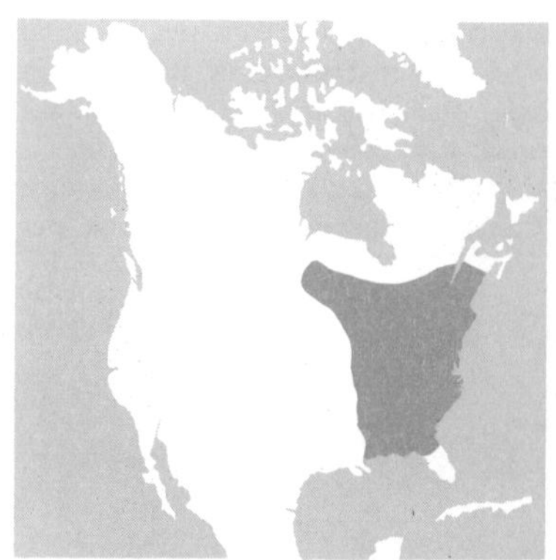

46 cm

93. ARISTOTLE'S CATFISH
Siluris aristotelis

33 cm

(◆) 94. CATFISH
Ictalurus nebulosus

principal food:

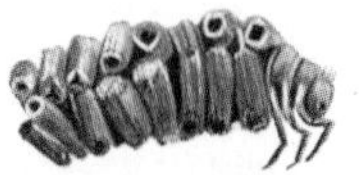

caddis-fly larvae 35 mm

pulmonate snail

fly larvae
12 mm

small crucian carp

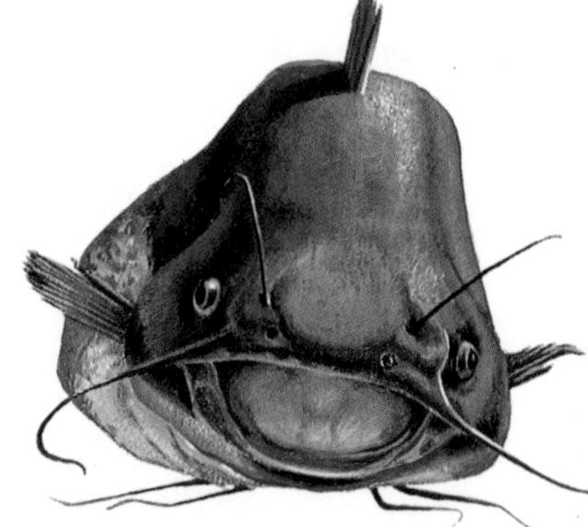

yellow eel 68 cm

♦ 95. EEL

Anguilla anguilla (L.)

Distinctive features: Very elongate body; dorsal, tail and anal fins are continuous; no pelvic fins. The gill opening is small and placed just in front of the base of the pectoral fin; the lower jaw is prominent.
Size: males 29–51 cm, females 42–100 cm. Maximum weight *c.* 3·5 kg.

The eel (family Anguillidae) is a sea fish which spends a large part of its adolescent life in brackish and freshwater. Its life-history is remarkable and still contains some unsolved problems. The eel spawns in the Sargasso Sea 4,000–7,000 km from the parts of Europe and North Africa where it grows up. The smallest known eel larvae, *c.* 5 mm long, are found from March-April at 100–300 m depth in water 6,000 m deep. The larvae are transparent, flattened from side to side and live pelagically in the upper water layers, feeding on diatoms. They are called leptocephali. With the Gulf Stream and the general north-eastward trend of surface current in the Atlantic they are carried across the ocean. It takes them 3 years to reach the European coastline and when they have penetrated into coastal waters they metamorphose into 65-mm long elvers (which are 10 mm shorter than the larvae). During their metamorphosis they do not feed. The elvers then migrate into shallow brackish water, and into rivers and streams in November-December in Spain and Ireland, January-March on the English west coast, and March-April along the coasts of the North Sea and in the Kattegat.

During summer the elvers become darkly pigmented. Some stay in brackish waters with a soft bottom and dense

silver eel 52 cm

map showing migration of larvae

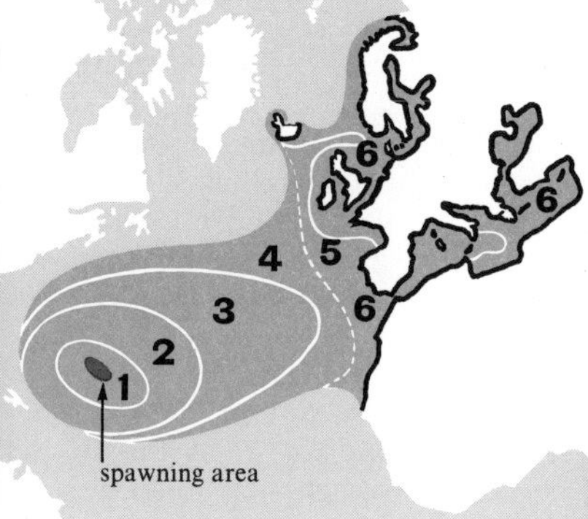

the numbers in the areas on the map correspond to the numbers on the diagram of larval growth and metamorphosis

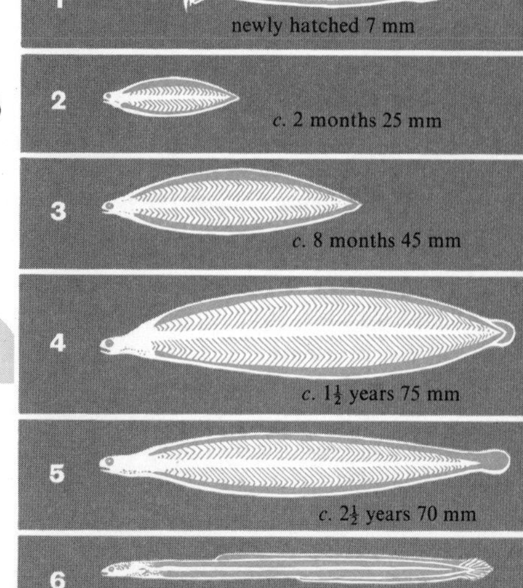

vegetation (e.g. eelgrass). Others spend the next few years in freshwater.

The ability of the elvers to overcome obstructions in their passage up-river is well known. Where free passage is barred by waterfalls or dams, eel-passes are constructed. These are often no more than a long bundle of heather or twigs covered by wire-netting, and so placed that the water runs slowly through the stuffing, giving the elvers an easier passage over the obstruction as they can wind themselves between the twigs.

The rate of growth depends upon food and temperature. During their first winter in freshwater the eels average a length of 8 cm, and in the second winter 17–19 cm. At this length small, oval scales are formed embedded in the skin. During their growth in freshwater they are called yellow eels. The eyes are small, the snout rather broad, and the body is very soft. The back is grey-brown, and the sides light lemon-yellow.

In freshwater the eel feeds on smaller fish, crayfish, frogs, mussels, snails and the larvae of insects. It is also said to eat fish roe. It is distinctly nocturnal, spending most of the day hidden in the mud or below stones or roots. Those eels which feed mainly on larger animals, and which therefore are more often caught on hooks, have a wide snout and have been called 'broad-snouted' or 'frog-mouth' eels to distinguish them from those with a narrow snout. At one time it was thought that there were two or more varieties of eel, but the two types belong to the same species, and are merely growth stages.

The eel is found up to an altitude of 1,000 m above sea-level. At low temperatures it is rather passive, and in the northern parts of its range it spends the winter hidden in the mud or below stones in frost-free places.

Between 4 and 10 years of age most eels begin to change from the yellow to silver form. The eyes increase considerably in size, the muscles of the jaws shrink, and the head becomes pointed. The skin becomes dark on the back, silvery on the belly. Gradually the eel ceases to take food, the intestine shrinks, and the body becomes hard and rigid—it is now ready to migrate to the sea.

The eel is unusual in that the ovaries and the testes develop late, and they are still undeveloped in silver eels when they leave the European coast on their way to the spawning places. Mature males have been produced experimentally by treating silver eels with hormones. It has been claimed that eels in brackish water develop mainly into males, which acquire their silver coloration about two years earlier than the females. The females grow up mainly in freshwater, and in the inner Baltic almost all eels are females. If an eel is prevented from migrating to the sea the yellow-eel stage is prolonged, and can continue to an age of 25–50 years.

The silver eels migrate in September-October, heading towards the Atlantic Ocean, but it is not known how they reach the Sargasso Sea. Outside the coastal region eels have never been caught and adult and mature males have been found only 3 or 4 times along the European coasts. It is assumed that they swim in mid-water. At the beginning of migration, up to a quarter of the eel's weight is fat, which provides the energy necessary for the journey. In order to reach the spawning places early in the next spring, an average daily speed of 20–40 km is required, and tagging experiments in the Baltic have shown that the eel is able to maintain this average. Its inability to feed does not affect its performance, for in aquaria the silver eel can live for 4 years without food.

The final maturation of the sexual products must be assumed to take place in the Sargasso Sea. There can be no doubt that the eels die after spawning.

Eels are caught in seines, traps, on hooks, with eel-spears and push-nets. Elvers and 1–2 year-old yellow eels are in places introduced into streams and lakes which

95. Eel

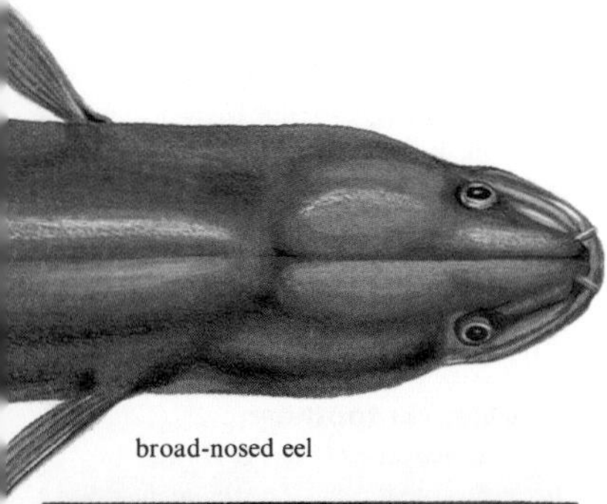

broad-nosed eel

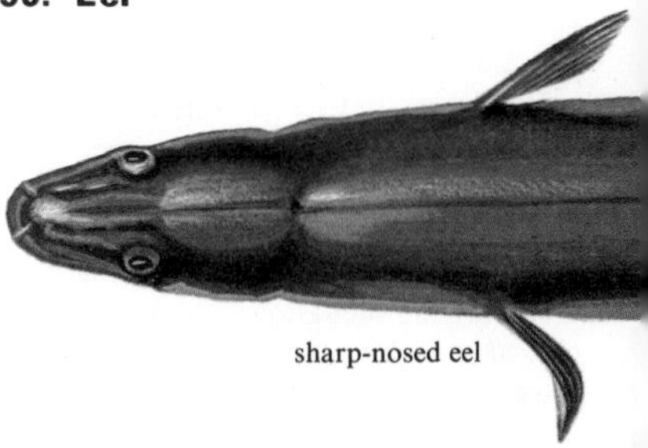

sharp-nosed eel

scale pattern exposed by scraping

principal food in brackish water:

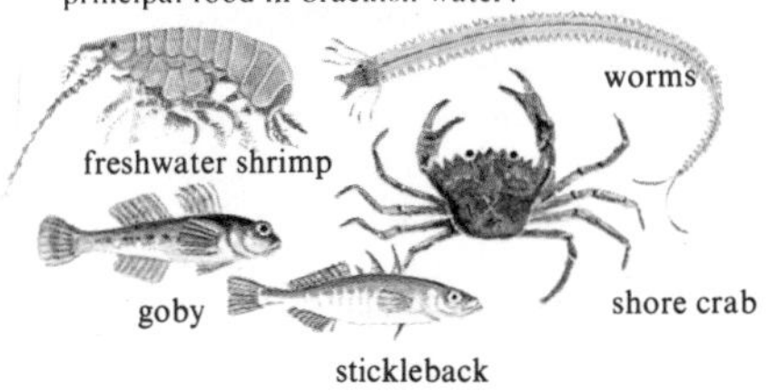

freshwater shrimp

worms

shore crab

goby

stickleback

principal food in fresh water:

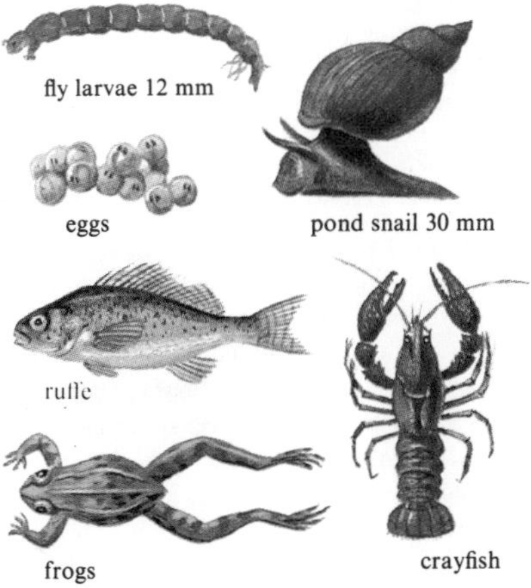

fly larvae 12 mm

eggs

pond snail 30 mm

ruffe

crayfish

frogs

they would not naturally ascend, and are cropped later when of sufficient size.

The fishery for silver eels is very lucrative, particularly in Danish waters through which the Baltic eels must pass. Holland also has important eel-fisheries.

Eels are surprisingly tenacious of life and can endure a long stay on land; the thick skin and the narrow gill-slits protect them against drying out.

The annual European catch of eels is 18,000–20,000 tons.

An eel pass should consist only of a tube made of chicken netting, stuffed with heather twigs (they last longest), and placed so that the overflow water filters down through it.

TOOTHCARPS

Toothcarps are small fishes found most abundantly in Central America. There are several indigenous European species, and one introduced from America as a control for malaria-carrying mosquitoes. Many tropical forms are kept in aquaria, including the well-known guppy.

They are frequently brightly coloured, with spineless fins and no lateral line. There are often no external differences between the sexes, though the males are more colourful and in the forms which bear live young the first rays of the anal fin are modified into an organ for transmitting sperm to the female.

96. Spanish toothcarp

Aphanius iberus (Cuv. & Val.)

Distinctive features: The male has 15 light blue, fairly distinct, narrow transverse bands across the body. The dorsal fin has a light blue edge and the tail-fin has 3–5 brown vertical bars. The female has 2–4 rows of brown spots along the body and colourless fins.

Size: 4–5 cm. The females are the larger.

This fish can live in weak brackish water, and thrives in almost all kinds of pools, ponds, ditches and swamps. It is little affected by fluctuations in temperature and oxygen content of the water. Its food consists of small snails, water-fleas (*Daphnia*) and the larvae of mosquitoes. It spawns during the summer and and the eggs, numbering *c.* 200, are deposited on water-plants and hatch after two weeks. Maturity may be reached in six months.

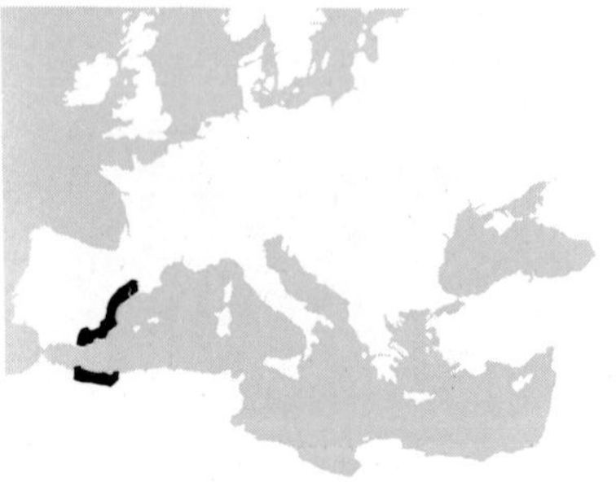

97. South European Toothcarp

Aphanius fasciatus (Humb & Val.)

Distinctive features: the male has 10–15 broad dark transverse bands on the sides. The dorsal fin has a dark border, and the caudal fin has a broad dark band. The female has narrow blurred transverse bands and greyish fins.

Size: 5–6 cm

98. Valencia toothcarp

Valencia hispanica (Cuv. & Val.)

Distinctive features: The male has 9–12 moderate, vertical, dark bars on the sides and a dark spot above the pectoral fin. The dorsal, anal and tail-fins are yellowish with dark edges. The female has an indistinct lead-grey, longitudinal band from the eye to the base of the tail.

Size: Females 8 cm, males 7 cm long.

Biology is similar to that of the previous species of *Aphanius*.

99. Mosquito-fish, Gambusia

Gambusia affinis (Baird & Girard)

Distinctive features: The male's anal fin-rays are modified into a copulatory organ. The female usually has a heavy, deep belly. A dark band through the eye in both sexes.

Size: Males 3·5 cm, females 5–6 cm.

Distribution: Introduced from North America in attempts to control the larvae of malaria-carrying mosquitoes and now found in southern France, Italy, Spain, the Balkans, in southern Russia and Central Asia. A hardy species living in all kinds of small ponds, pools, ditches and saline lagoons.

The female bears 10–80 young *c.* 30 days after fertilisation. Some sperm is retained in the oviducts, and several broods can be produced from a single copulation. 3–5 broods in a year. The young feed mainly on rotifers, and mature at 6–12 months old. It can compete with carp fry in ponds to the latter's detriment, and where it is present in the same waters in southern Europe, it tends to oust the native toothcarps.

male 4 cm

female 5.4 cm

96. SPANISH TOOTHCARP

Aphanius iberus

male 5.5 cm

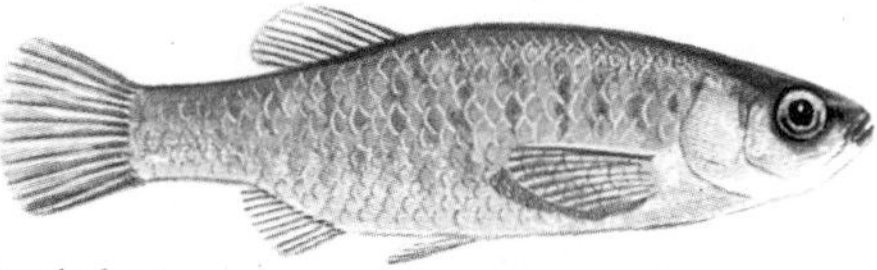

female 6 cm

98. VALENCIA TOOTHCARP

Valencia hispanica

principal food:

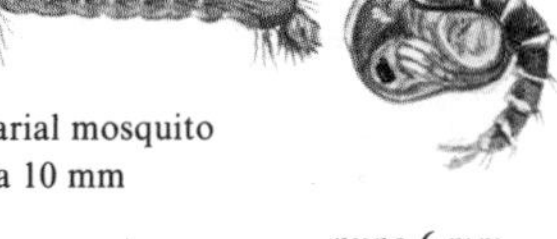

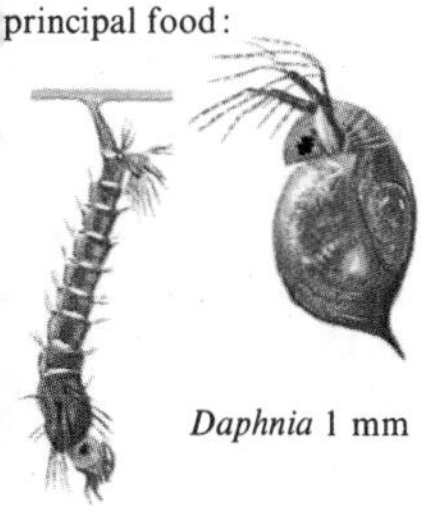

malarial mosquito larva 10 mm

pupa 6 mm

principal food:

Daphnia 1 mm

mosquito larva 10 mm

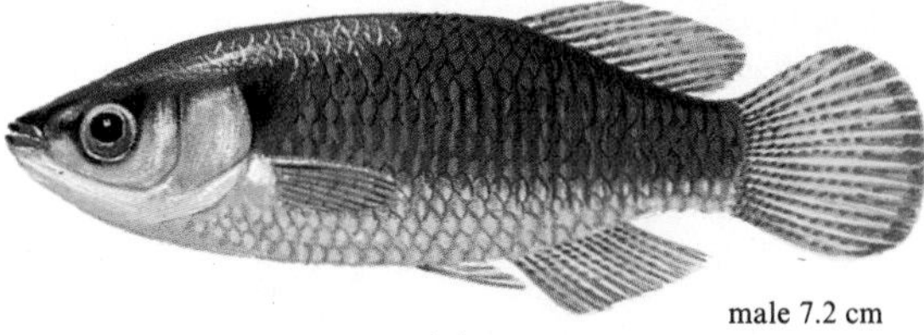

male 7.2 cm

97. SOUTH EUROPEAN TOOTHCARP

Aphanius fasciatus

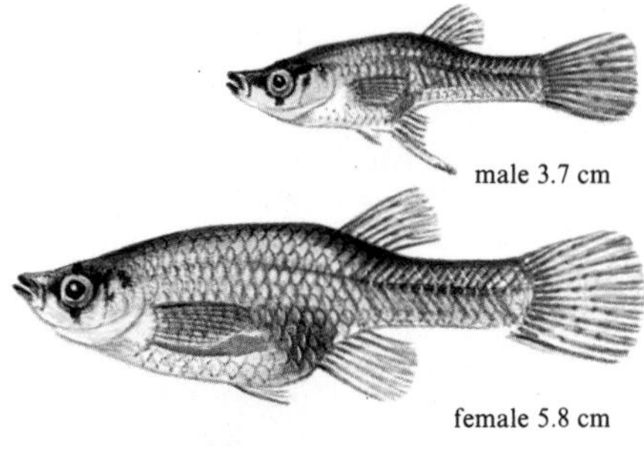

male 3.7 cm

female 5.8 cm

99. MOSQUITO-FISH

Gambusia affinis

THE CODFISH FAMILY

The cod family live in cold and temperate seas where very many species are known, but only the burbot is found in freshwater. The codfishes have 3, 2 or 1 dorsal fins, and the pelvic fins are placed well forward, on the throat. Most species have a barbel on the chin which serves as a food-detecting organ. The codfishes produce small, pelagic eggs, sometimes numbering more than a million.

100. Burbot

Lota lota (L.)

Distinctive features: Broad head; long barbel on the lower jaw, shorter barbel at each nostril; body slender with small, embedded scales. There are two dorsal fins, neither having spines and the second being much longer than the first.

The burbot belongs to the cod family, and may be related to the lings, which it resembles apart from its drab, blotchy colour, which may vary from lake to lake. Sometimes reddish-yellow 'golden burbot' are found. Three geographic races can be identified within its range.

Size: 40 cm (*c.* 500 g) at 4–6 years. Specimens up to 1 m 25–30 kg at 15–20 years have been reported, mainly from Siberia.

The burbot is a bottom-fish, living in lakes, and rivers with a gentle current and cool, clear water. It also occurs in brackish water, in the German haffs as well as in the eastern Baltic. In Alpine lakes it is found at over 1,200 m altitude, in Scandinavia at 500 m. The young stay in the weeded shore zone or in smaller streams, the older individuals frequent deeper water, down to 200 m.

The burbot is a nocturnal animal which during daylight hides under stones, roots, and in holes. The young feed on the larvae of may-flies, on water-slaters and other crustaceans, as well as mussels and snails. Older fish are voracious predators eating, in addition to these, fish mostly perch, roach, gudgeon. The burbot is also said to eat quantities of fish eggs. It feeds mostly in winter, and in summer moves into deeper water and feeds less.

The burbot spawns from December March, at 0·5–4°C and at depths of 2–50 m over a bottom of gravel, sand or hard clay. Many, mostly young, fish migrate into streams for spawning. The number of eggs is 35,000–5,000,000, varying with the size of the female. The transparent eggs measure 1 mm and have a large oil-globule and a specific gravity about that of water. However, in still water they often sink to the bottom. Similar pelagic eggs are characteristic of the marine codfishes but the greater density of sea water ensures that they float.

The eggs hatch in 1½ months at 2°C (*c* 80 day-degrees are needed). The larvae which are 3 mm long at hatching, disperse through the water-mass and, after the yolk has been consumed, feed on plankton in the upper layers. By autumn they measure 10–15 cm. They are almost coal-black, and may be found under stones or in dense weed-beds in streams or near the edges of lakes. Growth varies from lake to lake and maturity is generally reached in 2–3, less often 4, years. In the skerries of the central Baltic growth is

♦ **100. BURBOT**
Lota lota

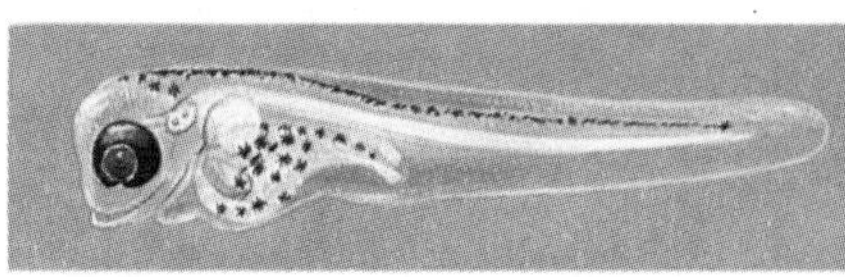
larva 5 mm

rapid and 40 cm and 500 g may be reached by the 4th year.

In the British Isles the burbot is now known to be very rare. It once occurred in eastern rivers, from Durham to Suffolk, and perhaps in the Thames.

In Europe it is caught with seines, stake-nets, traps and on hooks baited with worms or fish. It is often caught on eel-lines set overnight, and many are caught during the spawning migrations into streams. It is very resistant and can be transported easily if kept moist. The flesh is firm and tasty and is sold fresh, and iced. The liver is a highly valued delicacy, and the eggs are used for caviar in places. Even the skin is tanned in Siberia and put to various uses. The burbot is not considered a sporting fish.

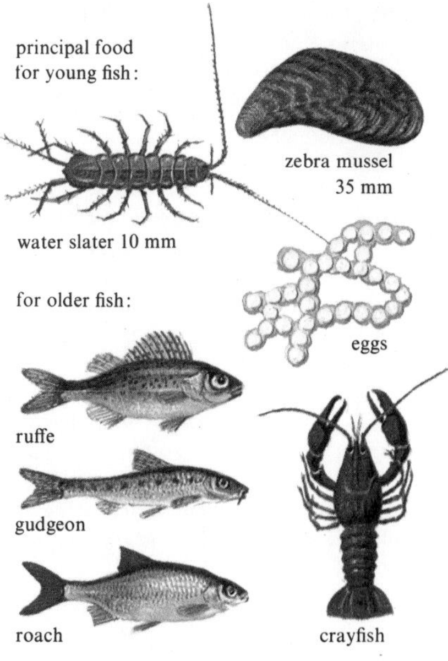

THE PERCH FAMILY

Two dorsal fins are present, the first with spiny rays and the second with mostly soft rays. The gill-covers have one or more flat spines and the scales have rough edges. A lateral line is present and the swim-bladder is without an air-duct.

There are very many species in the perch family, both in the sea and in freshwater, and a marine species, the bass *Dicentrarchus labrax* (Cuv.), is quite often found in brackish water in rivers.

101. Perch
Perca fluviatilis L

Distinctive features: The body is high in large fish, rather 'hump-backed', the first dorsal fin has 13–15 spines and posteriorly a black spot; the gill-cover ends in a strong spine.
Size: At 8–10 years *c.* 25 cm (0·2 kg), very rarely 50 cm (*c.* 3·5 kg).

The perch is abundant in lowland lakes and ponds and is found in lowland rivers even where currents are strong, as well as in brackish water, e.g. along the Baltic shores and in the Danish sounds. Perch are found up to an altitude of *c.* 1,000 m. It does not thrive in water with less than 3 ml of oxygen per litre.

The perch is rather sedentary, living usually in shoals which may include animals of different sizes and ages. They live in the upper 50 m of lakes, and it is is possible to distinguish the strongly-coloured perch of well-lit, shallow vegetation, from the lighter-coloured deep-water perch of the poorly lit bare bottom. In large lakes many are pelagic.

The food includes the larvae of insects, freshwater shrimps, young crayfish and young fish. Large perch are solitary predators, eating small roach, bleak, etc and as it is very abundant the perch itself, when young, often serves as food for larger perch, zander and pike. Deeply reddish-yellow perch have often derived their colour from the carotinoids in the flesh of the crustaceans which they have eaten.

Spawning occurs mainly in April (earlier in the south, later in the north), when the

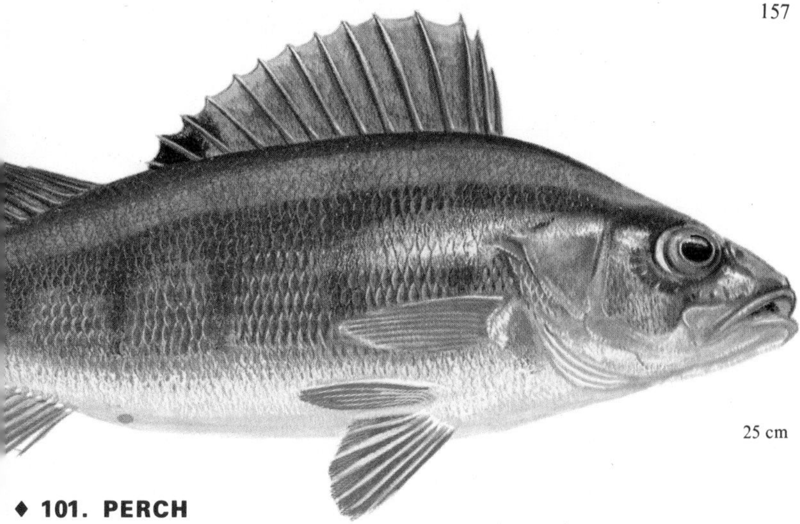

25 cm

♦ 101. PERCH

Perca fluviatilis

egg bands

larva 7 mm

principal food of young perch:

Cyclops 2 mm

young crayfish

mayfly larvae 7 mm

elvers

of adult perch:

bleak

roach

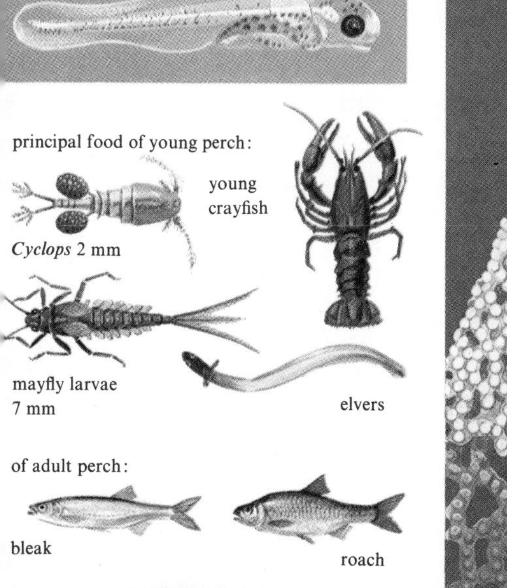

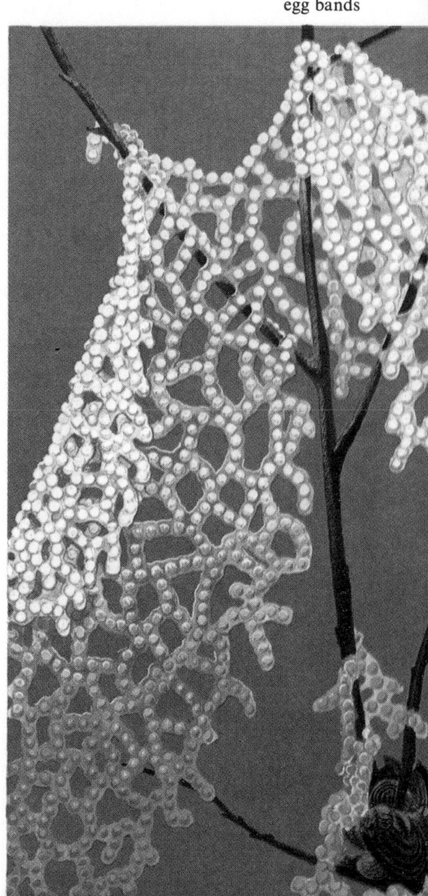

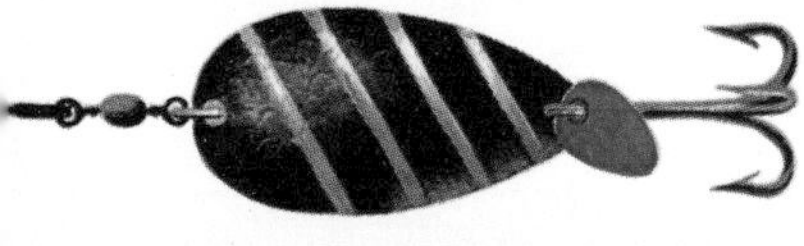

water temperature reaches 7–8°C. Shallow areas with dense vegetation, roots, fallen trees or twigs are particularly chosen for spawning, but it may occur in deeper water over a stony bottom. The eggs are 2–2·5 mm in diameter, have a considerable mucous layer which swells in water, and are shed in long threads which the female winds around plants, twigs or stones, while one or two males follow her and fertilise the eggs. The number of eggs varies from 4,000–300,000 according to the size of the female. They are all shed at the same time and hatch in 2–3 weeks. Hatching success is invariably high, probably due to the protection of the eggs by their mucous membranes. The young at hatching measure 8 mm. After the yolk is consumed they feed on plankton, chiefly crustaceans, and gradually disperse over the upper water layers. The presence of adequate supplies of food at this period is vital to the continued success of the year-class. At 15–20 mm they gather in big shoals close to the bank. At one year of age they measure 4–6 cm, after 2 years 8–12 cm. The males mature at 2–3 years, the females 1–3 years later, at a length of 15–25 cm. In places, mostly in the smaller lakes, growth is less, due to overcrowding and lack of food, and in these overpopulated lakes the males mature at a length of only 7–8 cm, females at 9–10 cm although they may, in fact, be older than mature fish in uncrowded lakes.

The total annual European perch yield is probably 20–30,000 tons, caught with seines, stake-nets, traps, and hooks. The perch is a good angling fish and may be taken with spinner, fly or hook baited with fish, worms or insects. Most European countries have local minimum sizes that can be taken, usually 13–25 cm. The perch is sold fresh, dried or salted, and its flesh makes very good eating.

The American yellow perch. *P. fluviatilis flavescens* is considered by some authorities to be a subspecies of the European perch.

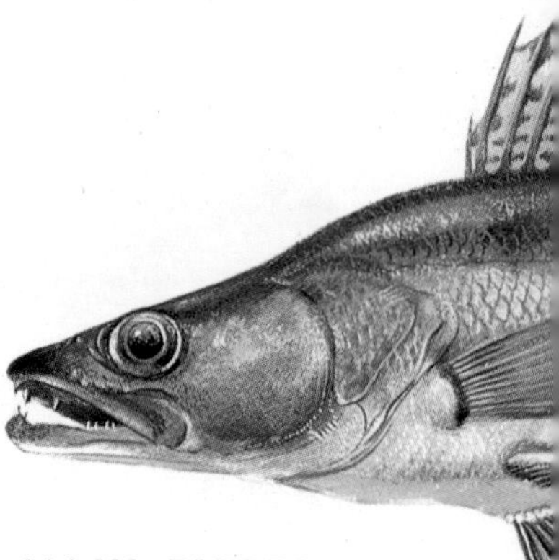

(♦) 102. ZANDER

102. Zander or pike-perch

Stizostedion lucioperca (L.)

Distinctive features: Slender body; gill-cover without a spine; mouth with several large fangs and many small teeth. The dorsal fin has 13–15 spines with dark elongate spots forming broken stripes, but does not have a black spot near the back edge. In large fish the upper jaw-bone extends well beyond the centre of the eye.
Size: At 5–6 years 35–55 cm and *c.* 1 kg. Maximum *c.* 120 cm, 12 kg, at *c.* 20 years.

The Zander (or pike-perch) is not as widely distributed as the perch. It is found mainly in large and medium-sized rather warm lakes with plenty of oxygen (at least 3·5 ml per litre). Also found in the lower reaches of rivers. It thrives best in turbid water and moves about in the free water-mass avoiding areas with vegetation. In this way it avoids competition with the pike, which prefers clear water with some vegetation. Zander when young live in small shoals, though as they get larger

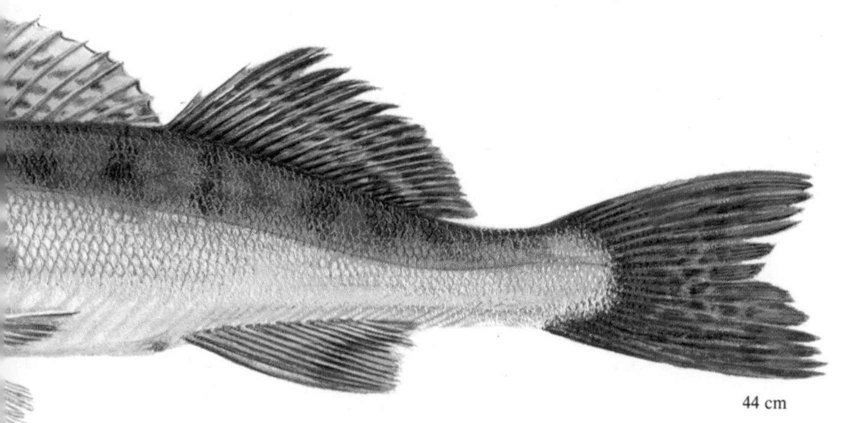

44 cm

eggs and larvae

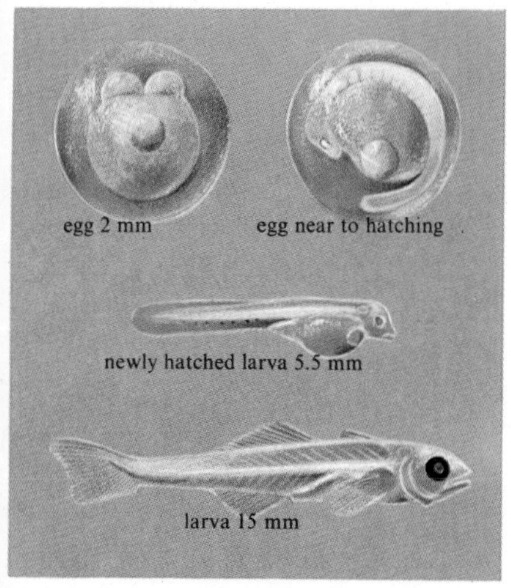

principal food of young fish:

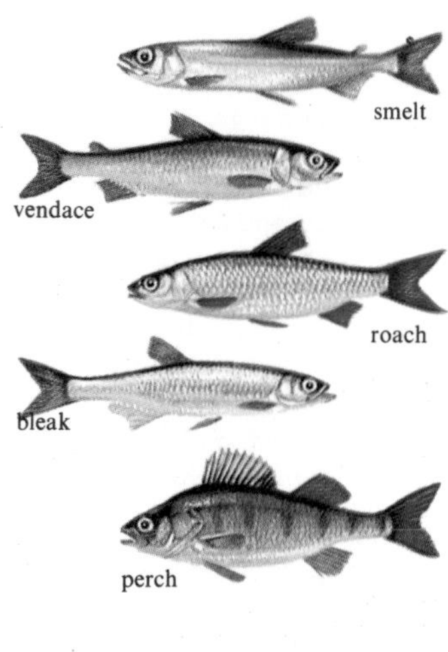

they become solitary, feeding on bleak, roach, bream, perch, and whitefish (*Coregonus*), in fact almost any suitable-sized fish present in the water they inhabit. The mouth is smaller than that of the pike, and it is unable to swallow prey larger than 12% of its own weight. Feeding is less in winter, and in the spawning season ceases altogether.

Spawning occurs at temperatures of *c.* 12°C during April-June, earlier in the south. It takes place usually over a firm sandy or stony bottom, though sometimes a bottom with plant-roots is preferred. The usual depth is 1–3 m. The eggs are deposited in shallow hollows, and stick to exposed roots and stones. The fish pair off and both guard the eggs, which measure 1–1·5 mm in diameter, and number 150,000–200,000 per 1 kg of body weight. They hatch in about a week (110 day-degrees C are needed) into larvae measuring *c.* 6 mm, but they are rather poorly developed and while living off the yolk of the egg both mouth and minute teeth appear. The fry later disperse in the surface waters, feeding on pelagic crustaceans (water-fleas and copepods). From *c.* 2 months they eat the pupae of mosquitoes and the young of other fish. Growth is rapid, and in autumn the young measure 6–10 cm. Growth does vary from water to water, but unlike the perch stunted stocks are not usual. Males mature at 2–4 years and a length of 33–37 cm. The females generally grow better than the males, but mature later at 3–5 years, and 40–44 cm.

In Europe the Zander is valuable both as a sporting fish and because it converts much inedible fish into tasty meat. For these reasons it has been introduced into many lakes, and is used as a secondary crop-fish in carp-ponds and to keep down the stock of young wild fish. Introduced to several waters in eastern England, for its angling value and is now well distributed and spreading in the Great Ouse river system.

In rearing zander artificial propagation is not general. Instead, ripe fish are introduced into ponds with a sandy bottom suitable for spawning, and the eggs are collected on artificial 'nests' of old fish-nets, or pieces of cloth, hung in a wooden frame and anchored in natural spawning places. Another method in use is to keep the spawners in cages or enclosures in shallow water, usually in the proportion of 1 male to 2 females. The cages are lined with willow-roots or juniper twigs and the eggs are deposited on these. They can then be transported while still attached to the moist twigs or packed in damp moss.

In southern Europe particularly, the collected eggs are hatched by means of the 'spray-method'. The egg-covered twigs are placed in closed containers, and at regular intervals are sprayed with water. Shortly before hatching the twigs are lowered into the water. This method has the advantage of avoiding fungal infections, and is usually very successful.

In lakes with few pike it is usual to introduce some 500–2,000 eggs per 100 areas surface. As perhaps 95% of these will perish while young, it is often easier to introduce 3-month-old fish at about 20–100 per hectare.

The pike-perch is caught with stake-nets, traps, seines and on hooks. It is a highly esteemed angling fish and is taken on spinner or baited hook. The total annual European catch is at least 10,000 tons.

103. Ruffe

Gymnocephalus cernua (L.)

Distinctive features: Resembles the perch but the dorsal fins are united. The head is scaleless and has conspicuous slime-filled cavities.

Size: Rarely over 12–15 cm, at 5–6 years. With good growth conditions up to 2[illegible] cm (400 g).

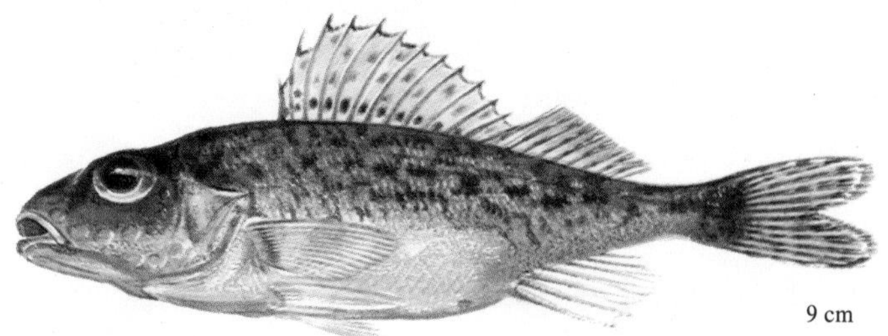

9 cm

♦ 103. RUFFE

principal food:

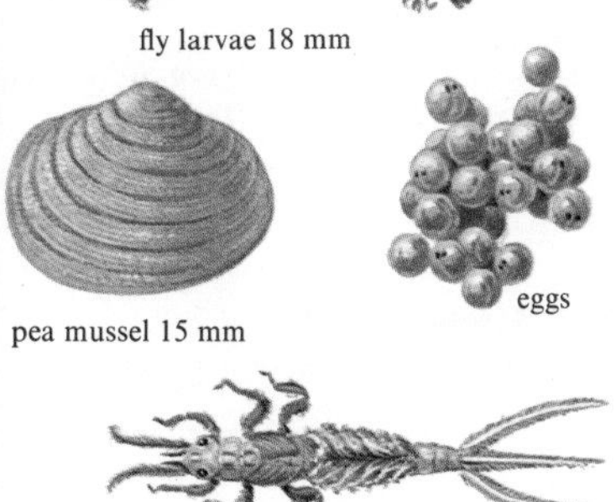

fly larvae 18 mm

eggs

pea mussel 15 mm

mayfly larvae 20 mm

The ruffe (or pope) is a bottom-living fish, occurring in the lower reaches of rivers (bream region) or on the bare bottom in lakes, and in summer also in smaller streams. During the day it is active, feeding on larvae of midges and other insects, water-slaters, snails, pea-mussels, fish eggs and fry, and at night lies close to the bottom.

In April-May, the ruffe gather in spawning shoals. Spawning takes place in shallow water at a temperature of 10–15°C, and the eggs, 1 mm in diameter and numbering 1,000–6,000, are deposited on stones and plants. The transparent larvae hatch after 8–10 days, at a length of *c.* 4 mm and with a large yolk-sac. Growth is rather slow and the ruffe, like bream, crucian carp and perch, are apt to form overcrowded poorly growing stocks. At 1–2 years they become mature. In open waters the ruffe is at times a competitor for food with bream and other more valuable fish. There is a general upstream migration after spawning to rivers and brooks, and a return in autumn.

Its flesh is tasty, especially when fried, but the fish is too small to be valuable as a table fish, although ruffe soup can be recommended. At one time the fishery in eastern Europe was important. In the eastern Prussian haffs the ruffe, which seem sensitive to sounds, were formerly driven into stake-nets by 'clap-boards' (the banging of boards which have ends sticking into the bottom).

The ruffe has no particular value as an angler's fish, and in fact is often regarded as a nuisance when it takes bait intended for bigger game.

104. Schraetzer (Ge.)

Gymnocephalus schraetzer (L.)

Distinctive features: The two dorsal fins united; the body elongate, and lemon-coloured with more or less distinct, broken, dark lengthwise stripes.

Size: Generally 15–25 cm, maximum 30 cm and 250 g.

Lives in the Danube catchment but is rather rare. It mostly occurs in deep places where the bottom is sand and gravel, and feeds on fresh-water shrimps, larvae of insects, worms, and the eggs of other fish. Spawns from April-May, *c.* 10,000 eggs are shed on a firm substratum in fairly rapid water.

Caught occasionally on hooks near the bottom.

105. Zingel (Ge.)

Aspro zingel (L.)

Distinctive features: Slender, rounded body with a pointed head and two well-separated dorsal fins, the first with 13–15 spines. The caudal peduncle is shorter than the base of the 2nd dorsal fin.

Size: 15–20 cm, maximum *c.* 35 cm.

Lives in the Danube and its tributaries in very shallow, rapidly running water. An inactive, bottom-living fish which in some ways resembles the freshwater bullheads. During the day it lives quiet and well-camouflaged between stones, at night it becomes active, swimming along the bottom hunting the larvae of insects, worms and young fish, in short rapid bursts of swimming.

Spawns from March-April in strong currents. Egg number: *c.* 5,000.

It is not common.

106. Streber (Ge.)

Aspro streber Siebold

Distinctive features: Slender, rounded body, with pointed head and two well-separated dorsal fins, the first with 8–9 spines. The distinctively slender caudal peduncle is as long as the base of the 2nd dorsal fin. Usually 4–5 distinct, irregular, dark cross bars on body; no swim-bladder.

Size: 12–18 cm, maximum *c.* 22 cm.

Lives in the Danube and its tributaries. Its biology resembles that of the larger zingel, except that it generally occurs in deeper water. Spawns from March-April. Caught only accidentally and used as bait.

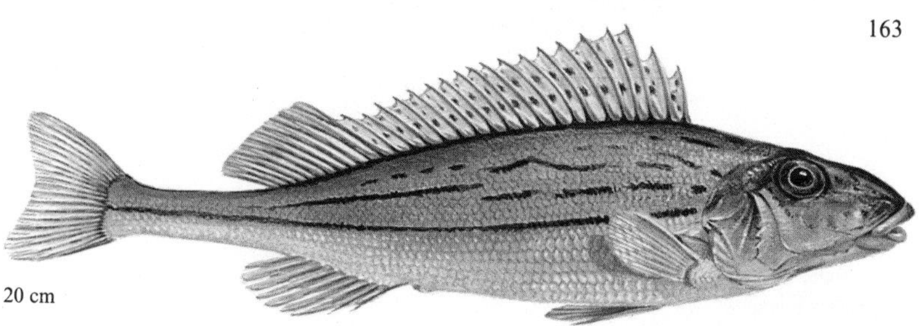

20 cm

104. SCHRAETZER
Gymnocephalus schraetzer

105. ZINGEL
Aspro zingel

28 cm

106. STREBER
Aspro streber

12 cm

107. Rhône streber

Aspro asper (L.)

Distinctive features: Resembles the streber, but the caudal peduncle is shorter than the base of the second dorsal fin. Usually 3 distinct, irregular dark bars of across the body. The Rhône streber may be only subspecifically distinct from the streber.
Size: 15–20 cm.

Found only in the Rhône basin. Lives on the bottom in shallow, running water and is nocturnal, as are the other *Aspro* species, feeding on the larvae of insects, freshwater shrimps, and the eggs and young of fish.

It spawns in spring, but otherwise its biology is little known.

108. Rumanian bull-head perch

Romanichthys valsanicola Dumitrescu, Banarescu and Stoica

Distinctive features: Similar in build to bullhead, but has scales. The 2 dorsal fins are well separated; the second is longer.
Size: c. 12 cm.

This small perch-like fish was first described in 1957. It is a fish which lives on the bottom in strong currents (trout or grayling region), and in daylight can be found under stones, often with the bullhead, which it resembles in biology. It is probably nocturnal in its habits.

Its biology is still little known, and it has been found only in the upper reaches of the Rumanian rivers Arges, Vilsan and Riul, all of which are part of the Danube system.

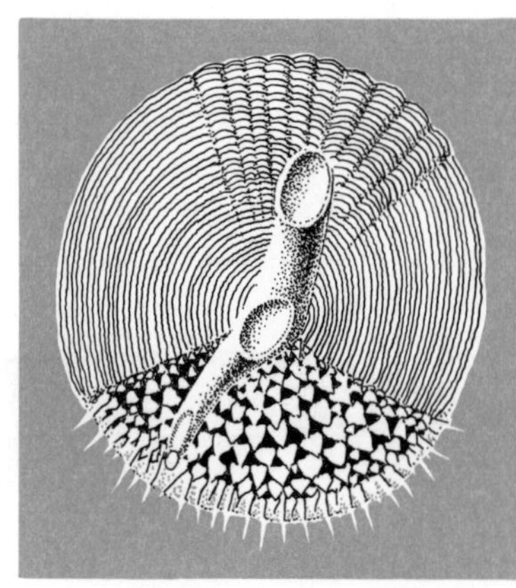

Scale for the lateral line—0.6 mm. The exposed part is at the bottom.

16 cm

107. RHÔNE STREBER

Aspro asper

principal food of schraetzer, zingel, streber and Rhône streber:

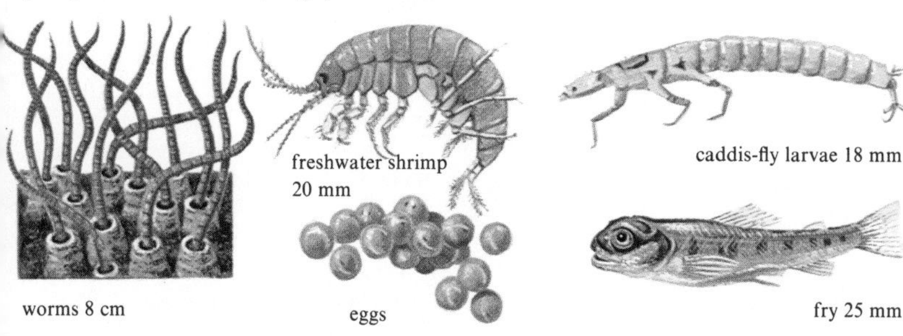

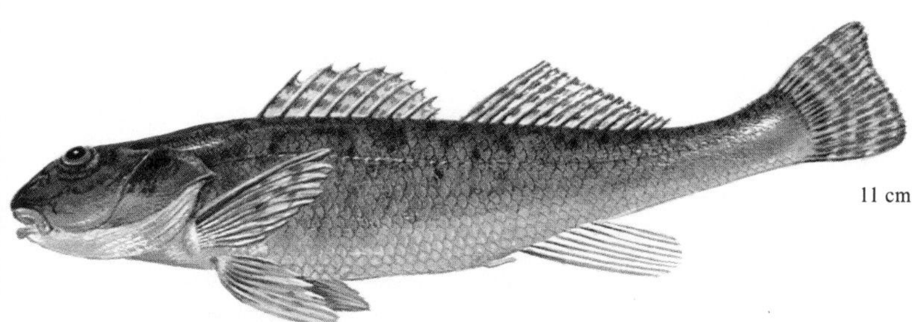

11 cm

108. RUMANIAN BULL-HEAD PERCH

Romanichthys valsanicola

fish seen from above

SUN PERCHES

The family Centrarchidae is essentially North American, but a few species have been introduced to Europe. Some have now become established and have spread.

Most species have a single dorsal fin divided by a notch in its outline. The front rays are spiny, while the second part has soft rays. The first three rays of the anal fin are strong spines.

109. Large-mouth black bass

Micropterus salmoides (Lacépède)

Distinctive features: The dorsal fin is very deeply divided into two sections, the first of which has low spines. Distinguished from the related small-mouth black bass (*M. dolomieu*—see figure), which has also been introduced, by the large mouth with the upper jaw reaching beyond the rear edge of the eye. 65–70 scales along the lateral line. Young fish have a dark pattern along the sides.

Size: 40–60 cm, *c.* 2 kg at 4–5 years. May reach 70 cm and over 10 kg.

Distribution: Introduced from North America into many European countries, including England, around the end of the 19th century.

Prefers stagnant or slow-flowing water. The young stay in shallow water among vegetation, older fish are found in deeper water. Feeds on most smaller fish in its habitat, frogs, tadpoles, the larvae of insects, crustaceans and fish eggs.

Spawns from March-July in water 1–2 m deep and at *c.* 20°C. The female prepares a shallow pit lined with plants, in which *c.* 1,000–4,000 eggs are deposited. They are guarded by the female who also guards the fry for the first few days. Growth is rather rapid in the first year, reaching 7–15 cm 10–50 g. Maturity is reached in 2–3 years when the fish measure 25–30 cm (½—1 kg). Rarely over 2 kg in Europe.

For fishery purposes, it is sometimes introduced into deep ponds with the object of keeping down valueless fish, and is also kept as secondary fish in ponds with carp. Its importance to fisheries is only small, and in northern Europe it does not thrive well. In North America it is a prized angling fish, and for this reason it is sometimes introduced into fishing waters in Europe.

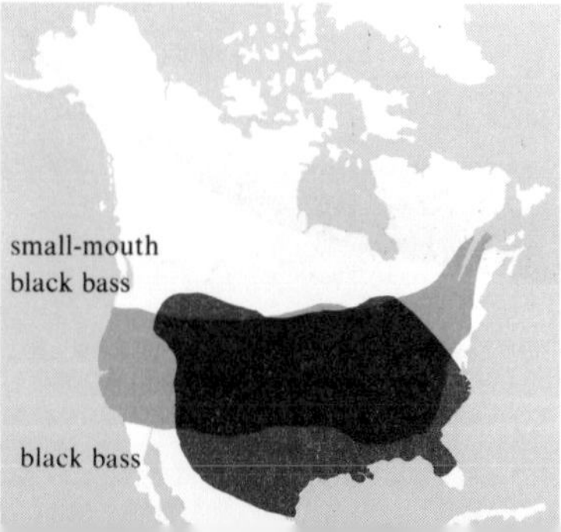

small-mouth black bass

black bass

111. Pumpkinseed

Lepomis gibbosus (L.)

Distinctive features: Deep, compressed body; the two dorsal fins united; a red, black-edged spot on the rear corner of the gill-cover.

Size: 8–15 cm, rarely 30 cm.

Introduced into Europe from America about the turn of the century. It now occurs in many places in central and southern Europe, and has occasionally been reported in England. It lives in shallow water in overgrown lakes and slow-flowing rivers, and feeds on water insects, small crustaceans and young fish. It spawns from May-June, the eggs being deposited in a hollow and guarded by the male until the young disperse.

Another introduced sunfish, *L. cyanellus,* is found around Frankfurt, West Germany.

26 cm

(♦) LARGE-MOUTH BLACK BASS

Micropterus salmoides

principal food:

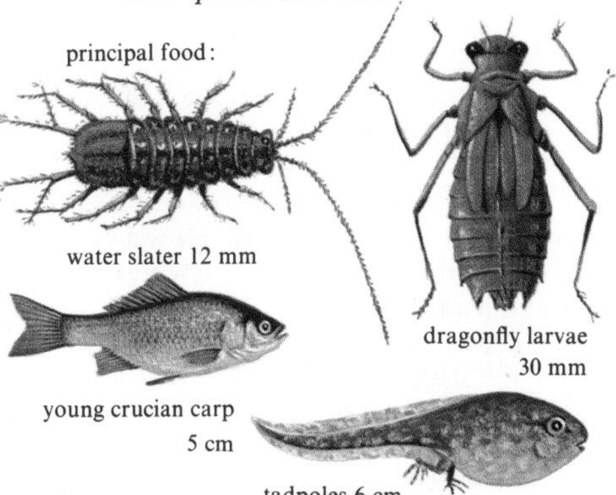

water slater 12 mm

dragonfly larvae 30 mm

young crucian carp 5 cm

tadpoles 6 cm

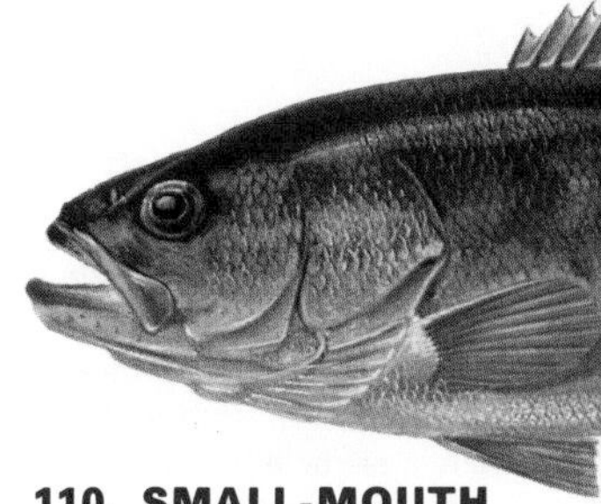

110. SMALL-MOUTH BLACK BASS

Micropterus dolomieu

9 cm

(♦) 111. PUMPKINSEED

Lepomis gibbosus

principal food:

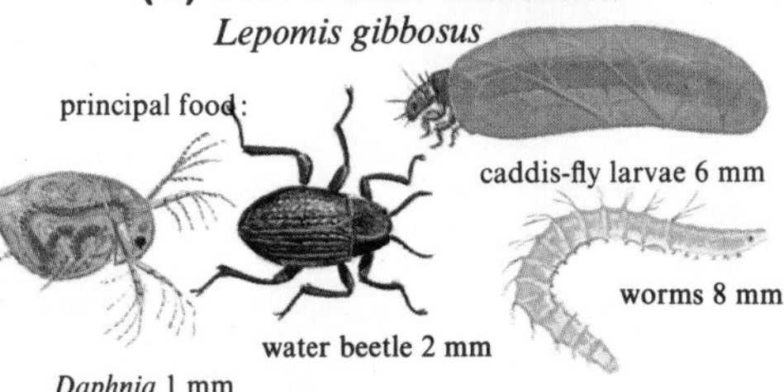

caddis-fly larvae 6 mm

worms 8 mm

water beetle 2 mm

Daphnia 1 mm

SAND SMELTS

The sand smelts (or silversides) are related to the grey mullets. They have 2 short, well-separated dorsal fins, and a distinct silvery band along each side. They are small shoaling fishes occurring in inshore waters, especially in estuaries, and in the south of Europe penetrating into rivers and lakes. Three species are found on the Mediterranean coast: *Atherina presbyter* Cuv., which also occurs on the Atlantic coast: *A. hepsetus* L. and *A. boyeri* Risso.

112. Little sand smelt

Atherina boyeri Risso

Distinctive features: First dorsal fin origin is just behind the level of the tip of the pectoral fin and above the pelvic fin base. The silvery stripe extends over the adjacent halves of the 4th and 5th rows of scales. Subspecies occur in the Black Sea and the Caspian Sea.
Size: Usually 12 cm, rarely to 15 cm.
Distribution: It is found in several Italian lakes and in Lake Albufera (Spain). Also in many Mediterranean rivers. Not found in freshwater in the United Kingdom.

Feeds on planktonic animals. Spawns in April-August, and the eggs, numbering *c.* 600, are shed in groups at intervals of several days. They are nearly 2 mm in diameter and have numbers of filaments by which they are fixed to plants.

sand smelts

GREY MULLETS

The mullets have 2 separate, short dorsal fins, the first with 4 spiny rays. The mouth is small with weak teeth on the lips. The scales are large and the lateral line is absent. There are 6–9 horizontal, dark bands along the sides of the body. The gills have 60–140 gill-rakers. Several species reach a length of 50 cm, a few even 70 cm.

About 100 species are found in tropical and temperate seas. They are active, pelagic shoaling fish which during summer are often found in brackish water, lagoons and estuaries with a soft bottom and dense vegetation. They are often found in the lower reaches of rivers.

Mullets feed on planktonic animals and on filamentous algae which they crush in a special, muscular gizzard-like part of the stomach. Their intestines are remarkably long, a regular feature among plant-eaters.

They mature at 5–8 years and spawn mainly during spring in inshore waters. The eggs are pelagic and number 100,000–7,000,000. The breeding biology of many species is very little known.

Caught mainly during the warmer months of the year when they are close inshore in fixed traps and seines. Total annual catch in southern Europe 15–20,000 tons; not much exploited in Britain, but some are caught by anglers.

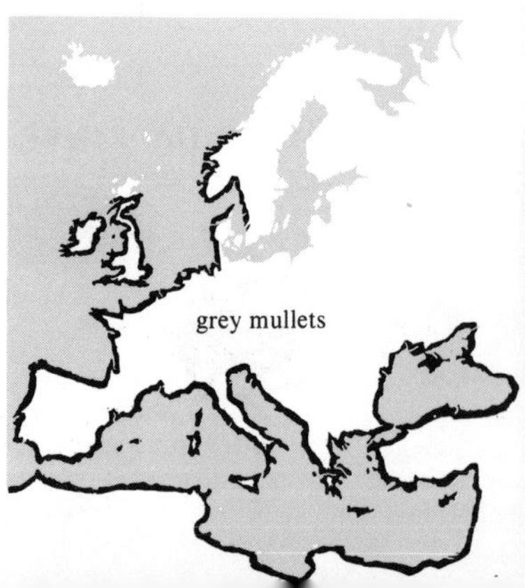

112. LITTLE SAND SMELT
Atherina boyeri

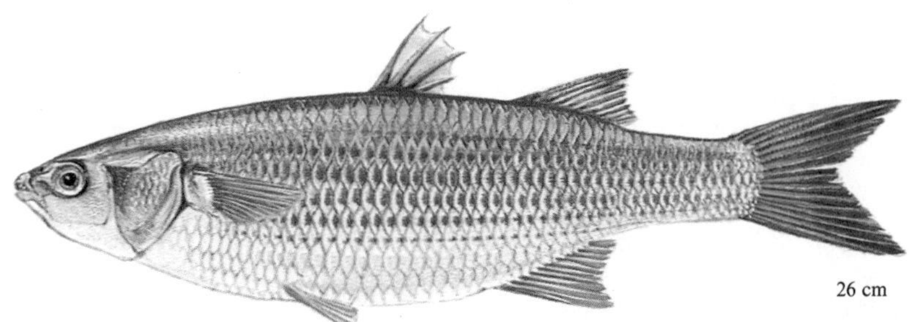

♦ 113. THICK-LIPPED MULLET
Chelon labrosus

thick swollen upper lip with 2 rows of small skin warts

narrow throat groove

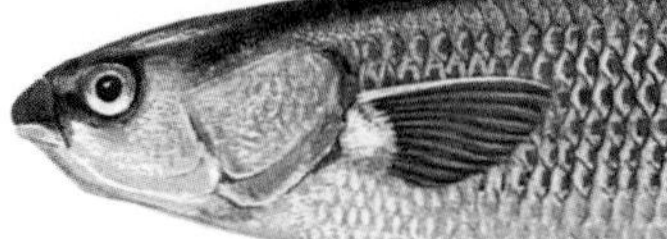

114. *Oedalechilus labeo*

upper lip smooth and as thick as the diameter of the eye

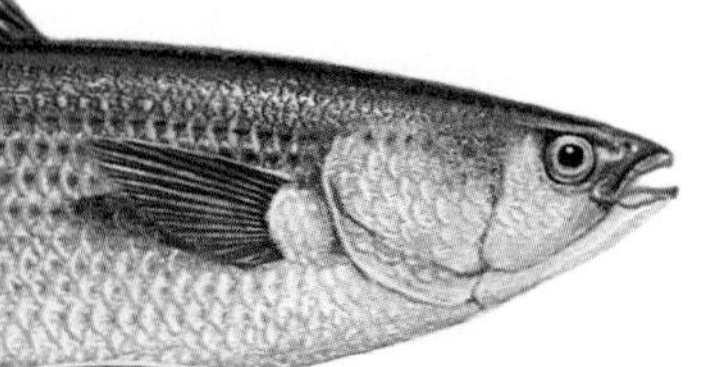

oval throat groove

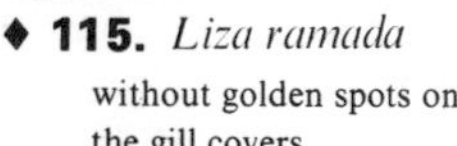

♦ 115. *Liza ramada*

without golden spots on the gill covers

117. *Mugil cephalus*

well-developed folds of fat around the eyes

♦ 116. *Liza aurata*

with a golden spot on each gill cover and one behind each eye

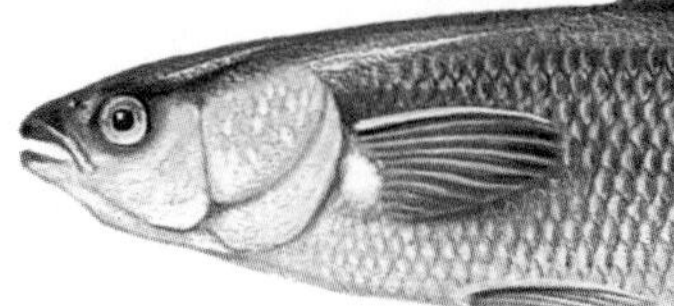

118. *Liza saliens*

several golden spots on the gill covers

GOBIES

Gobies are very abundant, small bottom-living fish in shallow inshore waters, in brackish and in freshwater. Very many species are known, distributed through all tropical and temperate regions. Some species live permanently in freshwater in southern Europe, others are occasionally found in rivers.

All gobies have one feature in common: their pelvic fins are joined to form a single fin capable of weak suction. They have 2 dorsal fins, the first being short with weak, spiny rays. The lateral line is missing or incomplete, and there is a pattern of sensory papillae on the head.

The only goby regularly found in brackish water in the British Isles is the common goby *Pomatoschistus microps* (Krøyer), which is not illustrated. It reaches a maximum total length of 7 cm.

119. Canestrini's goby

Pomatoschistus canestrinii (Ninni)

Distinctive features: The bases of the pectoral fins and the tail-fin are heavily pigmented; irregular dark dots on back and sides. Males have 6 indistinct dark bars on the sides of the body.
Size: 5–6 cm long.
Distribution: Populations are known in the river Jadro, near Split, Yugoslavia and around Venice.

120. Panizza's goby

Knipowitschia panizzai (Verga)

Distinctive features: Pectoral fins with a weak basal spot; dark spots or indistinct cross-bars along the sides of the body. Males have a dark blue, double spot on the hind end of the first dorsal fin.
Size: Maximum length 5·5 cm.
Distribution: Northern Italy in Lake Maggiore, Lake Garda, the rivers around Venice. A relative, *K. nigricans*, is described from the Rivers Tiber and Arno.

121. Kessler's goby

Neogobius kessleri (Gunther)

Distinctive features: Head large, heavy and flattened, its length about one third of the body length; lower jaw strongly projecting; the pelvic fins pointed.
Size: maximum 22 cm.

Migrates into Black Sea rivers. This is one of the commercially utilised gobies of the Black Sea, where it is caught in seines.

122. Mottled Black Sea goby

Proterorhinus marmoratus (Pallas)

Distinctive features: Head profile steep; 2 thread-like barbels on the snout.
Size: maximum 11 cm.
Distribution: Found in the Danube, upstream to eastern Austria.

123. Freshwater blenny

Blennius fluviatilis Asso

Distinctive features: Head with steep profile; dorsal and anal fins long, the dorsal not divided; body scaleless. Males, in particular, have a low longitudinal keel along the crown of the head. A small filament over each eye; the teeth are a a close-set row of low 'incisors' with long, curved 'canines' at the corners of both jaws; the sides of the body have large, indistinct oval spots.
Size: 8–15 cm long.

This is the only blenny, from a very numerous family (Blenniidae) of mainly sea fish, to be found in freshwater in Europe. It is found along the Mediterranean coastline, and occurs in some streams and lakes, notably Lakes Garda and Bouget in Italy. It prefers clear water and a stony bottom, and can be seen raised up on its finger-like pelvic fins. The eggs are deposited under stones and guarded by the male. The young fish form small shoals in shallow water.

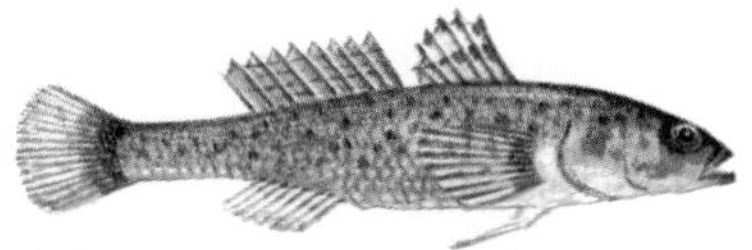

male 5 cm

119. CANESTRINI'S GOBY

Pomatoschistus canestrinii

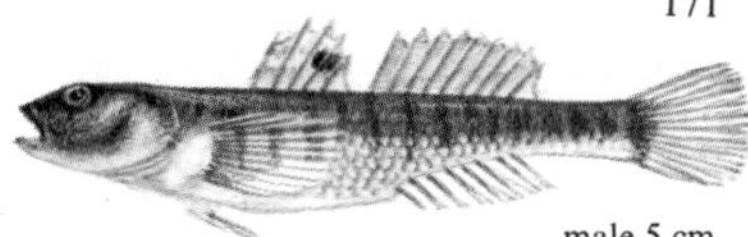

male 5 cm

120. PANIZZA'S GOBY

Knipowitschia panizzai

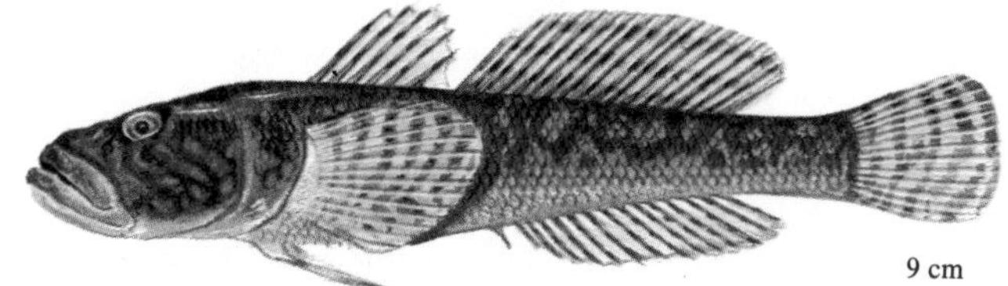

9 cm

121. KESSLER'S GOBY

Neogobius kessleri

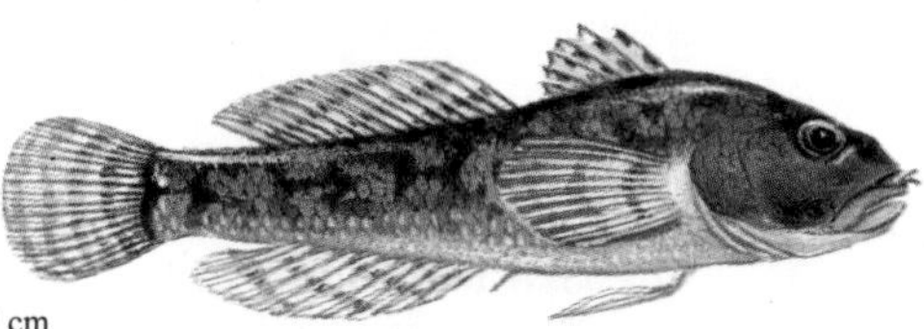

7 cm

122. MOTTLED BLACK SEA GOBY

Proterorhinus marmoratus

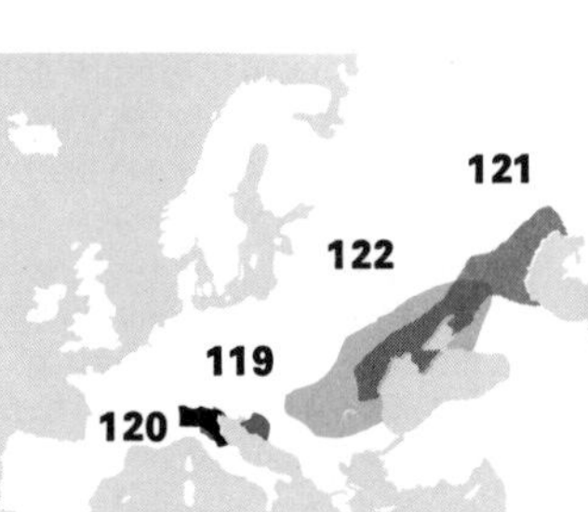

female 11 cm

123. FRESHWATER BLENNY

Blennius fluviatilis

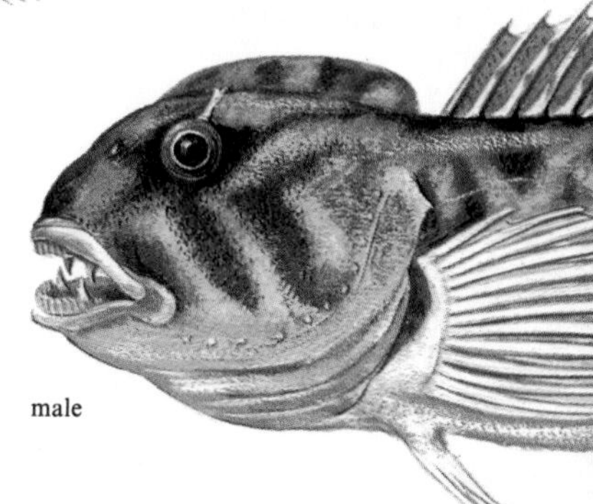

male

124. Miller's thumb or bullhead

Cottus gobio L.

Distinctive features: A bottom-living fish with large, wide, flat head; lateral line extends to the base of the tail-fin; pelvic fins light and unmarked with the inner ray more than half the length of the longest rays.
Size: 10–18 cm.

Lives on a stony bottom in strong to moderate currents and cool, clear, oxygen-rich water of streams (trout region) or around the edges of clear lakes. In the Baltic it occurs in brackish water. It is a crepuscular and nocturnal fish spending the day hidden beneath stones and plants. It is sometimes active on dull days. The bullhead is rather sedentary and moves only short distances at a time. It has no swim-bladder. Its food consists of the larvae of mayflies, blackflies and caddis-flies, also the eggs and fry of other fish.

Spawning occurs in Central Europe from February-March, and in northern Europe from March-May. The male displays to the female, which then deposits a clump of *c.* 100 sticky eggs in a hollow or beneath a large stone. The large eggs, 2–2·5 mm in diameter, are guarded by the male until hatching, at 3–4 weeks. The 6–7 mm long larvae have a large yolk-sac on which they subsist for 10–12 days, while living passively between stones. Later they feed on small animals. The bullhead matures in its second year and probably lives for 3–5 years.

The bullhead is in places eaten by brown trout, but it is not entirely an asset to trout waters for it may eat trout eggs and fry.

125. Siberian bullhead

Cottus poecilopus Heckel

Distinctive features: Closely similar to the common bullhead. The lateral line ends below the rear of the 2nd dorsal fin; pelvic fins marked with dark, transverse bands, and their innermost ray is less than half the length of the longest rays, which may reach as far as the vent.
Size: 8–12·5 cm.

The biology of the Siberian bullhead is similar to that of the common bullhead. It lives on a stony or sandy bottom in clear, running water, but in Europe is found in lowland rivers. It also lays its eggs in a guarded hollow.

It is not sufficiently common to have much standing as a competitor or predator to more valuable fish.

126. Four-horned bullhead

Oncocottus quadricornis (L.)

Distinctive features: On the top of the head are 2 pairs of grey-yellow, spongy bone clumps, often rather reduced in the freshwater populations, but well developed in the marine and coastal populations.
Size: Largest in Arctic coastal waters, and in the inner Baltic (*c.* 30 cm). The freshwater populations rarely grow longer than 10 cm.

This is an Arctic brackish-water and coastal species, which is found in freshwater in Europe as a glacial relict. During the last glacial period it was distributed farther south, but when the ice receded about 6,000 years ago some populations were cut off in deep lakes where they succeeded in adapting themselves to life in freshwater. As these populations are isolated, local races have developed.

Like other bullheads it is a bottom-living fish feeding mainly on crustaceans, some of which are themselves relicts from the glacial period.

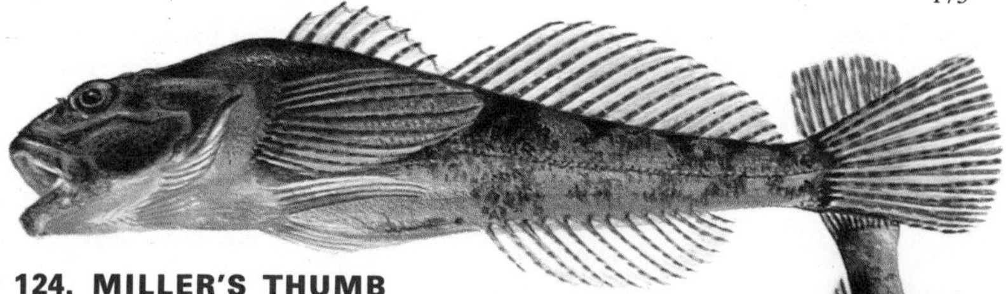

♦ 124. MILLER'S THUMB
Cottus gobio

11 cm

9 cm

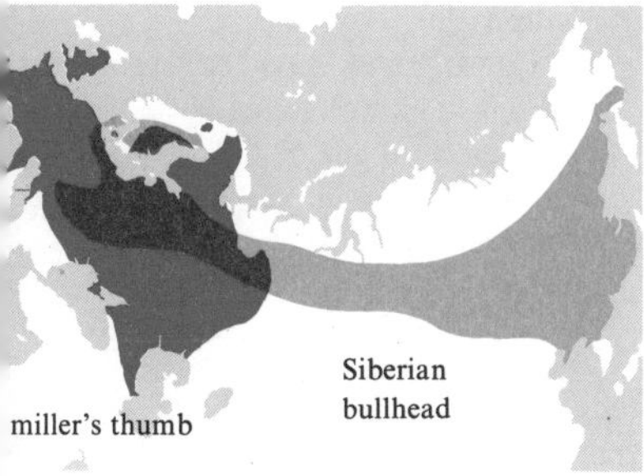

Siberian bullhead

miller's thumb

principal food:

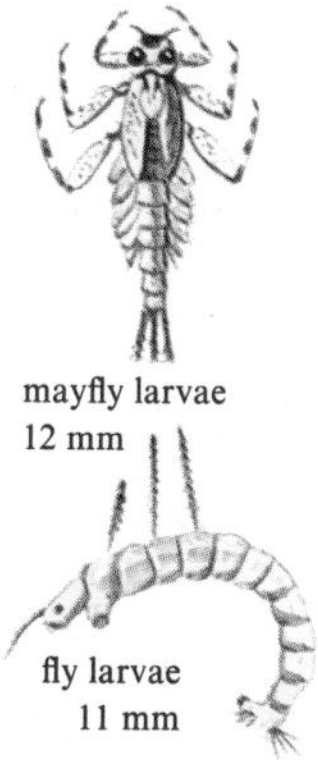

mayfly larvae 12 mm

fly larvae 11 mm

125. SIBERIAN BULLHEAD
Cottus poecilopus

male 20 cm

126. FOUR-HORNED BULLHEAD
Oncocottus quadricornis

head, from above

127. Three-spined stickleback

Gasterosteus aculeatus L.

Distinctive features: 3 isolated heavy spines on the back. The body is scaleless but the sides have bony plates. Three forms have been described according to the development of these plates: (1) the form *trachurus* with plates along the whole length; (2) the form *semiarmatus* with plates only on the front part of body and caudal peduncle; (3) the form *leiurus* with plates only on the front part of the body. Recently it has been shown that *semiarmatus* is a hybrid between the other two forms.
Size: 5–8 cm, but in the sea a maximum of 11 cm, at 3 years.

To the north of its range the stickleback is to some extent migratory. Those living in the lower reaches of rivers and estuaries (mainly of the forms *trachurus* and *semiarmatus*) spend the winter in the sea and return to freshwater in spring to spawn. The male, which is normally silvery, has a brilliant breeding coloration. It builds a nest in shallow water from bits of plants glued together by a secretion from the kidneys, and placed in a depression in the sand. The nest and the territory around it is defended against other males, and in some cases other species fish. Passing females are, however, enticed or drawn into the nest to deposit some of their 100–400 eggs, which are then fertilised by the male. Several females may lay eggs in the same nest, which may contain 300–1,000 eggs. The male fans freshwater over the eggs, which hatch in 4–27 days, depending on the temperature. The young stay in or close to the nest for about a week, guarded by the male. They then disperse in the vegetation, feeding on small animals. Later in the summer they migrate to the sea, where they form large shoals along the beaches. In the south of the British Isles and in southern Europe most sticklebacks do not migrate to the sea, but live in freshwater in ponds, lakes, ditches and rivers; these generally represent the weakly-armoured form *leiurus*. Their biology is the same as that already described.

The stickleback's food consists of most of the small animals found in its habitat. It matures at an age of 1–2 years, and is eaten by cod, salmon, eels, pike and many bird and mammal fish-eaters.

It has at times been used for the production of oil and fish-meal, especially in the White Sea and the German haffs, but is of no consequence today.

128. Nine-spined stickleback

Pungitius pungitius (L.)

Distinctive features: 7–12 free spiny rays on the back; caudal peduncle long and narrow.
Size: 5–7 cm.

A common fish in overgrown ponds, ditches, and shallow brackish waters. In general, its biology is like that of the three-spined stickleback, but it builds its nest in vegetation clear of the bottom, and appears to favour more densely weeded regions than its relative. Matures at one year old. Feeds mainly on planktonic animals.

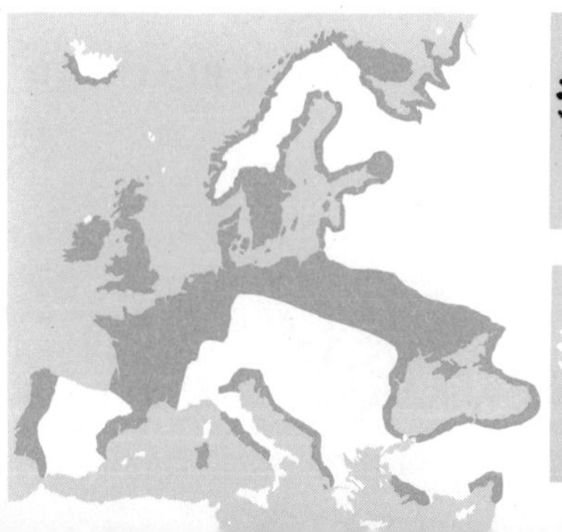

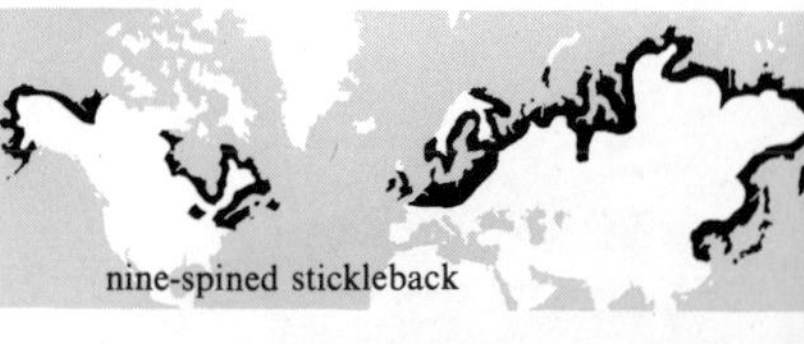

nine-spined stickleback

Ukranian stickleback

♦ 127. THREE-SPINED STICKLEBACK

Gasterosteus aculeatus

male in spawning colours

courtship dance

nest

principal food:

fry

eggs

Cyclops
2 mm

♦ 128. NINE-SPINED STICKLEBACK

Pungitius pungitius

129. UKRANIAN STICKLEBACK

Pungitius platygaster

A close relative, *P. platygaster* (see page 175), occurs in the Black Sea region, and is distinguished by its slightly curved spines, and its less elongate shape.

130. Flounder

Platichthys flesus (L.)

Distinctive features: Along the lateral line and the bases of the dorsal and anal fins are rows of fine, bony prickles. It is the only flatfish in Europe which is also found in freshwater.

Size: Rarely over 30 cm (½–1 kg) at 5 years. Maximum 50 cm (3 kg) at 15–20 years.

The flounder is found on the bottom, in inshore waters from the tidal zone down to 50 m. In summer it enters river mouths, lagoons and brackish fjords, and may migrate far upstream to be found many kilometres from the sea. The passage upstream often takes the fish through regions with strong currents. In winter they move further out to sea, and generally leave the estuaries, but it is said that they do over-winter in a few lakes.

Their food in the sea consists of worms, the smaller mussels, amphipod crustaceans and gobies. In brackish and freshwater they eat the larvae of midges (Chironomidae), amphipods and molluscs.

The flounder does not spawn in freshwater but migrates in February-May to depths of 20–40 m in the sea. In the central Baltic it spawns at a depth of 40–100 m, where the water is very salt. In water of a salinity below 10‰, as in the north-eastern Baltic, the eggs sink to the bottom and perish. At higher salinities they rise slowly to the surface and disperse. The number of eggs is from 400,000 to 2 million; they are 1 mm in diameter and hatch after 5–7 days at 10°C. The larvae are transparent and pelagic, measuring 3 mm in length and with a small yolk-sac which is consumed in about 2 days. Thereafter they feed on plankton, until in June-July they float into shallow water to complete the metamorphosis characteristic of the flat-fishes. The left eye moves over the top of the head until both eyes are on the right side, and the young fish begins to swim with its left side downwards. At 10 mm they abandon their free-swimming pelagic life and move into shallow coastal water. The right side, which is now spoken of as the eyed-side, is uppermost and heavily pigmented while the blind side normally remains uncoloured.

'Reversed' flounders (i.e. those with both eyes on the left of the head instead of the right) are not uncommon. In places, up to one-third of the population is reversed. Flounders with either partly or wholly coloured undersides are also common.

Growth depends to a large extent on the availability of food, and the length at one year may vary between 4 and 12 cm. Regardless of size males mature at 3 years, females at 4 years.

Fished in traps, set-nets and Danish seines. In freshwater the catch is not important. The flesh is fairly tasty especially when from freshwater, and it is sold fresh or frozen, although it is sometimes smoked. Total annual European catch is *c.* 10,000 tons.

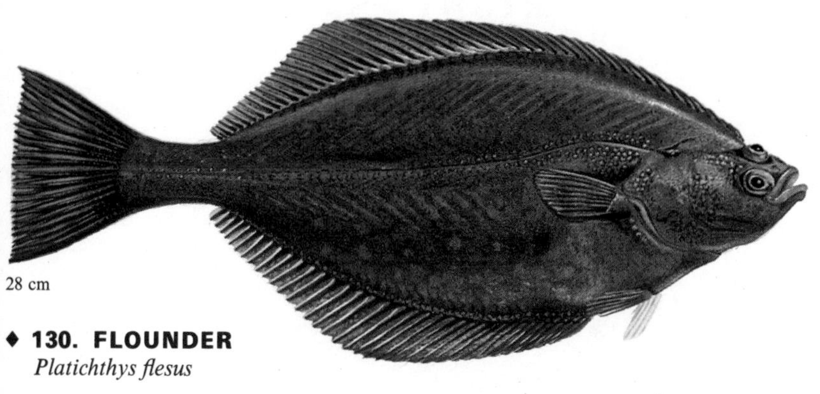
28 cm

♦ 130. FLOUNDER
Platichthys flesus

egg near hatching, larvae with yolk-sac, 3 pelagic larvae and young bottom-living form

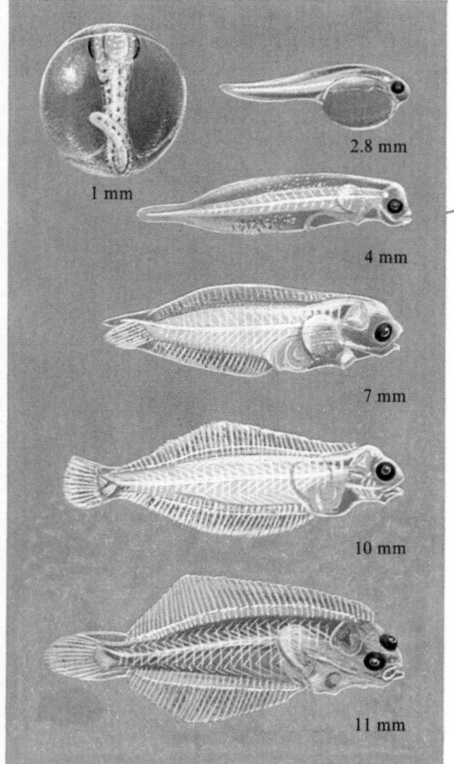

principal food in salt water:

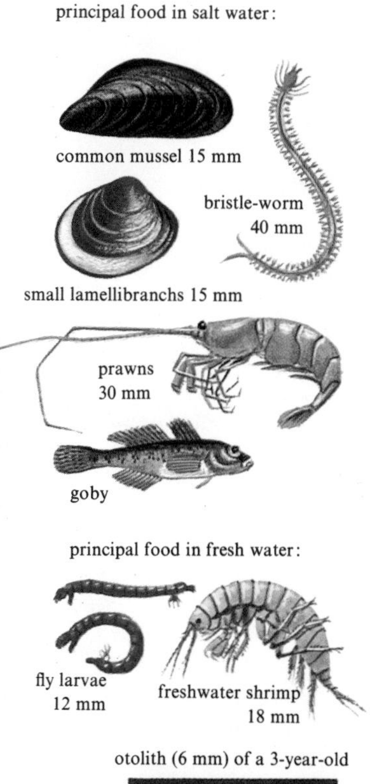

otolith (6 mm) of a 3-year-old

SOME IMPORTANT FRESHWATER INVERTEBRATES

The crayfishes, mitten crabs and pearl mussels are of such importance to European fisheries that it is natural to include them as an appendix to the freshwater fishes. Relatively few crustaceans are found in freshwater, compared with their abundance in the sea, and of the freshwater species most are small or microscopic, while large forms (the decapods) are few in number.

Two of the decapod crustaceans included here are not indigenous to Europe, viz. the American crayfish, which was deliberately introduced, and the mitten crab, which was accidentally carried by ships from China. The pearl mussel is also included as this is the only bivalve mollusc which has a direct economic importance.

131. European crayfish

Astacus astacus (L.)

Distinctive features: Body and claws broad; antennae shorter than body-length. The males are larger than the females, but have a narrower tail and can be recognised by the first two pairs of tail legs, which form tubes. The colour is greeny-brown or bluish, rarely red.

Size: The female attains *c.* 12 cm (80–85 g), the male *c.* 16 cm (150 g); larger individuals are very rare. They may live for 5–15 years but accurate age determination is not possible.

The crayfish lives in shallow water along the banks of lakes, ponds and smaller streams where the water is clean and well oxygenated, and where the bottom is firm, without dense vegetation. It avoids the cold water from springs and mountain streams. In central Europe it is replaced by its near relative the stone crayfish (*A. torrentium*) in mountainous regions. Another crayfish, *Austropotamobius pallipes,* the white-foot crayfish, is also found in Europe, and is native to the British Isles. *A. astacus* has been introduced into Britain.

The crayfish is not common in large rivers, but it can live in acid, lime-poor water, e.g. in peat-pits, provided sufficient oxygen is present. It is very sensitive to pollution and to oxygen deficiency. It digs deep holes in soft stream banks, or lives beneath tree-roots, stones or other hiding-

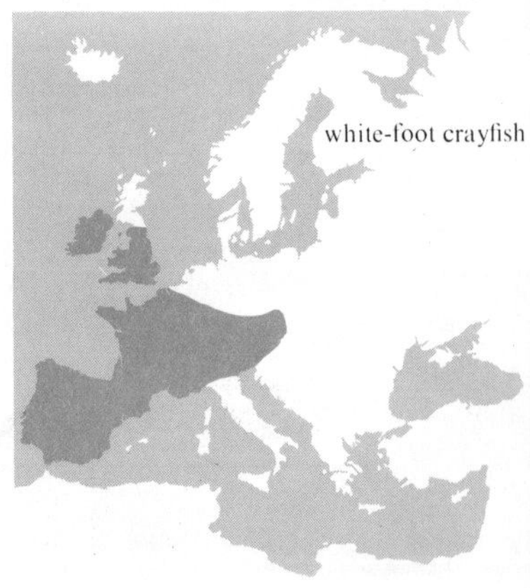

♦ 131. EUROPEAN CRAYFISH

Astacus astacus

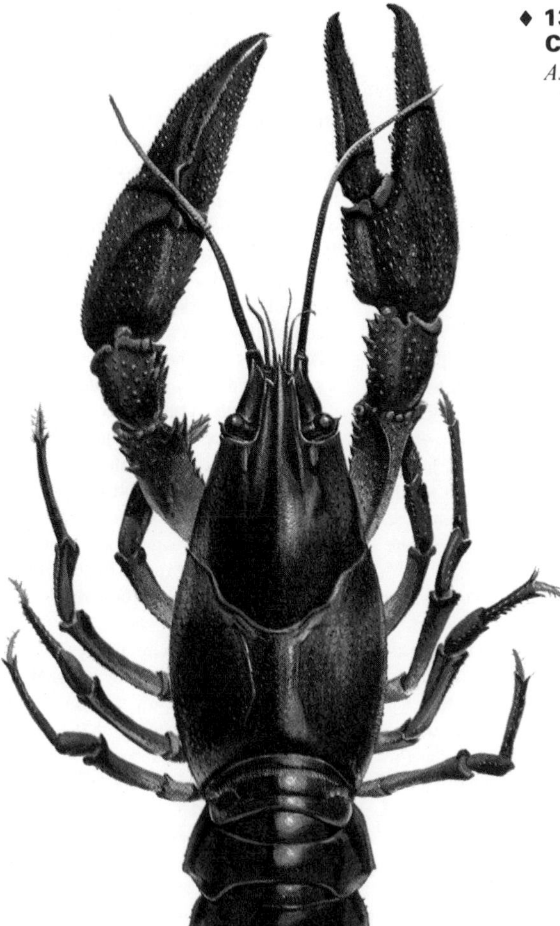

10.5 cm

places, and even in old cans and boots in rivers!

The crayfish is most active at night, hunting for food with extended claws. It is almost omnivorous, eating the larvae of insects, mussels, snails, other smaller crayfish, fish eggs and dead or dying fish. The young, particularly, also eat the roots of water-crowfoot, water-milfoil and stonewort. It does not, however, eat rotten meat, or feed in winter.

Its most dangerous enemies are the eel and burbot which, also being largely nocturnal bottom-feeders, are frequently encountered. Crayfish are also eaten by perch, otter, musk-rat and mink where the latter occur wild. Heron and other water birds also feed on them. Crayfish do not swim but can move backwards suddenly in quick jumps by clapping the tail powerfully against the underside of the body.

Mating occurs in September-November. The female turns belly uppermost and the male deposits its slimy sperm-capsules near the openings of the oviducts at the bases of the third pair of abdominal legs. The eggs are extruded 3–6 weeks later, and are deposited between the abdominal legs in a mucus which dissolves the sperm-capsules so that the liberated, mobile sperm cells fertilise the eggs. The female carries 50–350 eggs, each 2–3 mm in diameter, below the tail (abdomen) for about six months. The appendages on the tail fan fresh water over the eggs, which perish if removed from the mother. Normally 10–20% of the eggs survive to hatch into larvae, which are about 8 mm long. These remain on the mother for the first 10–15 days.

Growth in the crayfish, as in other crustaceans, is only possible by shedding of the hard shell covering the body. A slit appears at the junction of the thoracic shell and the first of the abdominal segments, and through this the 'new' crayfish crawls backwards out of the old shell. The actual moult lasts from 10 minutes to one hour, and following it the crayfish is soft-shelled and defenceless ('soft-backed crayfish'). It takes 8–10 days for the new shell to harden and become strong enough for the crayfish to move out of its hiding-place. During the moult and while the new shell is hardening, the body increases in size by the absorption of water. Growth thus occurs in spurts. During the first year the crayfish may moult 7–8 times to reach a length of 2–6 cm. Adult females moult once a year, adult males twice, and are thus larger. Maturity is attained at 3 years (central Europe), or 4–7 years (northern Europe).

It is difficult to be certain of the original distribution of the crayfish as it was introduced into many places during the Middle Ages. In the latter half of the nineteenth century an infectious fungal disease appeared in France and subsequently spread through Europe, severely reducing the crayfish stock almost everywhere.

Crayfish are caught in cages or drop-nets baited with fresh fish or meat. They are, of course, mainly caught at night, and while traps can be left overnight, drop-nets have to be examined every ten minutes or so. Marl-pits and bog-ponds can often be used to raise crayfish by laying out bundles of twigs or drain-pipes, and introducing berried (with eggs) females at a rate of 2–3 crayfish per 1 m of bank. The stocks are fed on offal and unwanted fish from stock-ponds. Crayfish are transported wrapped in moist plants or moss, and as long as they are carefully released back downwards in order to let the air collected around the gills to escape, they are relatively hardy. All European countries have local closed seasons, or minimum sizes of around 8–10 cm. The crayfish is not, however, farmed in the British Isles or much used as food.

The greeny-brown colour of the shell is due to the mixture of blue and red pigment. Cooking destroys the blue pigment leaving the red intact.

131. Crayfish

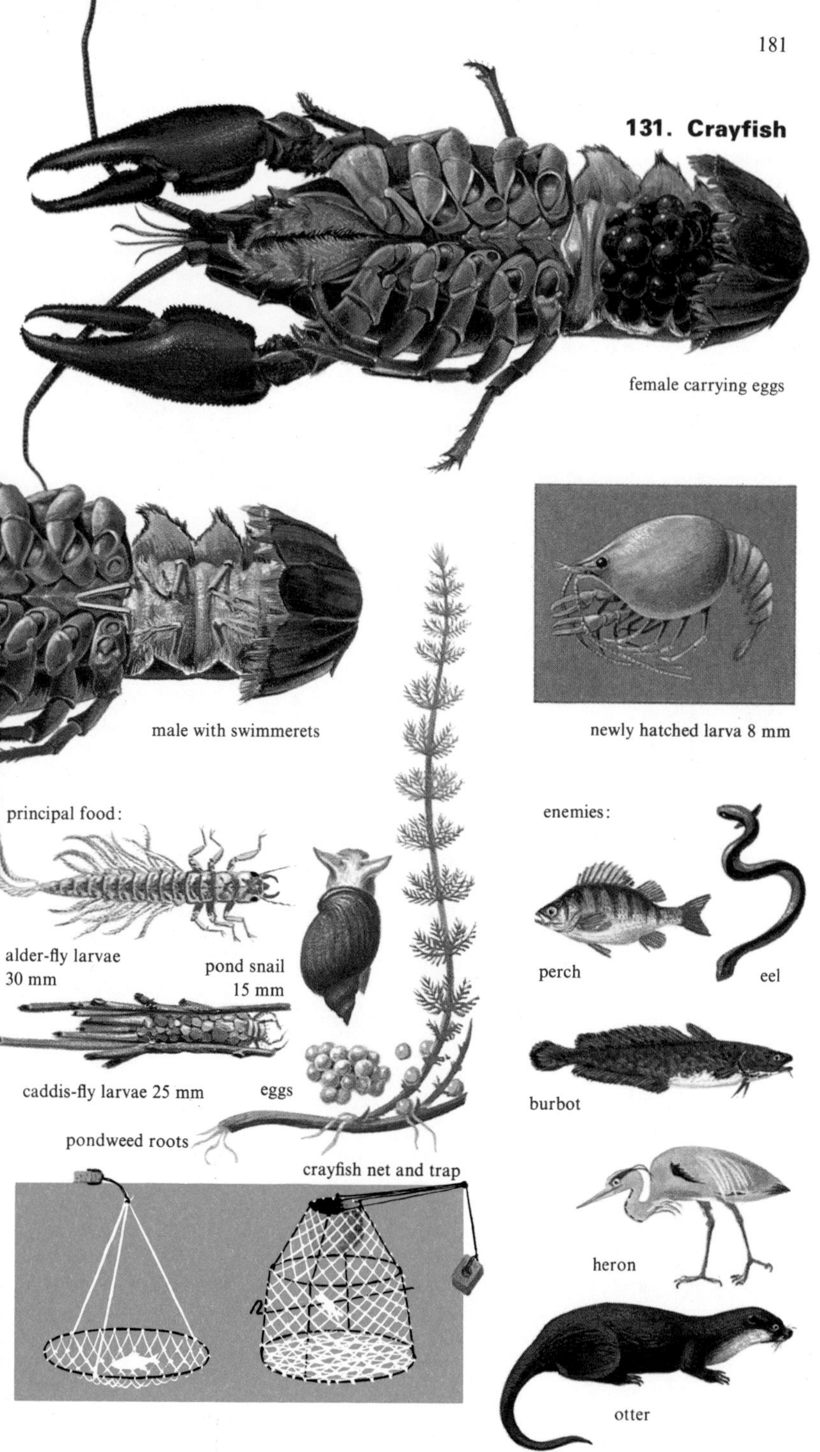

132. Eastern crayfish

Astacus leptodactylus (Eschscholz)

Distinctive features: Body and claws narrow, the antennae are longer than the body; shell softer than in *P. astacus*.
Size: 11–14 cm.

This is an eastern species which has been introduced into several places in Central Europe because it was thought to be unaffected by the fungal infection which decimated the common crayfish.

Its biology is similar to that of the common crayfish, but it is about four times as prolific. With its smaller tail and slender claws it has less meat, and as its flesh is rather soft, it is less popular as food than the common crayfish. It is not, therefore, a particularly good crayfish for the fish-farm, and should not be released into the wild where the European species is found.

When cooked its shell turns light red.

133. American crayfish

Cambarus affinis Say

Distinctive features: The tips of the claws on the walking legs are red; each segment of the abdomen has two elongate dark-red spots; claws are shorter than in the common crayfish.
Size: 7–9 cm, rarely 12 cm.

It was introduced into Germany from North America in 1890 and has since been introduced throughout central Europe and today forms much of the crayfish catch. It lives more in the open than the common crayfish, occurs in muddy bays with rich vegetation, does not burrow and is not especially bound to stony or firm bottoms.

Its food consists of plants, snails and the larvae of insects which are caught directly in the mouth without using the claws. It is less nocturnal and during daytime can be caught in small seines. It appears to be resistant to the crayfish disease, and is more tolerant of pollution than the common crayfish. It winters in deeper water, but feeds throughout all but the most severe winters.

Mating occurs in September at a temperature of over 10°C. The sperm is deposited in a sperm-pocket on the female's abdomen and is held there until fertilisation in April-May, when egg-laying occurs. The 200–400 eggs are carried by the female between the legs of the abdomen, and *c.* 100 young successfully hatch in 5–8 weeks. The young measure 4 mm, and stay attached to their mother until after two moultings they become free-swimming, feeding at first on filamentous algae and the larvae of midges. Development is rapid and after 5 months a length of 5–6 cm is reached. Adults moult three times a year, and the females spawn every year.

From the point of view of the fishery, the American crayfish has both advantages and disadvantages compared with the common crayfish. High fecundity, rapid growth, smaller demands on the environment, and the ease with which it is caught are balanced by its drawbacks of smaller size, poorer quality, and a tendency to oust the more valuable crayfish where both species occur. Many biologists consider the eastern and American crayfishes as valueless in a fishery.

132. EASTERN CRAYFISH
Astacus leptodactylus

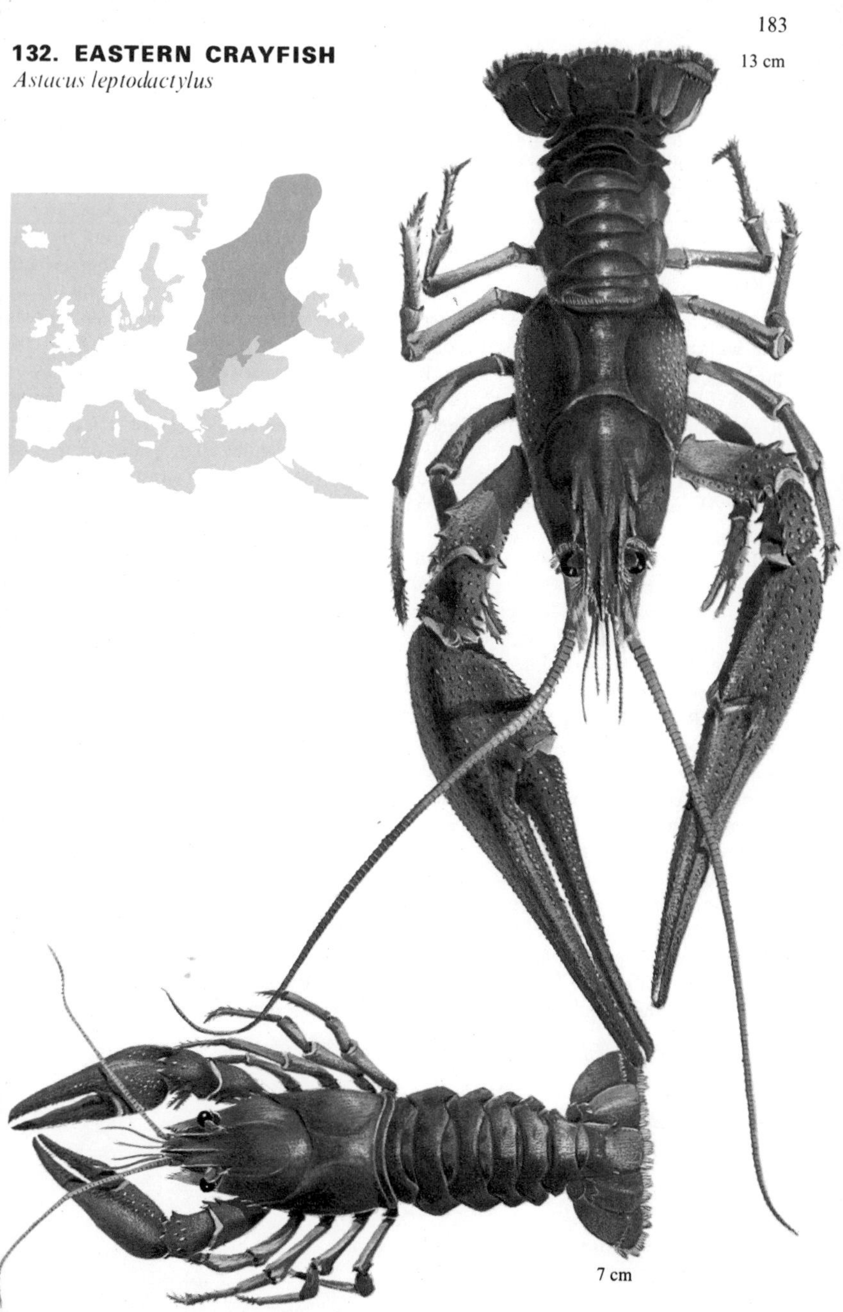

133. AMERICAN CRAYFISH
Cambarus affinis

134. Mitten crab

Eriocheir sinensis M.–Edw.

Distinctive features: The carapace is almost circular, and the claws, especially in males, are more or less hairy (hence 'mitten crab').

Size: The carapace reaches a width of 7–9 cm.

Distribution: This crab originated in China. and was accidentally carried to Europe, probably in the ballast water of ships. It was first found in Europe in 1912, in the River Aller, and has since spread to much of north-west Germany, Holland, Belgium and parts of Scandinavia. It was reported from London in 1932, and has again been found in the 1970s.

The crab occurs in shallow water in rivers, ponds and canals where it burrows in the banks and dams. It is nocturnal and feeds mainly on plants, supplemented with mussels, the larvae of insects, worms, and trapped or dead fish.

In the River Elbe area, the centre of its distribution in Europe, its life-history is as follows. From mid-July, large shoals of mature crabs start migrating towards the mouth of the Elbe, at a speed of 8–12 km in 24 hours. The males arrive first in September-October, and gather along a 20 km-long salt-water zone, where mating takes place on the arrival of the females. The number of eggs is 300,000–900,000, varying with the size of the females, which carry them under their tail from November to May or June, when they move into shallow water in the Wadden Sea. For development to proceed a salinity of at least 15‰ (one half normal seawater) is essential. After the eggs are hatched the females generally die.

The larvae are pelagic, and pass through several development stages until by October-December thay have reached a length of 3 mm at an age of *c.* 9 months. These young winter and live for a year between Cuxhaven and Hamburg. In April the following year (at an age of 2 years, size 20–25 mm) the young migrate by the tens of thousand up the Elbe for 150–200 km. This migration takes place during the night and in deep water. Dams and obstructions are by-passed by crawling over land, while tributaries and canals are colonised. After the winter, the remaining crabs at 3 years, (30–50 mm) continue their migration up the Elbe from April until August, reaching beyond Magdeburg, where they disperse and stay. A few may continue the following year to Dresden and even further. Maturity is attained at 5 years.

The mitten crab has proved to be a troublesome and unwanted animal, which undermines dams, destroys fish-nets and damages the caught fish. It can be caught during migration at dams and other barrages in grate-traps or pit-falls, but control of this pest has proved difficult and costly. It has been used for fodder and for fertilisers, while in China it is considered a delicacy.

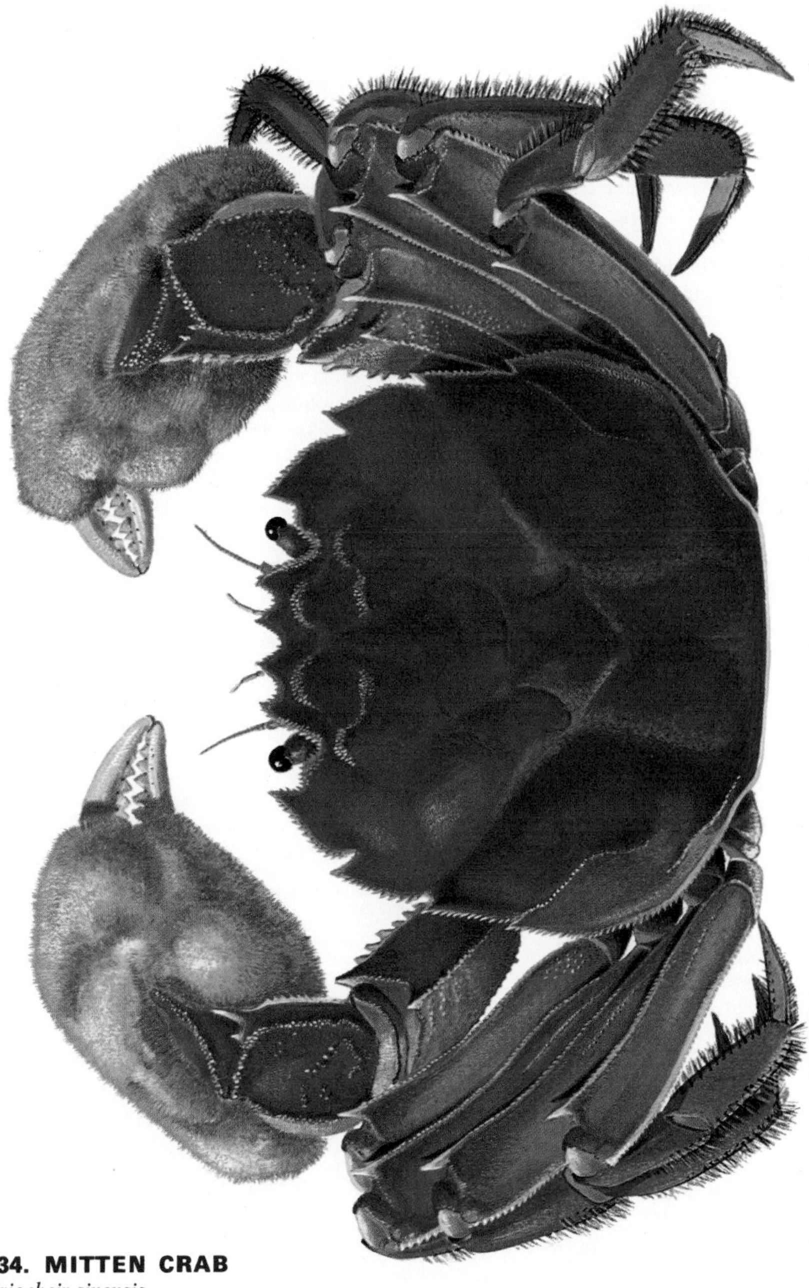

134. MITTEN CRAB
Eriocheir sinensis

135. River pearl mussel

Margaritana margaritifera (L.)

Distinctive features: The shells are thick, dark, almost black, and kidney-shaped, with a well-developed layer of mother-of-pearl on the inner side.

Size: 12–15 cm; lives for up to 60 years.

It occurs only in cool, running water, particularly in mountain streams with a bottom of stones and gravel, and a temperature not above 13–14°C. It is very sensitive to pollution, and the water must be rather acid. This mussel is therefore rather restricted in its distribution. It is not found in limestone regions, but occurs on peaty moors, for example on Lüneburg Heath, Germany and in southern Denmark (Varde and Sneum rivers), where it is regarded as a relict from the last interglacial period. It occurs in some west-coast rivers in the British Isles, but is absent from the central European lowlands.

The mussel anchors itself to the bottom with the rear end turned towards the current. The older mussels are stationary and virtually never move, sometimes occurring so densely that they almost form a pavement in the river. It feeds, like other freshwater mussels, by filtering plankton and other nutritive particles from the water.

Like the freshwater oysters and mussels, the pearl mussel has an interesting method of reproduction and of dispersing the young. The eggs are not shed in the water but are held in the four large gill-folds, where they are fertilised by the males' sperms, which are sucked in while respiring. The eggs, numbering between a half and one million, develop in the shell to form remarkable small larvae, called *glochidia,* which have a pair of triangular shells and a long thread. From July-August, after *c.* 4 weeks, these larvae are expelled through the respiratory opening of the mussel. They lie still on the bottom with gaping shells, waiting for a fish (e.g. a minnow or a trout) to pass close to them. The passage of a fish causes the larvae to open and snap their shells shut quickly and repeatedly, and some are fortunate enough to anchor themselves to the gills or fins of the fish. Most of them never succeed in this and perish within a few days. Once on the fish they irritate the skin tissues causing these to swell and envelop the glochidia, which are then enclosed in blisters where they feed parasitically by secreting digestive enzymes.

In between 2 and 10 weeks, depending on the temperature, the glochidium develops into a little mussel, the blister bursts, and the mussel drops to the bottom. At first it moves briskly about, but with increasing age it becomes more sedentary. The skin of the fish heals completely. Growth is slow, hardly over 2–5 mm annually, and the mussels become mature in *c.* 20 years.

The pearl mussel has from mediaeval times been famous for producing pearls. It has, therefore, always been a subject of proprietary interest, and in Saxony, for example, its fishery belonged to the State. In the mountainous regions of central Europe the mussels are collected in a basket, each is cautiously opened a little with special tongs, the edge of the mantle is searched for pearls and the mussel is

River fishing for freshwater pearl mussels. At top right are the crowns and rings in which the pearls were used. (Olaus Magnus 1555)

♦ 135. RIVER PEARL MUSSEL
Margaritana margaritifera

13 cm

then returned to the water. This inspection of the mussel streams is carried out at 6–10 year intervals.

Pearl formation itself is rather an enigma, but is thought to be the result of a small group of cells from the mother-of-pearl layer accidentally entering the connective tissue of the mantle below which they form a loose clump of mother-of-pearl, i.e. a pearl. It is possible that the original mother-of-pearl cells are loosened by the attack of a parasite. The number of pearls is small, as only one per cent of mussels contain a pearl, and only four in ten thousand hold a valuable one.

Large pearl fisheries exist in the northern U.S.S.R, but the harvest is nowhere rich. Elsewhere the crop is small and local and, due to the increasing pollution of streams and in places to over-exploitation, the stock of pearl mussels has become much reduced.

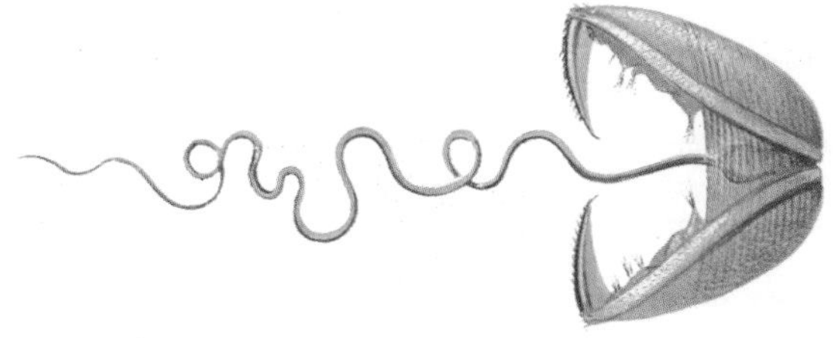

glochidium larva 0.3 mm

PREDATORS AND PARASITES

Fish have many natural enemies, from all classes of the animal kingdom, be they otters or insects. From the viewpoint of the owner of the heavily stocked fish-farm or the angling water, the animals described below are predators on fish. However, they all have to feed to live, and while we can remove some and discourage others we must be prepared to tolerate the remainder.

The **Water-shrew** can be distinguished by its very dark back and sides with a sharp transition to the white belly. All the feet are fringed with light-coloured swimming bristles. 10–12 cm long. It feeds on water insects, and possibly the eggs and young of fish. It is an excellent swimmer and has a silvery appearance under the water produced by the air trapped in its fur. It often lives in deserted burrows near the water. Two broods a year.

The **Otter** belongs to the marten family. Its maximum length is 1·5 m, 12 kg. It is an aquatic carnivore with nocturnal habits, and eats crayfish, fish, frogs and water-voles. It is only rarely seen, but may be betrayed by its broad foot-prints, which show the webbing on its feet, and by the remains of its meals. It has burrows in the river-banks with the entrance below water-level and also in natural hollows amongst stones. It lives in pairs or singly. The mating period is from February-March, and the 2–4 cubs are blind at birth and full-grown in two years.

The **Kingfisher** dives after fish and prefers clear streams. It eats many different sorts, including sticklebacks, minnows and young of other species. Its nest is built in a tunnel, which may be a metre long, in a bank.

The **Heron** lives in colonies in high trees. It is a migratory bird in northern Europe, but less so to the west and south. It takes fish, frogs and water insects when wading in quite shallow water, and can do great harm in pond-farms.

Other birds which to some extent feed on fish are terns, grebes, mergansers and the osprey.

Dragonfly larvae are found among weeds and on the bottom. The lower jaw is pincer-like and double-jointed and is pressed against the prey to catch it. These larvae eat newly hatched fish fry.

Some **Water beetles** and their larvae are carnivorous, eating tadpoles, water-insects, snails and the young of fish. They can often be seen hanging at the surface of vegetation-rich ponds. The larvae catches its prey with its curved, pointed mandibles. The bite is poisonous, and the flesh of the prey is dissolved by digestive fluids before it is sucked through the hollow mandibles into the intestine.

The **Fish Leech** sucks the blood of fishes. It has a sucking disk at each end and a pointed, knife-shaped head. Weak fish are often attacked and from 10–100 leeches may be attached to one fish. As about 160 cu mm blood can be sucked by a large leech in two days, an attacked fish loses much blood, weight and vigour. In fish-farms the leeches are narcotised with a 2·5% solution of common salt before they are removed.

The Water-boatman belongs to the water-bug group. It swims with its back downwards, and carries a reserve of air in a layer of hairs on its belly. A carnivore with piercing and sucking mouth-parts, like many other bugs it is harmful to fish fry.

water shrew 7 cm

otter 80 cm

kingfisher 16 cm

heron 90 cm

dragonfly larvae 6 cm

water beetle larva 5 cm

fish leeches 5 cm

water boatman 1.5 cm

THE HISTORY OF FRESHWATER FISHING

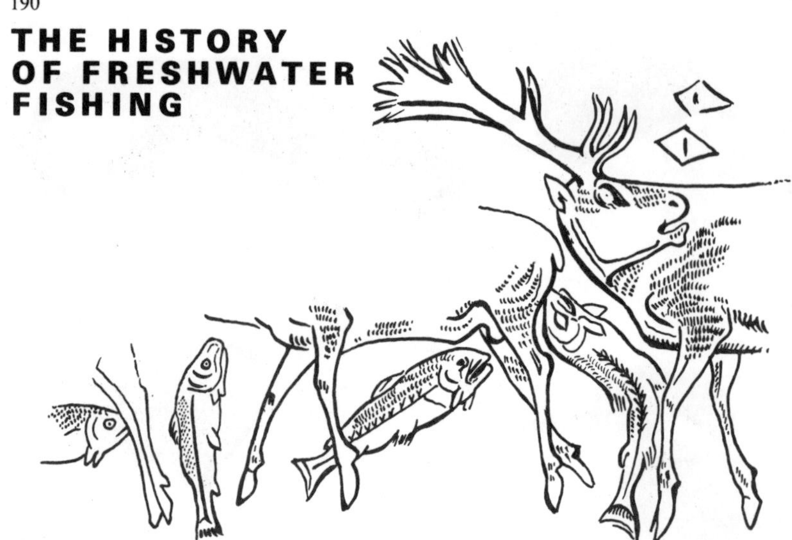

Stone Age drawing of reindeer antlers, found in Department of Hautes-Pyrenées, southern France. It probably represents deer in flight crossing a stream containing trout.

Fishing is no doubt as old as any other form of hunting. As early as the late European Stone Age there is evidence for the presence of fishermen—hooks made of bone, antlers or flint. At this time, when the major part of Europe was covered by forests, early man in inland areas founded settlements along the rivers and lakes, where he could supplement his diet of birds and mammals by fishing. Some years ago a team of Danish archeologists uncovered a summer settlement on a floating peat island where their ancestors had fished for perch, tench and pike 4,500 years ago. They found several hundred rods of willow and hazel arranged in bunches, cut in June for the weaving of fish-traps. This settlement had been inhabited until September and the fishing had been supplemented by the hunting of otters and beavers.

Bow and arrows were also used for fishing, and from the hunters' spear was developed first the barbed spear and then the forked fish-spear.

Early European fishing relied heavily on the pike, which was common, made good eating, and present all year round. An early fishing technique was use of the gorge, forced into a bait-fish and attached to a line which was either held or fastened to a float. The manufacture of lines from lime-bast or nettle-fibre was a first step towards making a net, and pieces of net are known from the pile dwellings in Holstätter Lake in Switzerland, and together with pine-bark floats and net-weights from a Stone Age site in Lake Ladoga, Finland.

As civilisation changed with the advance of agriculture the human population increased, and primitive hunting, fishing and food gathering was gradually abandoned. Commerce and more complicated economies developed. The concept of ownership became more refined with an increasingly complicated legislation. Special laws for inland waters were enforced, due firstly to the many legal problems connected with irrigation and drainage in combination with farming. Fish became a valuable food, and regulations concerning their capture were introduced. A 4,000-year-old Mesopotamian agreement stipulates an annual rent of 15 kg silver for the fishing rights of the river.

In arid but potentially fertile regions artificial irrigation was developed. The construction of canals and large reservoirs soon suggested the possibility of rearing and feeding those fish which were both easy to keep and tasty. Rational pond-farming seems to have originated in the ancient Asiatic civilisations. Keeping carp in ponds was presumably established in Asia Minor and brought to Europe by the Romans, for as early as the time of Cicero (106–43 B.C.) table fish were kept and fed by the Romans.

Stone Age hooks and net

Harpoon and spears made of bone

For many centuries the laws of Rome were a great influence on life in south and central Europe, and in accordance with these laws fish in public rivers and lakes were considered public property which everyone was allowed to catch. Only with the development of feudalism in the early Middle Ages were fishing rights gradually claimed by temporal and church magnates.

The Middle Ages

Freshwater fish were of much greater importance as food in the Middle Ages than now. In the first place, there were considerably fewer human beings in Europe, and at the same time far more fish because the water was cleaner. Secondly, fresh sea fish could not be carried far inland. Salted fish eventually became generally available inland but not until transport was well developed. Freshwater fish were of far greater importance in that they were available throughout the year. Freshwater fisheries, however, were at a primitive stage until the techniques of carp pond-farming spread from southern to central Europe with the establishment of monastries. It was late in coming to north Europe and, reached England in 1514, Denmark in 1560, and St. Petersburg (Leningrad) in 1729.

In northern Europe the right to establish eel- and salmon-weirs was a privilege which belonged mainly to the estates of noblemen and particularly to the Church. Fishing rights were leased for liberal sums, and prices of fish were often higher than those of meat. The construction of watermills proved to be of special importance to the freshwater fisheries. The watermill originated in Asia, and came into use in Greece and the Roman Empire at about the time of Christ. During the Middle Ages it was developed widely. Smaller streams were dammed to provide water reservoirs for the mills, and generally eel-weirs or some form of fish-trap were combined with the sluices. Tench, carp and pike were kept in the mill-pond, and the miller could pay his rent in fish or money.

Due to the hardiness of some of the freshwater fishes it was possible to transport them to distant mill-ponds and stews (fish-ponds). Eels and salmon were caught during their migrations and the surplus preserved for use as payments in the unlimited series of tithes, lease rents, taxes and services which burdened the European of the Middle Ages.

(Olaus Magnus 1555)

At the end of the Middle Ages a large number of watermills were built all over Europe. No attempt was made to tame the large rivers, but dams were built on the smaller ones in suitable places, creating new environments for those fish which really belonged to the bream region (bream, tench, pike, eel). The dams thus provided a source of income additional to the operation of the mill.

Men and women risk life and limb in fishing a large dam. From a book on freshwater fisheries of 1582.

More recent times

During the Middle Ages resources of fish began to show signs of exhaustion. Later, water power was utilised for a variety of purposes and from the seventeenth century countless powder-mills, paper-mills, cloth-mills, etc., were constructed along the rivers.

Carp pond-farming reached its greatest development in the seventeenth century, but after this it became more remunerative to change the large carp ponds into cultivated land. Pond-farming was often unprofitable, especially when all the year classes of carp were kept in one pond and where uncontrolled spawning also took place.

During the decline of the freshwater fisheries a south-German landowner, Jacobi, was the first to experiment with artificial fertilisation of fish eggs by mixing roe and milt from spawning fish. The results of his experiments were published and discussed in 1763 and 1765, but they were forgotten until two French fishermen, Remy and Géhin from the town of La Bresse, revived and developed the experiments in the middle of the nineteenth century. They gained recognition for these and the results were published as a guide book to the artificial reproduction of fish or 'the art of sowing fish like corn'. The French government financed the continuation of the experiments, and the *Etablissement de Pisciculture de Huningue* functioned in Alsace from 1854 onwards. After 1871 the institute was taken over by the German government as the *Kaiserlich-Deutsche Reichsanstalt,* but it was later let on lease. In 1861 Frank Buckland in England started hatching experiments and published his book *Fish Hatching* in 1863. Private hatcheries were soon started all over Europe and in America.

With the increase of industrialisation in the eighteenth and nineteenth centuries the pollution of the streams became more widespread. From about 1830 salmon no longer ascended the Thames and the same was true for the Seine. In the Rhine, the Weser and the Elbe the occurrence of a salmon nowadays is a sensation.

At the close of the nineteenth century the turbine wheel came into use. It harnessed the water power in the streams to an extent not known before. With the turbine-wheel, industry penetrated the hitherto untouched upper reaches of the streams, the grayling and the trout regions.

The present century has been marked by the advancing destruction of freshwaters everywhere in Europe. Even though the necessity for development has in many cases been proved, it is usually the unnecessary and pointless destruction of habitats which have had the greatest effect. The law—as it reads—provides a fair protection for fish stocks, but it is often not complied with. One of the reasons for turning a blind eye to violations to the freshwater laws concerning pollution and the free run of fish is, no doubt, that public authorities themselves are in many cases the chief violators.

Commercial freshwater fisheries have, as a result of these factors, steadily decreased and the stocks of many species of fish have now become so reduced that one fears their complete destruction in another 50 or 100 years if the present development continues. This holds true, for example, for the sturgeon, the shads (particularly the allis shad) and the huchen, while salmon and grayling are much threatened.

THE FISH'S ENVIRONMENT TODAY

Water has many meanings. To the sporting angler it means a countryside with fish, to the civil engineer it is either potential drinking-water or a sewer, to industry it represents turbines and kilowatts, or cooling and exploitable water; unfortunately it also receives their effluents. The farmer's interest lies in drainage, irrigation and the regulation of streams. We all have to realise that these interests often conflict with each other. The problem is to find a reasonable compromise which satisfies as many interests as possible.

To freshwater fisheries two problems are paramount; the unimpeded run of fishes in the streams, and pollution.

The free run of fish

Many freshwater fish, and among them the most economically valuable species, undertake migrations from the sea into freshwater, or from the lakes into feeder-rivers in order to spawn. Dams, locks, and high weirs prevent these vital migrations. The authorities of most countries have introduced various rules, very often too late, for the construction of fish-passes to allow migratory species to swim round obstructions built in the river. However, the actual functioning of these regulations is far from satisfactory. All too often fish-passes have been wrongly constructed, sometimes from short-sighted parsimony or from lack of local knowledge. Just as often the pass is built of perishable materials, and is not kept in good repair.

The so-called fish-ladder is widely used to provide a way around barriers in the river. At its simplest it consists of a channel divided into a number of stepped basins which form a staircase along the dam to be passed. These basins are connected through openings in the partitions between them, and the flow of water through them is moderate, 5–500 litres per second, while the difference in water-level from basin is generally 15–20 cm. Modern fish-ladders are usually constructed in cement. Migratory fish, especially salmon and trout, can swim from one basin to the next, and these are so shaped as to provide a sheltered corner where the fish can rest.

The siting of the entrance to the fish-ladder is all important so that the fish will have no difficulty in finding it.

A fish-pass, such as the one outlined here, is not suitable for the ascent of elvers, as the current between the basins is too strong. Elvers must have some support in order to advance against the current, but they can get over obstructions with the protection afforded by bundles of straw or brushwood at the edge of the current.

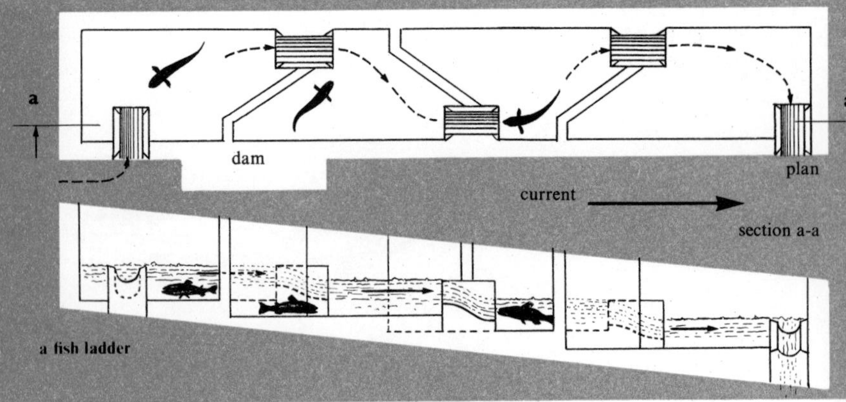

a fish ladder

The smaller weirs can be leapt by salmon and trout, though only if the depth of the water below the fall is sufficient to allow the fish to gather enough momentum for the jump.

Weirs are often the result of the regulation of the flow of the stream. Such control generally includes the straightening and deepening of the original bed, especially when drainage is also desired. Where the regulated stretch joins the natural reaches above it, the difference in the level of the bed is so pronounced that one or more weirs must be constructed—if only to prevent the bed of the river being washed down into the regulated stretch and deposited there. Weirs also offer the opportunity of controlling the flow of water in navigable waterways. Poorly designed weirs seriously hamper the passage of migratory fish, and an impassable one may mean that trout, for example, are cut off from all spawning places and nursery grounds in the higher reaches. Such a weir also results in a gradual diminishing of the fish in the upper reaches as it allows a downstream, but not an upward, migration. The control of streams almost always involves gross interference with the freshwater habitat and an adverse influence on the fish stock. The vegetation may be cut away or killed by chemical means; bays with deeper hollows where the fish can live are not spared in the levelling and straightening of the river. Shelter for the fish disappears, and the fauna of potential food animals is impoverished. The final death knell of the stream is sounded when the engineers culvert it in a concrete tube.

Pollution

When Izaak Walton in 1663 published his book *The Compleat Angler* England was still a rural country with countless rivers and brooks of clear, pure water. The Industrial Revolution of the eighteenth and nineteenth centuries resulted in the use of many of these rivers as water-supplies for the growing mining industry, gasworks, cloth-factories and paper-mills. The vast increase in population and the urban development in the Midlands, the North and around London produced a sewage problem of impossible magnitude. The untreated sewage was generally led directly to the nearest river in the, now

amazing, belief that the rivers and the sea would clean it away. England was not alone in this, for everywhere in Europe where industry spread it was rapidly surrounded by a wide belt of barren ponds, lakes and streams.

By the middle of the nineteenth century the condition of many of these waters was too foul to be ignored. In London, Parliament met with disinfected curtains hung over the windows of the House of Commons. It was also suspected that outbreaks of cholera and typhoid were in some way connected with polluted drinking-water. Initial control and the study of pollution was prompted more out of concern for human health than for the fishes' sake, but at least a beginning was made.

In the present day the problems of pollution in densely populated and industrialised western Europe are more pressing then ever before. The pollution of lakes and streams is not restricted to urban areas but reaches far into the open country. Intensive farming means using artificial fertilisers and chemical means for controlling animal pests, and both are a threat to the fauna of the streams. The gradual spread of industries into rural areas, where labour and building lots are easier to provide, has resulted in the greater risk of industrial pollution.

The most general form of pollution is the discharge of insufficiently cleaned sewage-works effluent, and of effluents with a high content of organic matter, e.g. slaughter-houses, sugar plants, breweries, silage, etc. Such organic matter is decomposed by bacteria and this decomposition uses oxygen. In bad cases, the water may completely lack oxygen and the bottom becomes black and smells strongly of hydrogen sulphide. In such a heavily polluted (polysaprobic) zone little besides bacteria and unicellular animals (Protozoa) can survive. The hover-fly larvae, the so called 'rat-tailed maggot' (*Eristalis*) can also be found here, but only in shallow water where they can reach the surface with their respiratory tubes.

The extent of the polysaprobic zone depends on the amount of the pollution and the water-supply of the streams. Ultimately, however, the organic matter becomes so decomposed that a state is reached where the proteins have been

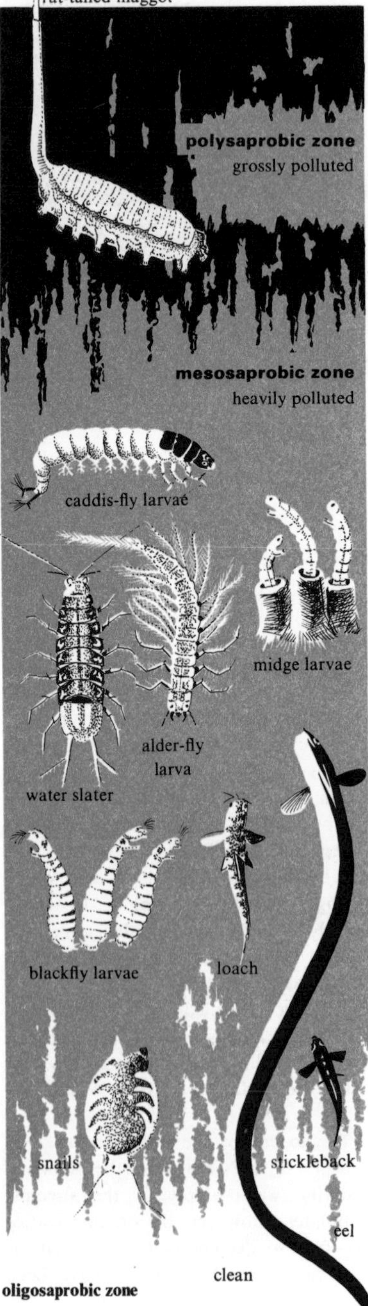

decomposed into amino acids, and where the water contains some oxygen produced by unicellular algae. The hydrogen-sulphide is oxidised and the surface of the mud is no longer black and smelly but yellow-brown. The number of bacteria decreases from over one million per ml of water to below 100,000. This zone is lightly to moderately polluted (mesosaprobic) and in it are found a few animals, net-spinning caddis-larvae (*Hydropsyche*), the larvae of the alder-fly (*Sialis*), and their prey the midge larvae (*Chironomus*). The water-slater (*Asellus*), and several snails become more common throughout this zone, and eventually several flowering plants appear. On the flattened floating leaves a sure indication of pollution can be found in the larvae of black-flies (*Simulium*) which feed on particles filtered from the water. A few of the more hardy fish occur here (e.g. eel, stickleback, and roach).

Finally, further downstream, we reach the non-polluted (oligosaprobic) zone which is distinguished by fewer bacteria still (less than 100/ml) and well-oxygenated, clear water. The polluting organic matter is now almost fully decomposed, and a normal fish fauna is present.

The biochemical processes involved in river pollution are very complicated. A relatively simple method of estimating the degree of pollution is based on the recognition of a number of more or less sensitive animals and plants which can be used as biological indicators of pollution. Thus the occurrence of black-fly larvae in numbers is one indication that the water is only lightly polluted—the zone termed β-mesosaprobic.

Especially noxious pollutants are found in several of the industrial waste products which are thoughtlessly, or accidentally, and often illegally discharged into streams. Such products are the dissolved salts of heavy metals such as lead, zinc, copper and mercury, discharges from chemical plants or the mining industry, etc., as well as a number of organic and inorganic acids which indirectly or directly kill the fish by preventing the intake of oxygen through the gills. Many other substances could be cited.

Large-scale disasters have resulted from the careless use of synthetic insect-killers (insecticides), e.g. DDT, which can kill fish in concentrations of as little as 0·04 mg/l. For the owner of valuable fishery a poisonous block of water drifting downstream may involve a loss of £100,000 in just ten minutes.

Less poisonous, but no more pleasant, are those pollutants from industrial processes (e.g. phenols) which taint the flesh of the fish.

Commercial freshwater fisheries

Freshwater fisheries use the same basic tools as sea fisheries, though they are usually reduced in scale to suit the more restricted local conditions. Among the nets, fyke-nets, stake-nets, seines and set-nets predominate. A gill-net is a wall of thin netting which catches around the fishes' gill-cover or fins when they swim into it. A special type of fixed net is the trammel, which consists of a fine-meshed net hung between two large-meshed ones. When a fish swims into the net, it pushes the fine-meshed one out through the meshes of the coarser, outer net, to form a bag holding the fish.

Hooks are used mainly on long lines, e.g. for eels, burbot and also wels.

Characteristic of freshwater fisheries are the many fixed fish-traps set in rivers for catching migratory fish. Many of

these traps are typical of certain districts, and their form is unique to a restricted geographical area. In general, a consider-

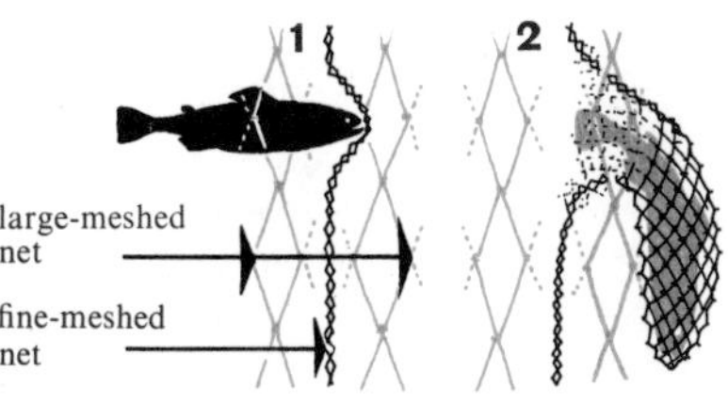

able ingenuity is used in adapting the type of trap to the surroundings, and they also reveal that their constructors had an intimate knowledge of the fishes' habits. The use of large fish-traps on rivers is, however, dying out, as they are expensive

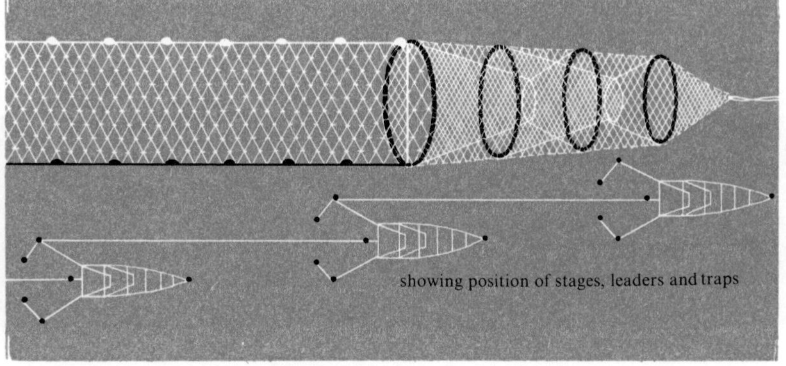

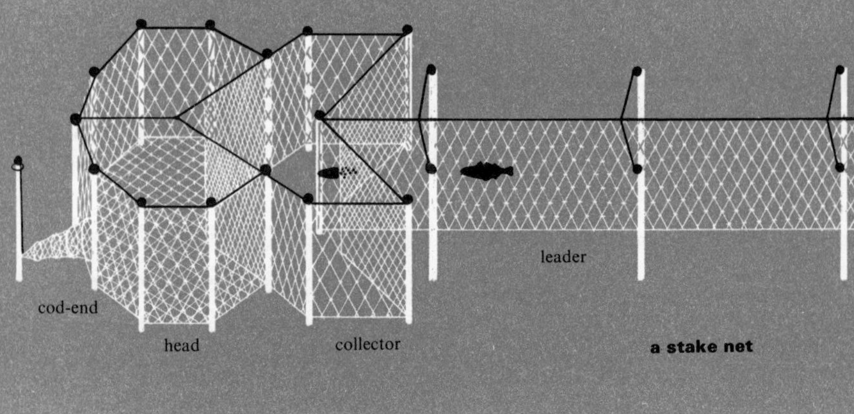

in man-power to repair and use. Many are not replaced when they fall into disuse.

In the British Isles commercial freshwater fisheries are not large, and only the salmon and eel support fisheries. In Europe the situation varies from country to country, but it is biggest in the inland regions of southern Germany and in the countries along the Danube.

The importance of sport fishing

From the number of fish which the sport fisherman takes from the water, and the often self-denying rules which govern his activities, it is evident that he makes no great impact on the fish fauna. Compared with the commercial fishermen in Europe, who take at least 95 per cent of all pike, eels and salmon caught, the sportsman removes a negligible number of fish. Paradoxically, the fish benefit from his activities as he is the backbone of the fight to preserve and save our rivers, streams and ponds.

Angling clubs and other bodies even protect the fish reserves by stocking with young fish, and have been known to ensure that fish-passages were incorporated in weirs and dams. Unfortunately, haphazard stocking often results in problèms of over-populated waters, and in the introduction of alien and undesirable predators, parasites, and disease. On the

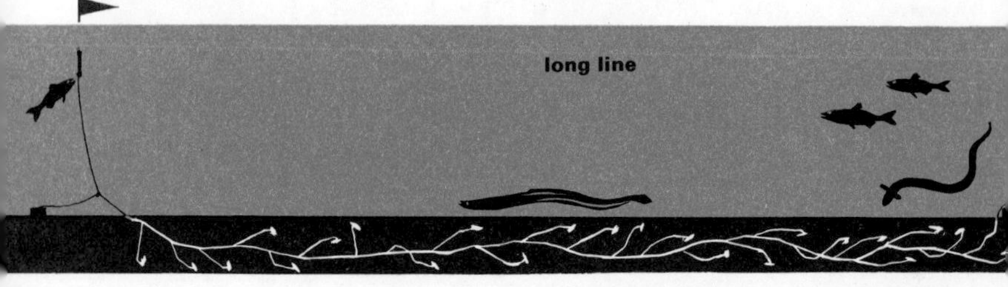

other hand, anglers are effectively organised as a body and vocal in their views, and their protests at the state of our freshwaters do serve to keep the more passive public alert to possible dangers.

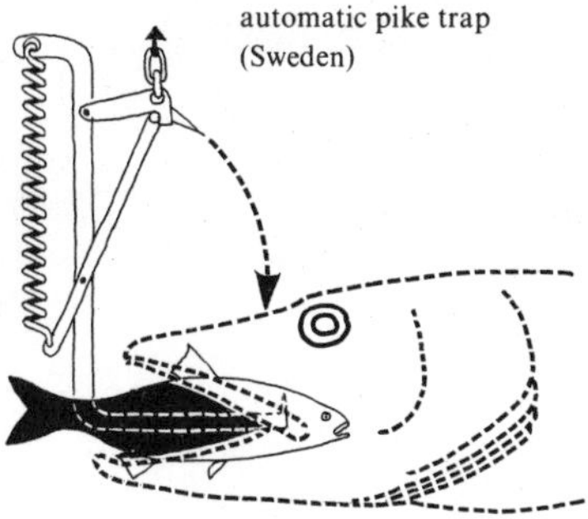

automatic pike trap (Sweden)

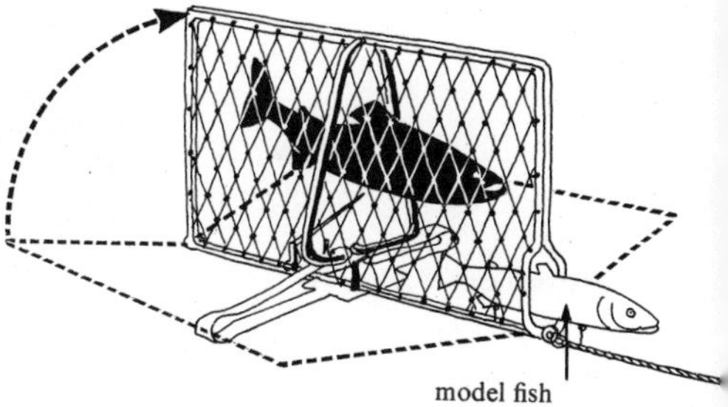

model fish

spring trap, salmon

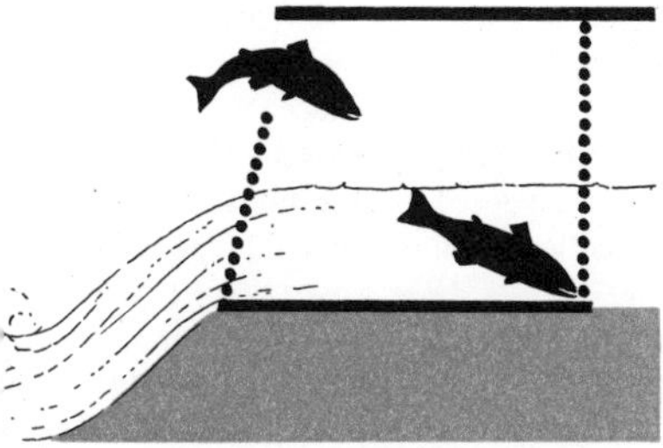

central European smack trap for salmon

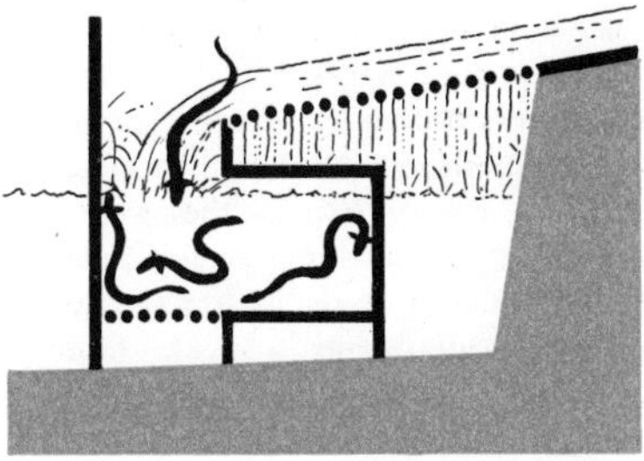

eel trap

various types of eel spear

EFFICIENT FISH-CULTURE

Hatcheries

The most difficult and dangerous time in the life of a fish is during the development of the embryo, hatching from the egg and the period until the yolk-sac is used up. Even if favourable temperatures obtain during all these stages, it is then that the first heavy mortalities occur. Many eggs are eaten, others are attacked by moulds, or fail to develop because they were not fertilised. After hatching, when the young fry rest passively on the bottom or remain fixed to water-plants and are feeding from the yolk-sac, many fall prey to carnivorous insects and fish.

The only way to prevent the heavy loss of eggs or larvae is to arrange for this particularly sensitive period to take place in the protection of a fish hatchery.

Maximum efficiency of a fish hatchery requires artificial fertilisation of the eggs. In fully ripe fish the sexual products are so liquid that they can be expelled by light pressure of the hand along the fish's belly towards the sexual opening. The simplest way is to press out the eggs and milt into an enamelled dish and stir them with a feather. Water should then be poured into the dish and fertilisation will take place, with the eggs swelling to almost twice their original volume. The sperms do not become active until they come into contact with the water, and as a rule their active life lasts only a few minutes, and in the salmonid fishes they live for 30 to 60 seconds only.

The increase in volume of the egg is brought about by water being absorbed through the permeable outer membrane which loosely surrounds the egg. In this way the egg is cushioned by a layer of water enclosed by the outer membrane. After fertilisation this membrane hardens, and in 2–6 days it has become a relatively tough envelope. If necessary, the eggs can be carried for several hours at this stage in an ordinary fish pail. The fertilised eggs are now carefully washed to remove slime and excess milt, and are then placed in trays or glasses which have a current of water passing through them. The respiration of the eggs demands a constant supply of clean, well-oxygenated water, and the supply is arranged so that it streams up through the perforated bottom or a grating in the tray on which the eggs rest. Large eggs (e.g. salmon and trout) are as a rule hatched in a single layer in flat trays, whereas small eggs (e.g. pike and whitefish) hatch best in high glasses with a slightly funnel-shaped neck (*Zuger-glass*), where water is supplied from below and overflows at the top.

Dead eggs, which can be distinguished by their opaque appearance, must be

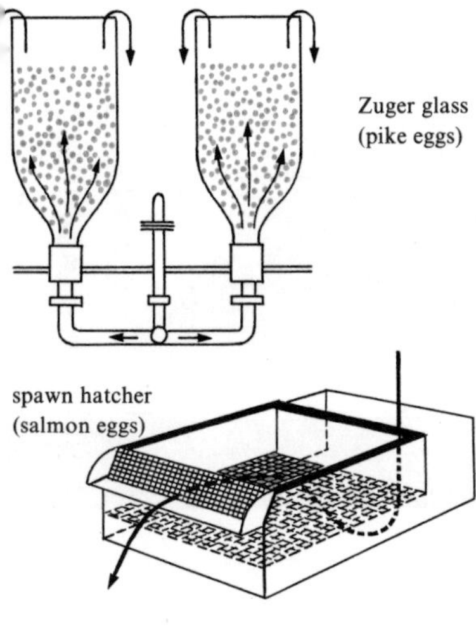

removed regularly with a pipette to avoid mould spreading to the healthy eggs.

In south-eastern Europe, frames holding carp eggs, or twigs with zander eggs, are hung in moist chambers where at regular intervals they are automatically exposed to water vapour until hatching. This is a particularly effective way of preventing fungus from attacking these rather sensitive eggs.

During the development of the eggs it is important to control the temperature, and to keep it within the optimum range. The hatchery is therefore usually built of brick on a foundation of concrete, and situated near a spring or other suitable stream with clear, well-oxygenated water. If necessary, the water is passed through a filter of gravel before being led into the hatchery. Sometimes ordinary tap-water can be used but this depends on the type of fish eggs and on the quality of the water. It is important that eggs and newly hatched fry should be protected from direct sunlight, as ultraviolet rays have a harmful effect.

In Europe, whitefishes are extensively farmed, but their eggs require very cold water for hatching (2–5°C). Pike eggs, however, develop best at 7–12°C. Each species has a relatively narrow range of heat tolerance, but within this range normal development will proceed, slower at the lower limits, faster when it is warmer. This is why hatching of fish eggs is spoken of in terms of day-degrees. Pike eggs, for example, take 110–130 day-degrees, or at 10°C development will be complete in 11–13 days.

With time the eyes of the embryo become clearly visible within the egg and they are then spoken of as eyed-eggs. It is generally at this stage that the eggs are distributed from the hatchery. Transport takes place in special boxes with a pile of flat frames covered with stretched fabric. Each frame carries one layer of eggs, but on the uppermost frame rests an ice-filled perforated box. Some form of insulating material is placed around the frames and ice-box.

Some time after hatching the yolk in the yolk-sac is used up, and the larvae start looking for food. Generally they are released into oblong wooden or concrete troughs for some weeks and are fed with scraped raw spleen, dry food or, if it is available, natural food (*Daphnia*, copepods, etc.), although these may introduce parasites to the fish.

Whitefish fry are usually released into the lake 3–5 days after hatching, and are put along the shore. Pike fry are kept for about a fortnight after hatching, but they have to be spread a few at a time around the water, for small pike are relatively non-migratory and quickly take to cannibalism.

In trout-farms fry are put into larger ponds not later than four weeks after hatching. Even as early as this in life there is a noticeable difference between them in length, and they often have to be sorted before release, so that the smallest can be kept away from the largest. Stocking a river with trout can either be done with early fry in spring, or later in the year with fingerlings. In any case the rate of mortality during their early months is very high.

Section through a dam with sluice and box for removing fish

Fish-farms

A fish-farm includes one or more specially constructed, shallow fish-ponds which can be emptied completely. The ponds are supplied with water from local springs or from a nearby river or brook, and the water-level is controlled by means of a sluice with adjustable wooden planks and a grating to hold back the fish.

The main principle of fish-farming is to put the young fish into ponds where they can be fed for one or more summers until they reach a size suitable for sale. They are then caught by lowering the water-level, sorted and distributed for sale. The most important pond fishes in Europe are rainbow trout and carp. Brown trout, American lake trout, cut-throat trout, tench, pike, black-bass and certain other species are also raised in fish farms. In Britain, however, fish-farms concentrate on the salmonid fishes, although a few raise carp.

The technique of intensive fish-rearing has been perfected in East Asia, where several species are raised together in known proportions. In this way the maximum productivity of the water is attained. Thus one species will feed on the plankton, another on vegetation, a third on bottom-animals, while the fourth is fed prepared food. An annual production of up to 90 tons of fish meat per hectare of pond area can therefore be obtained. Production at that level is, of course, a result of intensive feeding and a favourable climate, while natural production is considerably less.

The salmonid fishes demand well-oxygenated cool water below 20°C, while carp thrive best with summer temperatures over 20°C, and require less well-oxygenated water. The techniques of carp- and trout-farming are briefly reviewed below.

Carp pond-farming

Like all forms of animal stock-breeding the object of raising carp is to produce well-proportioned and healthy animals which grow rapidly. Stress is laid on the production of edible flesh, and cultivated carp are deeper bodied than their wild relatives. Some cultivated races are shown on page 139. Commercial producers have discovered that the scaleless leather carp sells better in some parts of Europe than the fully scaled forms, but only the scaled carp and mirror carp will breed true. The leather carp, and those with distinct rows of scales, are liable to produce many intermediate forms, and the latter particularly gives rise to stock of all varieties.

Carp-farming can be carried out as far north as 60°N, but there the summer growth is not particularly good. In central and southern Europe carp are sent to market in from two to four years.

Carp-farming can be more or less intensive. The more common means of carp-rearing is the release of young in large ponds which have a rich growth of submerged plants and plentiful natural food, the pond only being emptied when the carp have reached a size suitable for the table. However, the yield produced by this method is low compared with that of the more controlled farming which is now described.

In the beginning of May, a fortnight before the carp are ready to spawn, the animals to be used for breeding are selected. The males need not be more than 3 years old, the females preferably 5 years or more. The selected animals are then marked for identification with a metal tag, and are placed in a spawning pond, usually in the proportion of one male to two females.

The type of pond most often used in Europe for spawning is called a Dubisch-pond after the Austrian Dubisch, (1813–88) who first employed them. It takes the form of a flat, grass-covered meadow of 100–200 square metres, surrounded by a shallow ditch and bounded by a dike fitted with a sluice. Some days before the spawning carp are placed in the pond, it is filled with water to provide for a rich growth of planktonic algae and small animals. The depth of this water is maintained at between 20–30 cm.

By the end of May, or in northern Europe a little later, the water temperature reaches 17–20°C, and the carp start to spawn. The eggs, which are deposited on the blades of grass, hatch in a few days (100 day-degrees C are needed). After the yolk has been absorbed the young swim to the surface to fill their gas-bladder with air. After spawning the adults move to the rather deeper ditch from which they are easily removed.

A week after hatching the fry are carefully removed to another larger pond, the 'Vorstreckteich', where in the course of a month they grow to a length of about 5 cm. They are now sufficiently hardy to be transported and can be sold to carp-farms which do not rear fry themselves.

From this rearing pond the young are later transferred to rich nursery ponds of 2–10 hectares ('Brustreckseicke') which have previously been filled with water; from 1,000–5,000 young fish are stocked per hectare. In the autumn the young will have reached a length of 10–15 cm (*c.* 25 g), and the mortality will have been roughly 50 per cent.

The young carp, now one summer old (termed K_1) either over-winter in the nursery pond, or this is emptied to lie fallow through the winter. In this case the carp are transferred to a special wintering pond which is smaller and deeper than the nursery pond. During winter the young fish remain close to the bottom, and stop feeding at temperatures below *c.* 8°C.

In their second summer the carp are transferred to large growing ponds, at *c.*

300 per hectare, and are fed on special cereal food mixtures. The ponds are regularly fertilised to promote a heavy production of worms, snails, *Daphnia,* larvae of gnats, etc., which still make up half the food of the carp. The number of carp decreases during the year by 10–20 per cent due to various kinds of mortality.

After their second winter the fish are caught and sorted, and fine healthy individuals are transferred to fattening ponds, where they spend their third summer. In the autumn they will have an average individual weight of *c.* 1,250 g, and become in demand for food as 3-summers old carp. After sorting, they are placed in water-filled concrete basins, but are not fed. In a few days their intestines are empty and they lose their muddy taste. They are then transported in containers with water and an oxygen cylinder, or are simply packed in moist weeds and sacks.

In intensive carp pond-farming it is essential to avoid infectious diseases and attacks of parasites. It is therefore important to be able to leave the ponds dry periodically, to clean them of mud, to limewash them or to give them other kinds of chemical treatment. External parasites are usually removed by placing the carp in weak dilutions of salt, formalin, potassium permanganate. etc. Infectious diseases can be combated by means of streptomycin, penicillin, sulfonamides and other antibiotics.

Wild fish, such as crucian carp and bleak, are a potential source of infection in carp-farms. These unwanted fish also compete for food with the carp so zander, perch or young pike are often kept with the larger carp as a secondary fish-crop and to reduce the numbers of wild fish. These predators are then removed, before they become a threat to the carp, and sold. The tench is also a useful secondary fish in carp-ponds because of its hardiness and its efficient use of the natural food in the pond.

Artificial fertilisation of carp is not much used in European hatcheries. Carp can be made to mature earlier in the spring by the injection of acetone-treated, dried carp-hypophysis washed in 0·65 per cent brine. The eggs are ready for spawning about 24 hours after treatment. This method is used mainly in the U.S.S.R. and Hungary, where eggs and sperm are taken from carp ready for spawning and are artificially fertilised. The fertilised eggs stick to frames covered with netting and are kept in a moist atmosphere and automatically sprinkled with water at intervals of a few minutes. In this way mould is prevented from spreading from one egg to another. Hybrids between carp and crucian carp are produced by the artificial fertilisation of eggs from hypophysized carp, and sperm from crucian carp. The carp x crucian-carp hybrid is barren, but hardy and quick to grow.

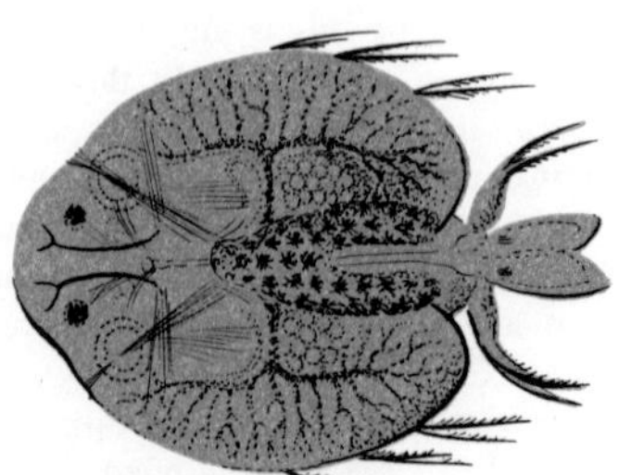

Parastic fish louse

6 mm

current
dam, with eel pass and fish ladder
hatchery
feeder canal
pond
sluice
pond
pond
pond
pond
to more ponds
food
ice
sorting
drainage canal

Trout pond-farming

Salmonid fish are more dependent than carp on the quality and temperature of the water, and need ample supplies of flowing, cool, well-oxygentated water. The ponds are considerably smaller than those used for carp, mainly because modern trout-farming is very intensive and is based entirely on artificial feeding.

A trout-farm is often planned as shown in the illustration on page 208. The ponds are rectangular and placed parallel between two channels, one to supply water, the other to remove it. The water is taken from a spring or a suitable stream, and is sometimes pumped into the ponds, such cases offering the opportunity of letting it fall as a cascade for further aeration of the water. The water level is regulated by a sluice which is also used when the fish are removed.

Among the salmonid fish kept in trout-farms the American species, the rainbow trout, is the most important. Other North American species, the lake trout, brook trout and cut-throat trout are also kept, as is the European brown trout too. These fish-farms either hatch their own fry, or buy them from other hatcheries, even from abroad, e.g. Denmark, where eyed-eggs and fry are raised for export.

In the nursery ponds trout are fed with offal from slaughter-houses which has been crushed and ground. In Denmark, which has the largest production of trout in Europe, the main food used is fish-meal from otherwise unexploited fish from the North Sea, especially sand-eels, herring and Norway pout, to a total of *c.* 50,000 tons annually. Trout kept in concrete ponds are fed mainly on a specially made and balanced diet of concentrated food in the form of pellets. These are scattered

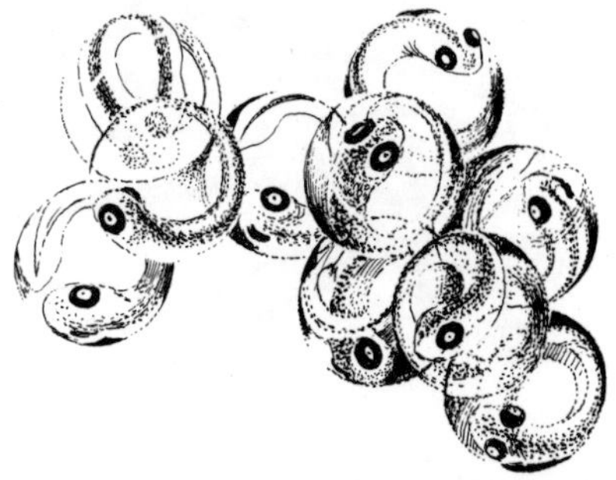

Eyed eggs

over the ponds 2–3 times a day. Using such food makes it possible to add any particular nutrients that the diet lacks. Experiments with automatic, mechanical feeding are also being carried out.

The rainbow trout is a spring spawner, and during the first summer the young grow 8–15 cm (5–25 g). In autumn the young trout are removed and sorted according to their size, either by hand or in a special sorting tray with an adjustable grid in the bottom. If the nursery ponds are frost-free they are returned, but if not the sorted fish are put out into deeper winter ponds.

After their first winter those which have made the fastest growth will be ready for market in May, and they are caught and selected then. The majority, however, will not reach marketable size until June or July.

In Europe most of the trout are sold as 'portion' fish at an individual weight of 160–260 grammes. They are for the most part transported alive in tanks of oxygenated water, which can be sent by rail or road. Larger portion fish are killed and delivered frozen, and the still bigger ones (over 500 g), the so-called 'salmon-trout', are iced.

The high population density in the ponds, from 10–25 fish per square metre, means that disease can be a serious threat. The most dangerous of these, 'Egtved-disease', is caused by a virus which attacks the kidneys, liver and other organs, and which can cause heavy losses (50–80%) in the winter months among the yearlings. Experiments have been made to breed resistant trout varieties. Good chemical remedies exist for other diseases, many of which are caused by parasites. The bottom and sides of the ponds can be chemically treated when they are periodically dried out.

As in carp-farming, trout can be reared and grown in large ponds where the fish feed on natural food only. This method, of course, requires good quality water and an abundance of food animals (larvae of insects, crustaceans and worms). The ponds do not need a constant current, but the fish have to be removed or reduced heavily in autumn, as there is a risk of a dangerous lowering of the oxygen in ice-covered waters.

FISHERIES BIOLOGY

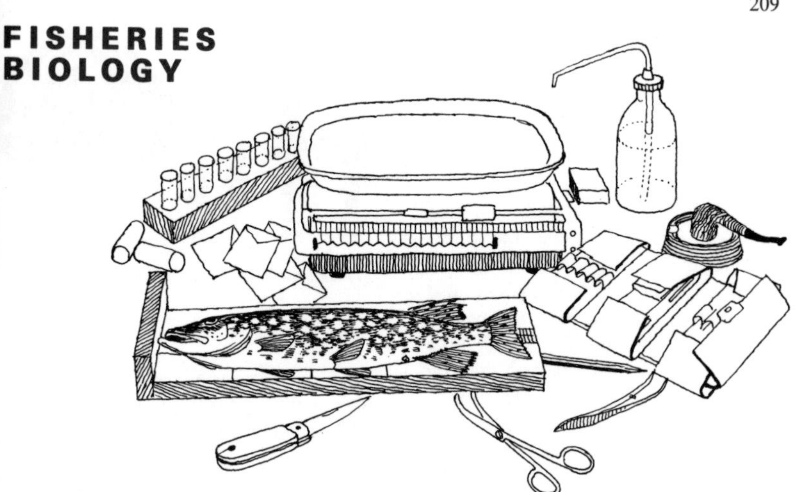

The simple object of fisheries biology is the logical unity of the theoretical and practical knowledge of fish to produce efficient and rational methods of raising more fish. Such an object, however, means that fishery biologists must have knowledge not only of fish but of all aspects of their environment. This is not so simple!

In the eighteenth and far into the nineteenth centuries, zoologists and botanists were mainly occupied with the description and cataloguing of the entire fauna and flora. Although this aspect is by no means exhausted, it has formed the basis from which wider studies have originated. Practical, scientific fisheries research first began in the middle of the nineteenth century in connection with the newly established hatcheries in France and Germany. Success in hatching delicate trout eggs and in keeping fry alive required the study and solution of many technical and theoretical problems. The slightly more vigorous science of the seas (oceanography) proved to be an inspiration as it developed as an independent and extensive science in the nineteenth century. An important support for fisheries research was also the development in the 1880's and 1890's of the basic study of freshwaters (limnology), founded by the Swiss scientist Francois Forel.

While much of the basic pure limnology is conducted at the universities and independent freshwater research institutes, fisheries research is usually run and staffed by local or national government fishery departments. Their work is therefore usually conducted as applied research, i.e. the solution of actual fishery or biological problems. Some experimental stations in Europe are financed privately by fishery unions, organisations of fish-farm owners, etc. In the British Isles most of the applied fisheries work is in the hands of the national fisheries and river authorities, while the internationally famous Freshwater Biological Association sponsors pure limnological studies.

The most important aspects of research in fisheries biology are briefly reviewed below.

Age and growth of freshwater fishes

A knowledge of the age-composition of a stock of fish furnishes information on recruitment and mortality, fluctuations in stock density and growth rate.

The age of fish can be read from their scales, ear stones (otoliths) and bones which form year rings. These rings are formed because growth is uneven, fast in summer and slow or absent in winter. During the winter the fish grows little and only a narrow dark band will show on the scale or otolith. Summer growth results in a broad light ring and this, with the preceeding winter zone, is counted as a year ring and so can give the age of the fish.

In scaleless fish, or those in which the growth lines in the scales are indistinct, the otoliths from the inner ear, or labyrinth (see page 12), can be used instead. The otolith is examined while held against the light, or it can be broken and the rings counted on the surface of the fracture. Most of the bones of the gill-cover, usually the operculum, and the vertebrae can also be used for determining age.

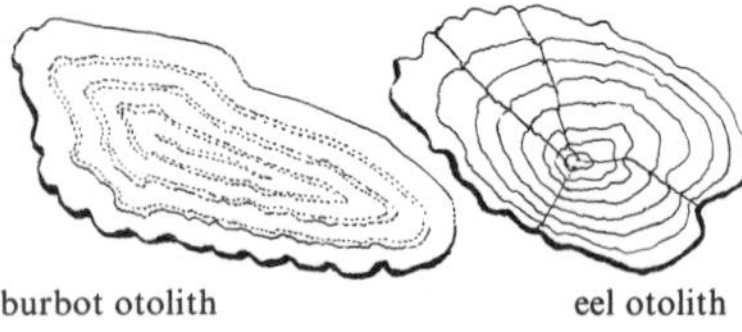

burbot otolith eel otolith

The Norwegian Einar Lea has observed that the growth of the scale is roughly proportional to the growth of the fish. From the year rings it can therefore be calculated how long the fish was at any given age. As scales can often tell us the number of times a fish has spawned (e.g. in the salmon), they too are an important source of information for fisheries biologists.

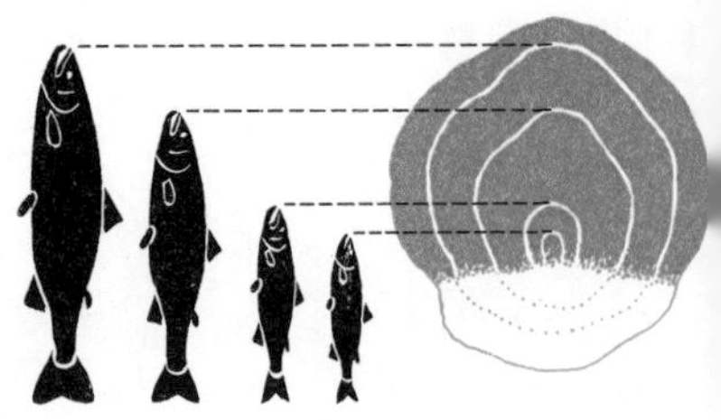

Relation between annual rings and length

The age-composition and growth of a fish population can often be determined approximately by measuring a suitable sample of the catch, and by plotting the measurements as a graph to make a distribution curve where the number of peaks corresponds to the number of year-classes. This method, which can be supplemented by analyses of scales, is less suitable for fish with a long spawning period, and for those with a highly varying growth (e.g. pike).

Fish tagging

Placing individual tags on fish helps solve a series of important questions concerning habitats and migrations. Many different types of tags are used. For freshwater fish the most popular one is a small tag of metal or plastic stamped with an index letter and a number, fastened to the fish by means of a wire of silver or stainless steel passed through the muscles just in front of the dorsal fin. Sometimes the tag consists of a rolled-up plastic letter with instructions to the finder, sometimes in several languages. The letter is generally placed in a small plastic cylinder, red or yellow and with a number marked on it. A simple variety is the arrow-tag, cut from yellow or red plastic and placed either in the muscles in front of the dorsal fin or passed through the gill-cover. Numbered metal clips are sometimes used and placed in the gill-cover.

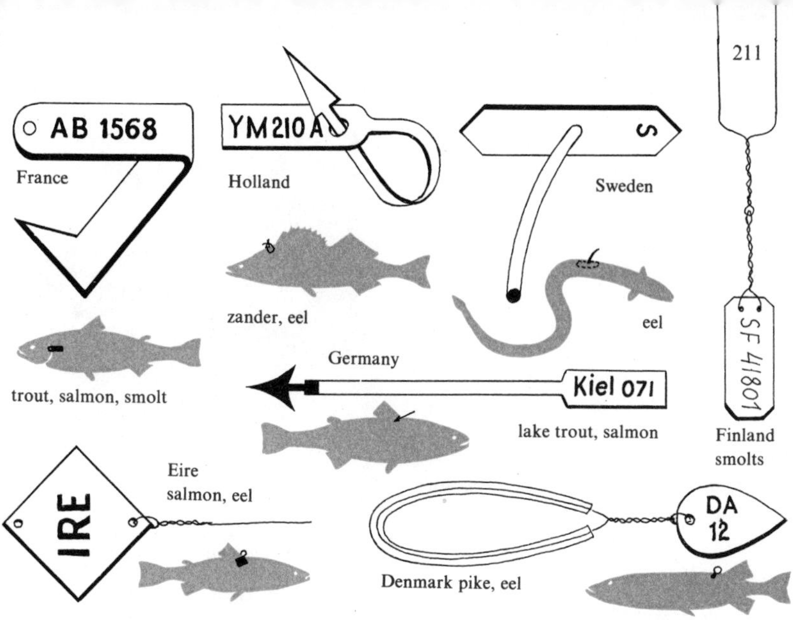

AB 1568
France
YM 210 A
Holland
S
Sweden
zander, eel
eel
SF 41801
Finland
smolts
trout, salmon, smolt
Germany
Kiel 071
lake trout, salmon
Eire
salmon, eel
IRE
DA 12
Denmark pike, eel

Examples of marking tags

Eels are often marked with coloured plastic tags which are pressed under the skin, and attached to an orange-coloured nylon thread which projects through the skin and is easily visible if the fish is caught.

Recovered tags, and sometimes the fish too, are sent in together with information on locality and time of capture. A small reward, generally 5–10 shillings, is paid together with compensation for the value of the fish. A letter telling where the fish was first tagged is then sent to its captor.

As one object of tagging is to deduce the migration pattern of the population from the behaviour of individual fish, the tag must be shaped and fastened in such a way that it does not harm the fish or hamper its normal life. At the same time, it is also necessary to ensure that the tag can be easily seen, and it must therefore be conspicuous. Internal tags, invisible from outside, are not seen until it is too late, perhaps when the fish is being prepared for the table, and by then it is impossible to learn where it was caught.

In the British Isles tagging is regularly used for commercial fish and sea fish, but the so-called coarse fish are tagged only in local schemes. Major tagging experiments are advertised in fishery papers or within

Eel migration routes from the Baltic Sea

the industry, and thanks to the keen interest of fishermen, a remarkably high proportion of tags sooner or later make their way to the fishery biologists. Extensive international co-operation must exist to make fish-tagging so successful. Recapture of 70–80 per cent of the tagged fish is in no way rare among heavily exploited species, e.g. eel and salmon.

Thanks to the many hundreds of thousands of such recaptures we now have a good record of both movements and life-history of migratory and non-migratory fish. Tagging returns also provide much important data on fishing intensity and on mortality.

Races and tribes

Almost all freshwater fishes tend to form geographical races. This is often caused when a species which was at one time continuously distributed through an area becomes divided into isolated units in later periods, perhaps by the formation of mountain ridges, or by climatic changes (e.g. ice ages). An example of a distribution which has become discontinuous, due to the deterioration of the climate in Siberia during the ice age, is the present range of the bitterling, with one race in Europe and another in northern China (see page 130). A long series of animals and plants have similar distributions to the bitterling, and occur as two closely related forms.

It is perhaps more remarkable that almost all salmonid fish and many cyprinids tend to develop local forms or races which can exist in the same water system, even within the limits of one and the same lake. In external appearance the differences between the races may be small, and they can often only be distinguished by numerical characters (the number of vertebrae or gill-rakers) or by precise assessment of the proportion of the head, or by blood-typing. Races such as these can, however, often be clearly distinguished from one another by their biology. Within the water system a species may form both migratory and non-migratory races. Races of other species may have different spawning times, spawning places and habitats. Also the number of eggs, food preferences and growth rate may differ.

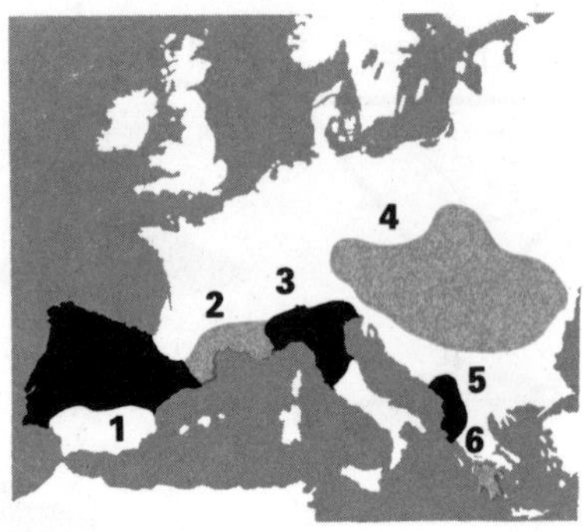

Races of the southern barbel Barbus meridionalis

1. Iberian, *B.m. graellsi*

2. Southern French, *B.m. meridionalis*

3. North Italian, *B.m. caninus*

4. Semling, *B.m. petenyi*

5. Albanian, *B.m. rebeli*

6. Southern Greek, *B.m. peleponnesius*

In addition to such variation within a species, which is evidently of a genetic nature, fish also vary in response to their environment. For example, dwarf races are formed where lack of space, or competition hamper normal growth (e.g. salmon, trout, and perch). This capacity of the species to vary both genetically and as a result of their surroundings is a positive character, and it ensures survival in an unstable environment.

Food-chains and production

Biological production in freshwater is a complicated amalgam of the processes of building up and of decomposition. One of the products we harvest from the lake is fish. On what factors does the production of fish depend?

The lake, according to the size of its feeder streams and outlet, is a more or less self-supporting system. Basic or primary production is brought about by plants. From the shore-line down to a depth of a few metres is a series of growing plant communities; inshore these are mainly marsh-plants, then come plants with both floating and submerged leaves, and farther out the completely submerged plants. In deep water insufficient light penetrates for the plants to grow, but in the surface layers float microscopic algae, which are also found along the shore zone.

Like all other green plants, water-plants are involved in the most vital of all processes in our world, photosynthesis. This is the process by which the energy of light plays a part in the chemical production of sugar, formed of carbon dioxide and water, and in which oxygen is a surplus product. Photosynthesis by water-

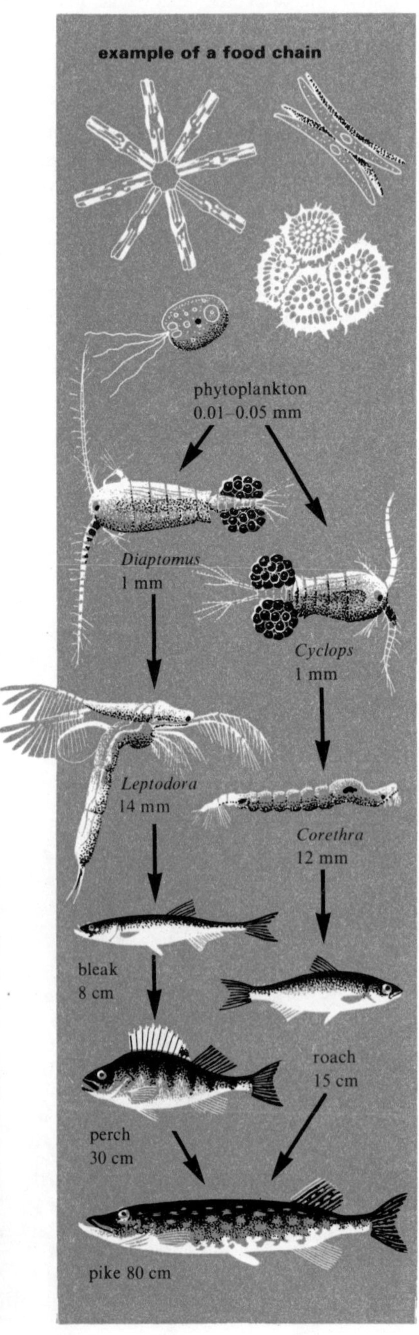

plants means that the oxygen becomes dissolved in the water, and this is of highest importance to aquatic animals for the natural exchange of oxygen from the air into the water is slow.

Dying plants decay slowly and some animals still find them suitable for food. Along the shore, most of the insects, snails and crustaceans will feed on living or decaying plants, and in the open water plant-plankton is the basic nourishment for the zooplankton (water-fleas and copepods). In their very early stages, many species of fish also feed partly on the plant-plankton, although within a couple of weeks of hatching they begin to eat mainly zooplankton which, of course, means that they are only one stage away from plant-eating.

Animals feeding directly on the plants are called primary consumers, while those which are meat-eaters and live only indirectly on plants are known as secondary consumers.

The basic production from water-plants of all kinds is distributed to animals through what is called, at its simplest, a food-chain. A food-chain always starts with the primary production of plants, and shows a succession of conversions. From link to link in the chain a loss of energy is observable, while some of the potential is lost in the faeces or by activity converted into heat.

The longer the chain is, the greater is the amount of plant-matter ultimately used to produce the last link in the chain, e.g. the pike in the case illustrated. This implies that the production of large predatory fish is never as great as that of fish for example, roach lower down the chain. It is a pity that the roach is not more tasty.

In a natural community many food-chains are interlinked, and a more accurate impression of the food relationships can be obtained by thinking in terms of a a 'food-web', i.e. many-linked chains.

The fishing methods used by biologists

Biologists very often use perfectly ordinary fishing gear to sample the fish fauna in a lake, pond or stream. Sometimes, however, they have to use special methods such as poison or electric fishing.

Poisoning

In Asia and South America the natives often 'fish' with the bark or roots of various plants which contain strong nerve poisons. The different parts of the plants are pulverised and spread over the water, and the fish come to the surface more or less helpless and can easily be caught. In Europe various plant-poisons lethal to fish are found in native plants; for example, a decoction of flowers of mullein, containing saponin, was used by the Greeks, and the juice of cyclamen by the Romans.

Derris elliptica

The use of such poisons to catch fish is strictly illegal in the British Isles and Europe. However, exceptions may occasionally be made where, for scientific analysis of the stock, it is desirable to catch all the fish in a certain area. Here, fishing with the use of poison can be very effective.

The fish-poison used most often is rotenone, which can be manufactured from several plants of the genus *Derris* growing in southern Asia—the roots of derris plants contain up to 10 per cent rotenone, but it can now also be manufactured synthetically. It causes the fine blood vessels in the gills to contract so much that the respiration of the fish stops. It is active in weak concentrations (0·5 litre per 1,000 tons of water), but it is not poisonous to humans. It becomes inert relatively soon after it is applied.

Rotenone is used where it is desired to eradicate a valueless fish stock in a pond before introducing more valuable varieties. It is sprinkled as an emulsion from a boat, and the fish float to the surface within half an hour to two hours of its application.

Electric fishing

Twenty-five years ago the use of the electric fish stunner was unknown; today, anyone interested in the study or care of fish stocks must have one. With an electric fishing machine a stream can be cleared of unwanted fish, while growth investigations, tagging experiments and stock analyses can be carried out with an efficiency which no other fishing gear could ensure. No wonder that electric fishing has become an indispensable method for fishery biologists and workers. Its very efficiency makes the machine a dangerous tool in the hands of the ignorant, and in all countries electric fishing is permitted only for special purposes and with special permits.

Electric fishing is based on the principle that fish under certain conditions act towards a direct current by swimming towards the positive pole (the anode). At the waterside the procedure is as follows: current is produced by a portable generator, e.g. a light petrol motor running a dynamo, and the current is led through long rubber cables which allow a stretch of *c.* 100 m, up or down-stream, to be fished. The negative electrode (the cathode)

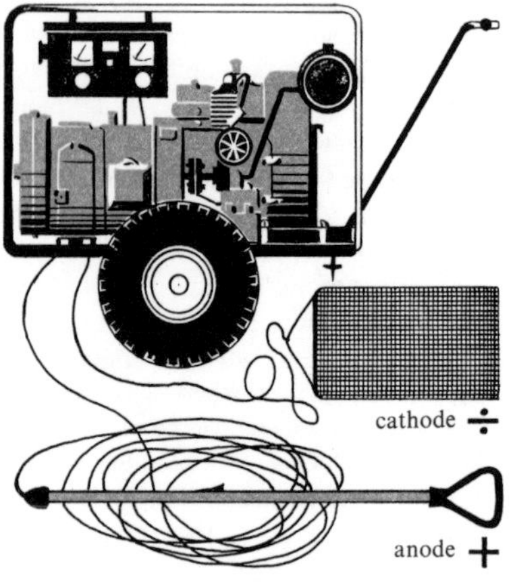

consists of a good conductor, e.g. a cylinder of wire netting which is thrown into the stream, while the anode may be a ring of metal on an isolated shaft. During fishing the operator wades slowly up-stream probing the stream with the anode. Within a radius of *c.* 3 m fish will swim towards the electrode, where they may become completely paralysed. The operator, or more usually an assistant, nets the fish as they come up.

Direct current is usually used with a voltage of 220, occasionally up to 700, volts, and the capacity is 0·5–1·5 kilowatt. The anode must be handled with caution!

The following factors have a bearing on the efficiency of electric fishing. The fish reacts to the difference in potential—the 'body-potential'—occurring between head and tail, and one of five reactions may be produced: (1) on the edge of a field of current the fish will be scared and swim away; (2) when the body-potential passes a certain limit the body of the fish will vibrate; (3) at rather higher body-potential the fish will swim towards the anode (electrotaxis); (4) if the body-potential increases further the fish will become paralysed (electronarcosis), and (5) with the continued influence of the current or at still higher potentials the fish will be killed (electrocution).

The object of electric fishing is to make the fish swim towards the anode and if possible to catch it in a net before it becomes paralysed. The fish do not suffer any after-effects from the reactions 1–4, although stage 4 is best avoided, and they recover shortly after the current stops.

In order to arrive at electrotaxis (reaction 3) a suitable body-potential must be inflicted upon the fish. Experience has shown that frequent current shocks act more strongly on the nerves of the fish than a constant current. Therefore an alternating current with 40–100 cycles per second is often used.

It seems that the difference in potential between head and tail (the body-potential) for many freshwater fish should be between 1 and 4 volts to make them swim towards the anode. The trout, for example, shows electrotaxis at a body-potential of 1·2–2·0 volt, while with higher potentials it is paralysed. Larger fish will receive a higher body-potential than small ones because their length covers a larger part of the current field.

Close to the anode the potential decreases rapidly. This is shown diagrammatically in the figure, where a difference in potential of 1 volt between the lines must be visualised. This shows that a big trout (A) has a body-potential of 1·2 volts, when two metres from the anode in this hypothetical case. This is just the threshold value causing it to swim towards the anode. The potential lines, however, occur closer

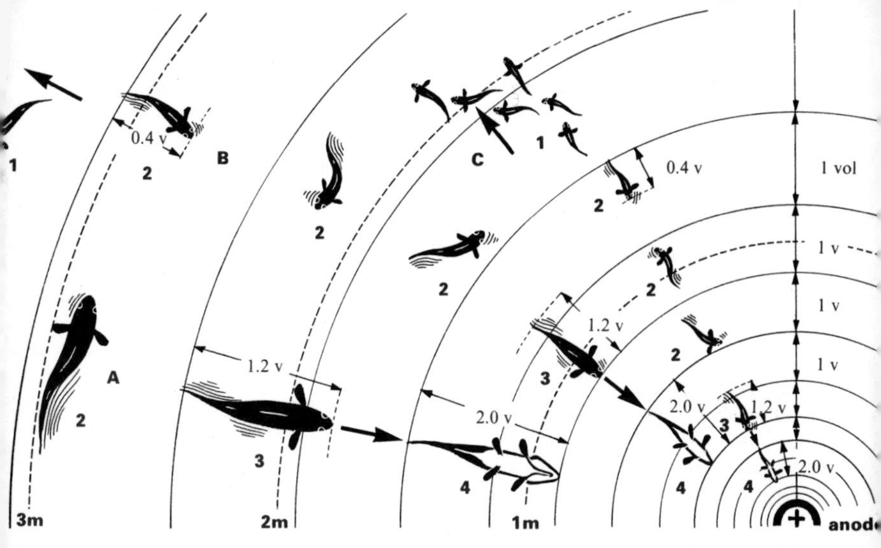

and closer, and *c.* 1 m from the anode the length of the fish covers two lines, or 2 volts. A body-potential of 2 volts is necessary to paralyse the fish, causing it to turn over on its back. A smaller trout (B) must, as shown in the figure, be much closer to the anode before its body-potential reaches 1·2 volts, causing electrotaxis, and it is not paralysed until it is *c.* 60 cm from the anode. A young trout (C) will not be paralysed until it is within a radius of 40 cm of the anode.

In practice this means that the anode catches bigger fish more effectively than smaller ones. One must therefore work with potentials well adjusted to the length of the fish one wishes to catch.

The radius of action of this technique depends on the size of the area for which an electrical field can be obtained with potential lines close enough to produce the necessary body-potentials. As already mentioned, the length of the fish is important, and the conductivity of the water is another critical factor. A high conductivity means less resistance, and with this comes a smaller fall in potential resulting in greater distances between the potential lines, that is, the fish must be closer to the electrode to get the necessary body-potential. Electric fishing in estuaries or salt water is therefore very difficult, for salt water is a good conductor. In some freshwaters, too, conductivity can be embarrassingly high, for example in polluted water and in marl pits, while generally it is low in waters on granite and in many spring-fed brooks.

The uses of electric fishing

One obvious advantage in using electric fishing is that unwanted fish can easily be removed. In a good stream with grayling and trout, large pike can be removed from deep hollows, or the stock of ide and chub can be thinned out. Any paralysed trout or grayling need not be touched but will float downstream and recover quickly. The method is also often used to obtain fish for stocking in other places or spawning fish for hatcheries.

The effect of an electric current on fish can also be used for making a barrage. A series of electrodes can be placed across a stream, establishing a continuous current field which scares the fish away. This method has been used in places in hydro-electric dams to prevent fish from entering the turbines. By the same method fish can be led into fixed traps.

Planned exploitation

The preparation of working plans for lakes and ponds which are to be rationally exploited is an important part of the consultative activity of the fishery biologists. The potential productivity of a lake can be estimated from quantitative bottom-samples, and limited fishing can provide an analysis of the existing fish fauna. The topography of the lake, its feeder streams and outlets are studied and the quality of the water is examined. Based on these data the future of the fishery in the lake can be planned. This plan consists primarily of an estimate of which fish species the fishery should be based upon, and how their production can most expediently be furthered.

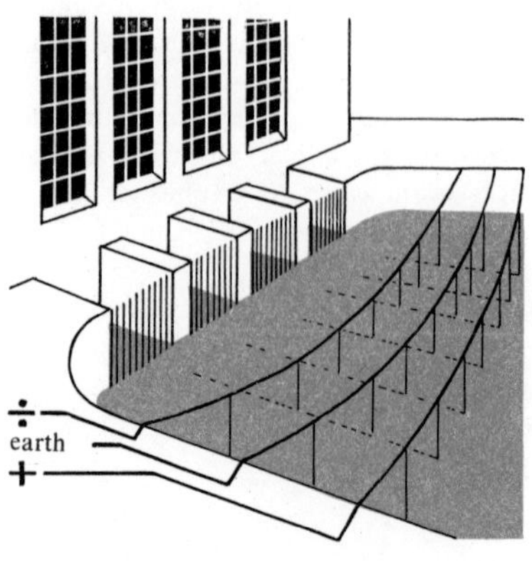

Electric barrier above power station

One of the methods of increasing number and quality of the fish is to improve, or to establish, adequate spawning places, and to provide the newly hatched fry with adequate shelter and protection. In lakes with poor vegetation one can deposit bundles of willow or juniper brushwood, on which perch, pike and roach will spawn, and in which the young can later find shelter. Similar steps will also improve the vegetation-poor shores of larger lakes.

A number of fish are spring spawners and spawn in shallow water, e.g. flooded meadows, and one must take care that these shallow areas do not become traps for the young when the water-level falls following the spring floods. This can be done by digging ditches which act as channels to the lake, and can be used when the water level drops. It is also sometimes necessary to cultivate those water-plants suitable for providing the fry with shelter.

The production of rivers can be improved, e.g. for grayling and trout, by ensuring that there are adequate spawning places. By taking advantage of the possibilities offered by the natural formation of the bed, and by the currents, it is possible to excavate hollows and pits in the bed. These will provide suitable shelter for bigger fish than would otherwise be found in the river.

In smaller lakes the vegetation often becomes so dense that the fish literally have difficulty in moving. A dense growth of plants with floating leaves (water-lily, pond-weed and duck-weed) is also undesirable as they shade the water, the bottom and submerged plants. A plentiful growth may also cause a deficiency of oxygen in the water during winter, when the plants wither and decay. Over-dense vegetation is therefore often cut and removed with various cutting equipment, used from the bank or a barge as appropriate.

Another method of improving the production of fish is by introducing tiny fry or fingerlings. This can be done either to supplement the stock of a species which does not spawn successfully in the water, but which will grow well there, or in order to introduce a new fish species in a lake.

Regulation of the stock through fishing is an important method of preventing undesirable fish from becoming too abundant (e.g. bream in many lakes and chub in many streams). Over-populated, slow-growing stocks can be improved by intensive fishing because the competition for food and living space is lessened (trout and perch in lakes). The object of good fishery management is to regulate the stock density in such a manner that it is of a reasonable size in proportion to the amount of food.

The production of natural food for the fish can often be increased, but this is difficult in streams and larger lakes. In ponds and smaller lakes it is easier to control both the flora and the fauna. Such waters can even be carefully treated with fertilisers to increase primary production, a process which will also improve the production of fish.

The climatic, topographic, chemical, and biological factors determining the character of a lake or stream are many and variable. Freshwaters can, of course, be divided into a series of different types, but at another level one can go to the other extreme and say that in reality no two lakes are exactly alike. A work-plan for a fishery is therefore at best a series of suggestions based on the experience and judgement of the advisor. When his advice is followed and careful records are kept, the catch statistics will soon demonstrate where the plan has to be adjusted, and whether it could be supplemented to raise production still further.

LIST OF FOREIGN FISH-NAMES

(G = German, F = French, Du = Dutch, Da = Danish, I = Italian)

BARBEL: Barbe (G), barbeau (F), barbeel (Du), flodbarbe (Da)
BLEAK: Laube (G), ablette (F), alver (Du), løje (Da)
BREAM: Blei, Brachsen (G), brème (F), brasem (Du), brasen (Da), abramide (I)
BURBOT: Rutte, Quappe (G), barbotte (F), kwabaal (Du), ferskvandskvabbe (Da)

CARP: Karpfen (G), carpe (F), karper (Du), karpe (Da), carpio (I)
CHARR: Saibling (G), ombre chevalier (F), fjeldørred (Da)
CHUB: Döbel (G), chevaine (F), kopvoorn (Du), døbel (Da)
CRUCIAN CARP: Karausche (G), carassin (F), kroeskarper (Du), karuds (Da), carrassio (I)

DACE: Hasel (G), vandoise (F), serpeling (Du), strømskalle (Da), lasca

EEL: Aal (G), anguille (F), aal (Du), ål (Da), anguilla (I)

GRAYLING: Äsche (G), ombre (F), vlagzalm (Du), stalling (Da), témelo (I)
GUDGEON: Gründling (G), goujon (F), grondel (Du), grundling (Da), ghiozzo (I)

IDE: Orfe, Aland (G), ide (F), winde (Du), rimte (Da)

LAMPERN: Flussneunauge (G), lamproie fluviatile (F), rivierprik (Du), flodlampret (Da), lampreda (I)
LOACH: Bartgrundl (G), loche (F), bermpje (Du), smerling (Da)

MILLER'S THUMB: Groppe (G), chabot (F), rivier donderpad (Du), ferskvandsulk (Da)
MINNOW: Elritze (G), verón (F), elrits (Du), elritse (Da), pesciolino (I)
MULLET: Meräsche (G), muge (F), herder (Du), multe (Da), muggine (I)

PERCH: Barsch (G), perche (F), baars (Du), aborre (Da), pesce pèrsico (I)
PIKE: Hecht (G), brochet (F), snoek (Du), gedde (Da), luccio (I)

ROACH: Plötze, Rotauge (G), gardon (F), blankvoorn (Du), skalle (Da), lasca (I)
RUDD: Rotfeder (G), rotengle (F), ruisvoorn (Du), rudskalle (Da), scardola (I)
RUFFE: Kaulbarsch (G), grémille (F), pos (Du), hork (Da), acerina (I)

SALMON: Lachs (G), saumon (F), zalm (Du), laks (Da), salmone (I)
SMELT: Stint (G), éperlan (F), spierling (Du), smelt (Da), eperlano (I)
STICKLEBACK: Stichling (G), epinoche (F), stekelbaars (Du), hundestejle (Da), spinarello (I)
STURGEON: Stör (G), esturgeon (F), steur (Du), stør (Da), storione (I)

TENCH: Schleih (G), tanche (F), zeelt (Du), suder (Da), tinca (I)
TROUT: Forelle (G), truite (F), forel (Du), ørred (Da), trota (I)
WHITE BREAM: Güster (G), brème bordellière (F), kolblei (Du), flire (Da)

Index of Scientific Names

Index of English Names